PERGAMON INTERNATIONAL LIBRARY
of Science, Technology, Engineering and Social Studies
The 1000-volume original paperback library in aid of education, industrial training and the enjoyment of leisure
Publisher: Robert Maxwell, M.C.

THERMAL DESIGN of NUCLEAR REACTORS

Other Titles of Interest

CARTER et al.: Management of Low-level Radioactive Waste (2 volumes)

CHICKEN: Nuclear Power Hazard Control Policy

COMMISSION OF THE EUROPEAN COMMUNITIES: Fusion Technology, 1980

DE VOLPI: Proliferation, Plutonium and Policy

HUNT: Fission, Fusion and The Energy Crisis, 2nd Edition

JUDD: Fast Breeder Reactors

KEMENY: Report of the President's Commission on the Accident at Three Mile Island

LEWINS: Nuclear Reactor Kinetics and Control

MURRAY: Nuclear Energy, 2nd Edition

SECRETARIAT FOR FUTURES STUDIES: Solar Versus Nuclear: Choosing Energy Futures

SHABALIN: Fast Pulsed and Burst Reactors

WALTAR & REYNOLDS: Fast Brccdcr Rcactors

WILLIAMS: Nuclear Safety

Related Journals

Free specimen copies gladly sent on request

Annals of Nuclear Energy
Energy
Energy Conversion and Management
International Journal of Heat and Mass Transfer
Letters in Heat and Mass Transfer
Progress in Nuclear Energy

THERMAL DESIGN of NUCLEAR REACTORS

R. H. S. WINTERTON

Lecturer in Nuclear Engineering
Department of Mechanical Engineering
University of Birmingham
England

PERGAMON PRESS

OXFORD · NEW YORK · TORONTO · SYDNEY · PARIS · FRANKFURT

U.K.	Pergamon Press Ltd., Headington Hill Hall, Oxford OX3 0BW, England
U.S.A.	Pergamon Press Inc., Maxwell House, Fairview Park, Elmsford, New York 10523, U.S.A.
CANADA	Pergamon Press Canada Ltd., Suite 104, 150 Consumers Road, Willowdale, Ontario M2J 1P9, Canada
AUSTRALIA	Pergamon Press (Aust.) Pty. Ltd., P.O. Box 544, Potts Point, N.S.W. 2011, Australia
FRANCE	Pergamon Press SARL, 24 rue des Ecoles, 75240 Paris, Cedex 05, France
FEDERAL REPUBLIC OF GERMANY	Pergamon Press GmbH, 6242 Kronberg-Taunus, Hammerweg 6, Federal Republic of Germany

---

First Edition 1981

British Library Cataloguing in Publication Data

Winterton, R. H. S.
Thermal Design of Nuclear Reactors — (Pergamon International Library).
1. Nuclear reactors — Design and Construction
I. Title
621.48′32 TK9202 80–41187

ISBN 0–08–024215–4 Hard cover
ISBN 0–08–024214–6 Flexi cover

Printed in Great Britain by A. Wheaton & Co. Ltd., Exeter

Preface

This book is intended as an introduction to the thermal design of nuclear reactors, either for people starting work in the field or for university students studying the subject. The emphasis is on power reactors, and all the main reactor types are covered. SI units are used.

Basic understanding of many topics in turbulent flow is poor. Consequently empirical correlations of experimental results are used, and many different equations can be proposed for the same phenomenon. In this book no attempt has been made to list all the methods available, instead for most topics just one reasonably accurate and simple method is presented in detail. The more recent of the references at the end of each chapter provide an entry point to the literature for those wishing to pursue a topic further.

The first two chapters contain a minimum of background information. Chapter 1 summarises the reactor physics of the core. Chapter 2 describes the main reactor systems, since the choice of material in Chapters 3 to 9 is strongly influenced by its relevance to the reactor types that are used for power production around the world. The last chapter looks forward to the heat-transfer and fluid-flow problems of a quite diffierent type of reactor, the fusion reactor.

Many of the problems at the ends of the chapters are based on tutorial or examination questions set either to final year Mechanical Engineering students or to students on the MSc course in the Physics and Technology of Nuclear Reactors, and I am grateful to the University of Birmingham for permission to use them. Also I would like to thank the friends and colleagues who have read sections of the typescript and suggested improvements.

Contents

CHAPTER 1

Summary of Reactor Physics

INTRODUCTION

This chapter briefly summarises the basic principles of reactor physics. It is difficult to understand the need for many of the components of a nuclear power plant without some appreciation of the way in which the release of nuclear energy is achieved. More detailed information can be found in textbooks on reactor physics, e.g. [1,2].

FISSION

The source of the heat that is produced in a nuclear power plant is fission, i.e. the splitting of a large atom into two smaller atoms. The only naturally occurring isotope that is capable of a self-sustaining fission reaction is uranium-235. One possible reaction when this isotope is bombarded by neutrons is as follows:

$$_{92}U^{235} + {_0n^1} \rightarrow ({_{92}U^{236}}) \rightarrow {_{56}Ba^{141}} + {_{36}Kr^{92}} + 3{_0n^1}. \quad (1.1)$$

The superscripts in this equation are the mass numbers of the various isotopes, i.e. the number of nucleons (neutrons plus protons) in the nucleus. The subscripts are the atomic numbers, i.e. the number of protons in the nucleus, or the number of positive electrical charges. In nuclear reactions the number of nucleons is conserved and electrical charge is conserved.

Equation (1.1) is only one of many possible U^{235} fission reactions. The first step is always the formation of a compound nucleus of uranium-236. This immediately splits into two smaller nuclei plus two or three neutrons. As shown in Figure 1.1 there are a large number of possible fission products. The fission products are radioactive, having too many neutrons in the nucleus for stability, and in a few cases decay after a time of the order of a few seconds by emitting a neutron. The usual decay mode is to give out beta particles and gamma rays, i.e. a neutron in the nucleus turns into a proton plus an electron, and the electron (or β-particle) is ejected at high velocity. The β-emitters have half-lives ranging from seconds to years.

The two most important features of the fission reaction are the fact that more neutrons are produced than were required to initiate the reaction, and the large amount of energy released. On average 2.43 neutrons are produced per U^{235} fission, so there is the possibility of a self-sustaining chain reaction, at any rate in pure U^{235} (natural uranium is 0.7% U^{235} and the rest U^{238}). The total energy released per fission is about 200 MeV and the neutrons produced in

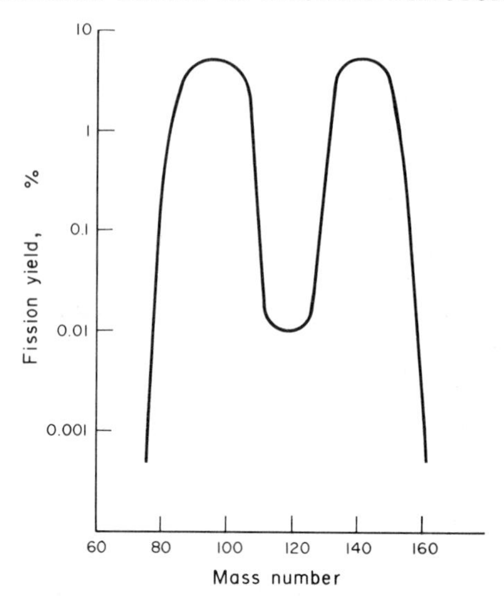

Fig. 1.1. Yield of the different fission products as a function of their mass number. Each fission produces two fission product nuclei, that tend to be of unequal size.

fission have an average kinetic energy of about 2 MeV. These quantities are related to SI units by

$$1 \text{ electron-volt} = 1 \text{ eV} = 1.602 \times 10^{-19} \text{ J}.$$

The distribution of this energy release in time and space is important, and the first step is to know how the energy is divided among the various particles. There are a number of extra points to note. Firstly, the particles produced in equation (1.1) are accompanied by γ-rays emitted instantaneously in fission. Secondly, there are other particles, antineutrinos, given off in association with β-decay. These go straight through the concrete shielding of the reactor, taking their energy with them. They contribute nothing to the heat output of the reactor, and will be ignored in what follows. Thirdly, some of the neutrons in the reactor are captured by other nuclei and do not undergo fission. A small amount of energy is released in the capture reaction, and more later if the new isotope is radioactive. This energy is not produced directly in fission, but must be taken into account in estimating the total heat output. The energy associated with each type of particle is given in Table 1.1.

TABLE 1.1. ENERGY RELEASED PER THERMAL FISSION OF U^{235} [3]

	MeV	%
Kinetic energy of fission products	166.2	82.4
Kinetic energy of neutrons	4.8	2.4
Initial γ-rays	8.0	4.0
β-particles	7.0	3.5
γ-rays associated with β-decay	7.2	3.6
Capture of neutrons	8.8	4.4
Total	202.0	100

The distance that the fission products and the β-particles travel in giving up their energy is short, so all their energy will appear as internal energy in the uranium fuel elements, i.e. the initial kinetic energy is converted to the random energy of movement of the individual atoms in the fuel. The fast neutrons and γ-rays have a range of several cm or more. The core is the region of the reactor containing the fuel, and there must in practice be other materials apart from uranium present, so the energy of the neutrons and γ-rays may appear anywhere in the core. However, the fuel elements are very massive, and most of the remaining energy will end up in the fuel as well. So perhaps 95% of the thermal energy will appear in the fuel, and 5% elsewhere in the core, the precise figures depending on the detailed design.

The next problem is what happens when the reactor is shut down. About 7% of the energy released is associated with the decay of the fission products. This will continue after the fission reactions have ceased, and there is no way of stopping it. While the 7% figure only applies for the first second or two heat will continue to be produced at a lower level indefinitely (equation (7.12)). The cooling system must therefore be capable of operating at a reduced level even when the reactor is shut down and no fission is taking place.

The value of 202.0 MeV for the total energy produced has an error of $\pm$ 0.6 MeV, and anyway depends slightly on assumptions made about the structure of the core in estimating the capture contribution, so for most purposes the energy released per fission can be taken as 200 MeV or 3.20×10^{-11} J.

NEUTRON FLUX AND REACTION CROSS-SECTIONS

In practice there will be many other isotopes present in the reactor in addition to U^{235}, and each of the isotopes is capable of at least two distinct types of nuclear reaction with the neutrons. We need some method of quantifying the probability of a particular reaction occurring, and this is given by the reaction cross-section. The definition of the reaction cross-section is itself bound up with the definition of neutron flux.

Suppose we have a beam of n neutrons per unit volume travelling in the same direction with velocity v. Then the *neutron flux* is

$$\phi = nv, \tag{1.2}$$

i.e. it is the number of neutrons striking unit area in unit time.

If this beam encounters a medium containing N atoms per unit volume of a particular isotope, and each atom has a microscopic *cross-section* for a particular nuclear reaction σ, then the rate of reaction is

$$R = nv\sigma N = \phi\sigma N \tag{1.3}$$

events per unit volume per unit time.

It is as if each nucleus presents an area σ to the flow of neutrons, and any neutrons striking this area cause a nuclear reaction. However, σ should not be thought of as the real physical cross-section of the nucleus since σ varies enormously with neutron speed v.

Numerical values of σ turn out to be of the order of 10^{-28} m^2, so it is convenient to measure σ in units of *barns*.

$$1 \text{ barn} = 10^{-28} \text{ m}^2$$

In addition to the microscopic cross-section we have just defined, there is a macroscopic cross-section $\Sigma = \sigma N$. So the reaction rate is given by $R = \phi\Sigma$.

The neutrons in a reactor are travelling in different directions and at different velocities, and the situation is much more difficult to visualise. The neutron flux is now defined as the number of neutrons crossing unit area perpendicular to their direction of travel per unit time integrated over all directions. Equation (1.3) still applies.

In addition to the *fission* reaction there are three other types of reaction that are important. There is *elastic scattering* in which the neutron simply bounces off the nucleus. Total kinetic energy is conserved which means that the neutron loses kinetic energy. All isotopes exhibit this form of scattering, so neutrons that escape any other type of reaction steadily slow down. Also there is *inelastic scattering* which is significant in U^{238} at energies over about 0.1 MeV. The neutron is absorbed to form a U^{239} nucleus, which immediately reverts to U^{238} giving out a neutron and a γ-ray. The net effect is that much of the kinetic energy of the neutron is lost to the γ-ray. Finally, there is *capture*, where an isotope of one higher mass number is formed. For example, in U^{238} at lower energies:

$$U^{238} + n^1 \rightarrow U^{239}.$$

In this case the neutron is lost to the system.

CRITICALITY

Since the process of separating U^{235} from U^{238} is very expensive, we can assume that at the start of any nuclear power programme the reactor will contain both isotopes. The problem of obtaining a self-sustaining chain reaction can perhaps best be understood by looking at Fig. 1.2, which shows the main reaction cross-sections for the two isotopes as a function of energy.

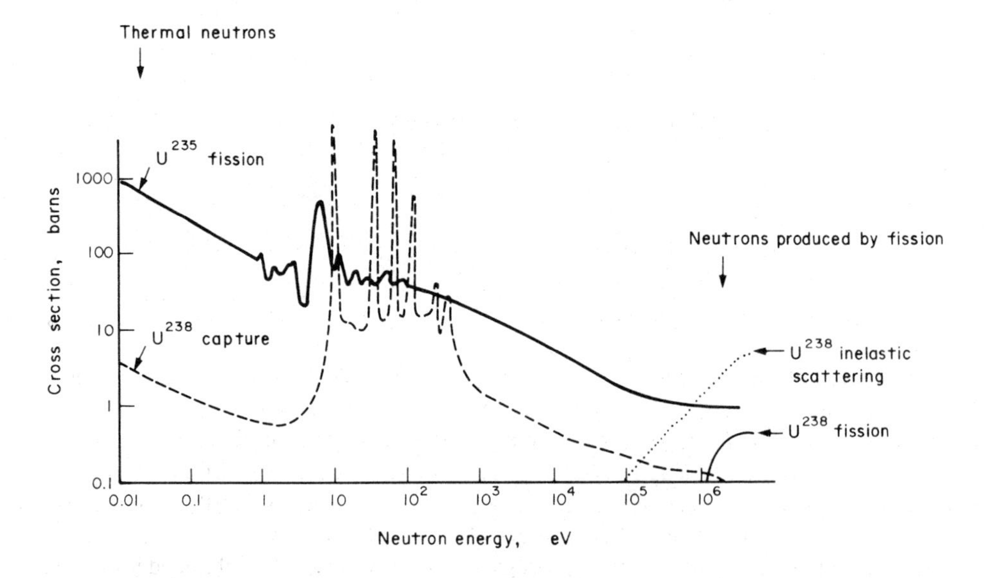

Fig. 1.2. Principal neutron reaction cross-sections for uranium.

The enormous range of energy shown can be explained as follows. The fast neutrons produced in fission have an energy of about 2 MeV, and if they are not absorbed in capture or fission reactions they will lose energy in scattering collisions. Their energy does not fall to zero, however; eventually they come into equilibrium with the energies of the nuclei, which themselves have a slight movement due to thermal vibration. This means that the neutrons slow down to an energy of rather under 0.1 MeV, and are then known as *thermal* neutrons.

To simplify the figure some of the cross-sections have been omitted. The elastic scattering cross-sections are a couple of barns and not strongly influenced by the neutron energy. U^{235} also has a capture cross-section, which is smaller than its fission cross-section but follows a similar pattern. The variation of the cross-sections with energy is obviously complicated, but can be partly explained by saying that at low energies what matters is the time that the neutron spends in the vicinity of the nucleus. This time is proportional to $1/v$ where v is the neutron velocity, so there is a range where the cross-sections are proportional to $1/v$. At higher energies, corresponding to the peaks on the graph, *resonance absorption* occurs. The energy available, i.e. the kinetic energy of the neutron plus the energy resulting from the initial capture reaction, is just right to bring the compound nucleus formed to one of its excited energy levels. When this happens the probability of reaction is greatly increased.

The fission process will be self-sustaining, i.e. the reactor will be *critical*, provided one of the neutrons produced in fission in due course causes another fission reaction. To start with we can dismiss the possibility of a chain reaction in U^{238}. The fast neutrons resulting from fission are more likely to be inelastically scattered than involved in a U^{238} fission, and just one inelastic collision is enough to reduce the neutron energy below the threshold for fission in U^{238}.

In natural uranium it is difficult to obtain a chain reaction because only 0.7% of the material is U^{235}. To offset this it is necessary for the U^{235} fission cross-section $\sigma_f(235)$ to be much larger than the U^{238} capture cross-section $\sigma_c(238)$. Simplifying the problem slightly by assuming that only two neutrons are produced per fission, i.e. the remaining 0.43 of a neutron is an allowance for capture in U^{235} and in the other materials that must in practice be present in the reactor, then one of these two neutrons must cause a fission in U^{235} and the other may be captured in U^{238}.

The rate of fission reactions is $\phi\sigma_f(235)\,N(235)$.
The rate of capture reactions is $\phi\sigma_c(238)\,N(238)$.

We require these to be equal, so

$$\frac{\sigma_f(235)}{\sigma_c(238)} = \frac{N(238)}{N(235)} = \frac{99.3}{0.7} = 142.$$

The only region of the graph (Fig. 1.2) where the ratio is as high as this is at thermal energies. The problem then is to get the fission neutrons from around 2 MeV to under 1 eV without them being captured in the U^{238} resonance region. This can be done if the uranium is distributed in a *moderator*, a substance that slows the neutrons down without absorbing them significantly. This type of reactor is called a *thermal reactor* because most of the neutrons are slowed down to thermal energies before they cause fission.

The above argument is for natural uranium, but the conclusion is unchanged if the uranium is enriched to two or three times the natural proportion of U^{235}. Enrichment does have the practical advantages of allowing more absorption in the moderator and in structural materials, and a longer period before the fuel has to be replaced.

Only with about 20% U^{235} (or plutonium in place of the U^{235}) is it possible to dispense with the moderator. The chain reaction now takes place with the fast neutrons and the reactor is a *fast reactor*. Up to now only prototype fast reactors have been built; all commercial power reactors are thermal ones.

MODERATORS

The moderator must have a very low capture cross-section, also a high elastic scattering cross-section is desirable. Equally important is the question of how much energy the neutron loses in each collision, which determines the number of collisions required to bring the neutron to thermal energies. A large number of collisions not only increases the chance of capture, it implies a large quantity of moderator. The energy lost in each collision can be analysed quite simply using classical mechanics. If a small object (the neutron) bounces off a large, massive object (the nucleus), and the total kinetic energy of the system is conserved, then the kinetic energy of the small object is only slightly reduced by the collision. The smaller the nucleus the more kinetic energy will be transferred to it. In the extreme case of the nucleus having the same mass as the neutron, and with a direct hit, then all the momentum of the neutron would be transferred to the nucleus, and the neutron would be brought to rest in just one collision. In fact, with hydrogen atoms in the moderator, this could happen, since the mass of the hydrogen nucleus is very nearly equal to that of the neutron. However, hydrogen captures neutrons too strongly for use with natural uranium fuel, so we will consider the other isotopes of low mass number as well. The first six elements in the periodic table are listed in Table 1.2.

TABLE 1.2. ELEMENTS OF LOW MASS NUMBER

Atomic Number	1	2	3	4	5	6
Name	Hydrogen	Helium	Lithium	Beryllium	Boron	Carbon
Mass Numbers	1,2	4	6,7	9	10,11	12
Comments		Gas	Absorber		Absorber	

Lithium and boron both absorb neutrons strongly; helium only exists as a gas and a prohibitively large volume would be required. Hydrogen, of course, is also a gas, but in the form of water it is possible to obtain a high density of hydrogen atoms (the oxygen does not absorb neutrons significantly). With hydrogen it is worth distinguishing between its two isotopes, ${}_1H^1$ and ${}_1H^2$, the first ordinary, or light, hydrogen, the second heavy hydrogen or deuterium, normally given the symbol D. Since heavy hydrogen has a very low neutron capture cross-section it is necessary to consider heavy water, D_2O, separately from light water, H_2O. Of the remaining elements in Table 1.2 beryllium is a potential moderator material, but it is expensive, toxic and difficult to fabricate. It has not been used in power reactors.

So we end up with only three moderator materials, ordinary water, heavy water and carbon (in the form of graphite). Only heavy water and graphite can be used with natural uranium. Ordinary water requires slightly enriched uranium, but it is cheap, very little is needed to thermalise the neutrons, and it can also be used as the coolant.

Both enriched uranium and heavy water require separation. The processes for separating the isotopes are large scale and expensive. There are only a few suppliers of enriched uranium around the world, and heavy water is only produced in large quantities in Canada. Until recently enriched uranium has only been available from plants that were initially set up to provide highly enriched material for military puposes.

BREEDING

U^{235} is the only naturally occurring *fissile* isotope, i.e. that fissions with neutrons of low energy and is capable of a self-sustaining reaction. However, other fissile isotopes are formed during the operation of nuclear reactors, in particular plutonium-239. The reactions leading to Pu^{239} are:

$$U^{238} + n^1 \rightarrow U^{239} \rightarrow Np^{239} + \beta \rightarrow Pu^{239} + \beta.$$

The half-lives of the intermediate isotopes are very short.

In a thermal reactor the rate at which Pu^{239} is produced is less than the rate at which U^{235} is burnt up, because the thermal fission of U^{235} (or other fissile isotopes) does not produce enough spare neutrons. However, fast fissions, in particular that of Pu^{239} itself, produce more neutrons. A fast reactor fuelled with plutonium and natural (or depleted) uranium is capable of producing more plutonium than it consumes. Such a reactor is a *breeder*. In this way, eventually, nearly all of the atoms in natural uranium can be burnt up in fission, instead of less than 1%. The initial supply of plutonium for fast reactors comes from thermal reactors.

THE MULTIPLICATION CONSTANT

The multiplication constant is defined as

$$k = \frac{\text{number of neutrons in one generation}}{\text{number of neutrons in previous generation}}. \tag{1.4}$$

If $k = 1$ then the neutron flux and power level stay constant; the reactor is *critical.* If $k < 1$ the neutron flux dies away to zero; the reactor is *subcritical.* If $k > 1$ the neutron flux and power increase; the reactor is *supercritical.*

For an infinitely large reactor, i.e. ignoring the problem of neutrons leaking out of the sides of the core, the multiplication constant is k_∞. The value of k_∞ depends on the materials used in the core and upon their arrangement. It does not depend on the overall size or shape of the core because we have assumed no leakage from the sides. In an infinitely large reactor the condition for criticality is just $k_\infty = 1$. In a finite reactor with leakage we will require $k_\infty > 1$ for criticality.

With natural uranium-fuelled, graphite-moderated reactors it is difficult to get k_∞ values of much over one. In particular it is important to use large diameter fuel rods to reduce the number of neutrons captured in the U^{238} resonance region. The effect of segregating the fuel and moderator is to ensure that the neutrons of intermediate energy, corresponding to the resonance absorption peaks, are found largely in the moderator.

NEUTRON FLUX DISTRIBUTION

To find the condition for a finite reactor to go critical, and the distribution of neutron flux within the core, we need to study the diffusion of neutrons. The simplest approximation is to assume that the neutrons all have the same energy (thermal). This is called *one group neutron diffusion theory*. The diffusion equation for the rate at which the number of neutrons per unit volume n increases with time is

$$\frac{dn}{dt} = D\nabla^2\phi + s - \Sigma_a\phi \tag{1.5}$$

where s is the source of neutrons per unit volume and $\Sigma_a\phi$ the rate at which neutrons disappear through absorption (i.e. the reaction rate equation; Σ_a is the total absorption cross-section for all the isotopes present). $D\nabla^2\phi$ gives the rate at which the neutrons diffuse into the volume of interest from outside. D is called the diffusion coefficient.

Considering a uniform, *homogeneous* reactor, where even the smallest elementary volume can be considered to contain some fuel, moderator, coolant, etc., and the proportions of these constituents remain constant, then the values D and Σ_a are independent of position. In a reactor the source of neutrons is fission and, since the ratio of new fission neutrons produced to neutrons absorbed depends only on the materials of the reactor and is not affected by leakage, we can write $s = k_\infty \Sigma_a \phi$. Further, for an exactly critical reactor, $dn/dt = 0$, so equation (1.5) simplifies to

$$\frac{\nabla^2\phi}{\phi} = -\frac{(k_\infty - 1)\,\Sigma_a}{D} = -\frac{(k_\infty - 1)}{L^2} \tag{1.6}$$

where L is the diffusion length and $L^2 = D/\Sigma_a$ (it is possible to show that L is a measure of how far the neutron diffuses before being absorbed).

The one group neutron diffusion theory takes no account of the distance travelled by the neutrons while they are slowing down to thermal energies, with the result that equation (1.6) is a poor approximation. Consequently, it is modified to take account of the neutron slowing-down length L_s as follows:

$$\frac{\nabla^2\phi}{\phi} = -\frac{(k_\infty - 1)}{(L^2 + L_s^2)} = -B_m^2; \tag{1.7}$$

B_m^2 is the *material buckling*, and depends purely on the materials and lattice structure. The quantity $\nabla^2\phi/\phi$ depends only on the geometry of the reactor and the boundary conditions and is called the *geometrical buckling*. For a critical reactor the two bucklings are equal to one another (the term buckling comes from the similarity of equation (1.7) to the equation for the buckling of a loaded rod).

The boundary condition for the solution of equation (1.7) is very nearly that the neutron flux falls to zero at the edge of the core, and for large water-moderated reactors it is sufficient to take $\phi = 0$ at the edge. When graphite-moderated reactors are surrounded by more moderator to act as a reflector, reflecting neutrons back into the core, the neutron flux behaves as though it is going to fall to zero some distance outside the core. So equation (1.7) is solved with the flux falling to zero at the *extrapolated* boundaries of the core. (This is an approximate solution, and gives erroneous values for the flux level in the reflector itself.)

From the point of view of minimising neutron leakage the best core shape is a sphere, but it is convenient to make all the fuel elements and coolant channels the same length, with the result that the cores of power reactors are roughly cylindrical. In terms of the extrapolated length L' and radius r_0 of the cylinder (i.e. the physical dimensions of the core plus the extra distance on each side), the neutron flux is given in z, r coordinates with their origin at the centre of the core as

$$\phi = \phi_0 \, J_0(2.405r/r_0) \cos(\pi z/L') \tag{1.8}$$

where J_0 is the Bessel function of the first kind, zero order, and ϕ_0 is the maximum value of the neutron flux, which occurs at the centre of the core.

For a given fuel enrichment the rate of fission reactions and hence the rate of energy production is directly proportional to the neutron flux. So the distribution of ϕ is also the distribution of power.

Substituting ϕ from equation (1.8) back into equation (1.7) gives the geometrical buckling as

$$\frac{\nabla^2\phi}{\phi} = \left[\frac{\pi}{L'}\right]^2 + \left[\frac{2.405}{r_0}\right]^2. \tag{1.9}$$

Note that the absolute level of the neutron flux, given by the value of ϕ_0, cancels out of equations (1.7) and (1.9), and does not enter the condition for criticality. The reactor can be critical at any level of ϕ_0. Nothing in the reactor physics restricts the neutron flux or the heat output that can be achieved. In practice the heat output is limited by the ability of the cooling system to remove the heat and by the ability of the materials to withstand high temperatures.

Equation (1.8) is a quite close approximation to the overall flux distribution in a reactor with uniform enrichment. There are local variations in flux within fuel elements and between the fuel and the nearby moderator, but we have excluded these from equation (1.8) by assuming a homogeneous reactor. In practice it is usual to vary the radial enrichment, as will be explained in more detail in Chapter 8, so the radial variation in flux is more complicated. The axial variation remains a cosine however.

PRACTICAL REACTOR SYSTEMS

Both fuel and moderator are essential for a thermal reactor to go critical. To produce power other components are required. The fission products are highly radioactive and must be contained, normally by sealing the fuel in metal cans. The heat must be removed, normally by coolant flowing in direct contact with the cans. The power output must be controlled at the desired level and it must be possible to shut the reactor down. This is usually done by means of rods containing a material that absorbs neutrons strongly, such as boron.

In most reactor designs the coolant operates at a high pressure, either to raise its boiling point (water-cooled reactors), or to reduce the pumping power required to circulate it (gas-cooled reactors).

All the materials and equipment required for the core are manufactured to a high standard, and obviously the system is more expensive than the combustion chamber of a conventional power station, where finely divided coal or oil is burnt in a stream of air. A feature of nuclear power stations is the high capital cost. Fuel costs on the other hand are low, since the total amount of energy produced by a kilogram of uranium is enormously greater than that produced by a kilogram of coal or oil.

SUMMARY

The behaviour of the neutrons in the core, and in particular the conditions needed to obtain criticality, impose a number of constraints on the design of the rest of the system, which can be summarised as follows.

For thermal reactors a moderator material of low atomic weight is essential.

Only materials with low neutron absorption cross-sections can be used.

The high capital cost of the core requires a high rate of return if the system is to be economic, and this in turn implies a high rate of energy generation and an efficient heat-transfer system.

With natural uranium fuel only graphite or heavy water have low enough neutron absorption to be used as moderators. It is not easy to get a natural uranium reactor to go critical; the arrangement of fuel and moderator must be carefully chosen, and very few materials are suitable for the fuel cans.

With enriched uranium fuel a wider range of materials may be used, in particular ordinary water may be used as the moderator.

References

1. BENNET, D. J. *The elements of nuclear power*, Longman, 1972.
2. LAMARSH, J. R. *Introduction to nuclear reactor theory*, Addison-Wesley, 1966.
3. JAMES, M. F. Energy released in fission. *J. Nucl. Energy* **23**, 517–536 (1969).

CHAPTER 2

Reactor Systems

INTRODUCTION

In this chapter the main reactor systems are briefly described. The summary is confined to those reactor types that are either currently in use for power production or are reasonably likely to be brought into use in the near future. More detailed information on reactor systems may be found in the articles that appear from time to time in the journal *Nuclear Engineering International*, and in the relevant volumes of the *Directory of Nuclear Reactors* [1].

In the course of the last 10 years or so a small number of reactor types have each acquired a significant amount of operating experience as commercial power plants. The very high development costs associated with the introduction of these systems have been paid. It seems unlikely that the cost of developing a new, untried, system can now be justified simply on the basis of some minor, claimed, advantage. Probably the only new systems that are likely to stand a chance of future development are those with some really distinctive feature: for example, the fast breeder reactor, with its utilisation of nearly all the atoms in natural uranium instead of under 1% and the high temperature reactor, with the possibility of process heat applications.

Since nearly all of the systems to be described have a number of common features it is worth listing them here. The fuel is normally in the form of uranium dioxide, enclosed in metal cans. The fuel cans are cooled on the outside by a coolant flowing parallel to the axis of the cans. The primary coolant circuit is usually pressurized, so either the whole core is enclosed in a large pressure vessel or the individual coolant channels are enclosed in pressure tubes. Normally the primary coolant from the core then goes to a boiler to produce steam, and the steam then expands through a turbine to drive the electricity generator.

THE PRESSURIZED WATER REACTOR

This reactor type, normally abbreviated to PWR, uses ordinary water as both moderator and coolant. Water is particularly effective as a moderator, containing as it does a high density of light hydrogen atoms, so the fuel rods may be packed close together and the core is quite small for a given power output. This made the PWR the natural choice for a nuclear submarine propulsion unit; the early development of the PWR was for this purpose rather than for electricity generation. To prevent the water boiling it must be kept at a high pressure (around 150 bar). This is done by placing the core in a steel pressure vessel. Reactors of this general type are in operation or under construction in most of the industrialised countries of the world.

The primary coolant circuit of a PWR is shown in Fig. 2.1. The hot water from the core leaves the main pressure vessel and enters tubes inside the steam generator. A separate supply of water at a lower pressure flows round the outside of the tubes, boils, and produces steam. The steam is separated from any remaining water by devices similar to those to be described later for boiling water reactors, and dry saturated steam is passed to the turbine. After expansion in the turbine the steam is condensed back into water and returned to the steam generator (details of the steam cycle are given in Chapter 9). In the primary circuit the cooler water leaving the steam generator enters a centrifugal pump and is returned to the core. The number of coolant loops is variable, but typically for a large reactor there would be four steam generators, each with its own primary circuit pump.

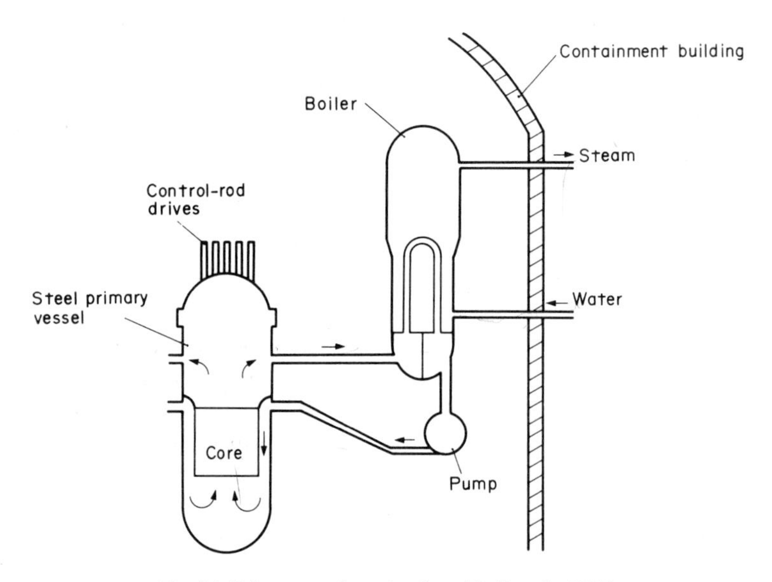

Fig. 2.1. Primary coolant circuit and boiler of a PWR.

In addition to the features shown in Fig. 2.1 there are other tanks connected to the primary circuit pipework. A surge tank is required to accommodate thermal expansion of the water. This tank contains steam and water. The steam pressure and temperature are kept constant either by electrical heaters or by spray injection of cooler water. This determines the pressure levels throughout the circuit, so the surge tank is called the *pressurizer*. Other tanks are associated with the emergency core cooling system. Water is stored in these tanks, under nitrogen which is maintained at a pressure lower than the normal primary circuit value. If, as a result of an accident, the pressure in the primary circuit falls below that in the tanks, then valves open automatically to allow the emergency cooling water into the core. There is also a pumped high-pressure water injection system for use in emergencies.

The steel reactor vessel is about 4 m diameter and has walls about 200 mm thick, protected on the inside by a thin layer of stainless steel. The whole of the primary circuit is surrounded by a reinforced concrete containment building, designed to prevent the possible escape of radioactivity should a pipe in the primary system burst.

A cross-section through the pressure vessel in the region of the core is shown in Fig. 2.2. The core is made up of square fuel assemblies arranged, so far as is possible, into a cylindrical shape. The core is surrounded by a baffle to confine the flow of coolant to the fuel assemblies. The baffle is supported by the core barrel. The thermal shield is a thick sheet of steel, designed to reduce the neutron and γ-ray dose received by the wall of the pressure vessel. The cooling water flows down on both sides of the thermal shield before entering the core.

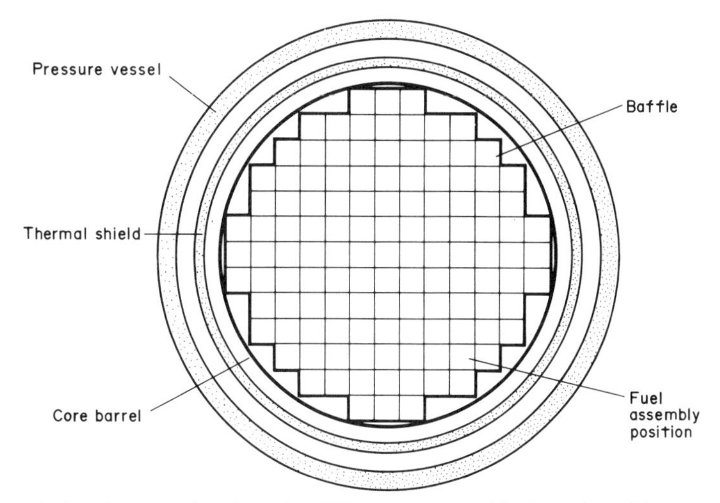

Fig. 2.2. Cross-section through a PWR pressure vessel in the region of the core.

The assemblies of fuel rods are generally open, i.e. there is no physical barrier preventing flow of coolant from one assembly into another. The following information applies to the Sequoyah nuclear power station [2,3], but a number of other stations built at about the same time have the same design of fuel assembly. This power plant is in Tennessee, U.S.A. It was designed by the Westinghouse Electric Corporation and has been in operation since 1978. Each of the two reactors has a net electrical output of 1140 MW. A cross-section through a fuel assembly is shown in Fig. 2.3. The fuel rods consist of 9.3-mm-diameter pellets of uranium dioxide inside 10.7-mm o.d. Zircaloy tubes. The rods extend the full 3.66 m height of the core. The pitch of the rods is 14.3 mm. Not all of the lattice positions in the 15 by 15 arrray are occupied by fuel rods; there are 204 fuel rods and 21 hollow guide tubes. The assembly is held together by grids at several axial positions, that are themselves attached to the guide tubes. The main function of the guide tubes is to permit the several elements of the control-rod assembly to move in and out of the core. Since it is not necessary to have a control-rod assembly for every fuel-rod assembly the guide tubes in many of the fuel assemblies are redundant, and consequently blanked off to prevent a wasteful flow of coolant through them.

The water enters the core at 285°C, flows past the fuel rods at an average velocity of 4.7 m s^{-1} and leaves the core at 321°C. These are rather low temperatures and lead inevitably to a low overall plant efficiency. The ratio of electrical power sent out of the plant to thermal power produced in the core is only 0.33.

Short-term control of reactor power is achieved by movement of the control rods, which contain indium and cadmium absorbers. Long-term changes in reactivity are allowed for by varying the concentration of boric acid dissolved in the water.

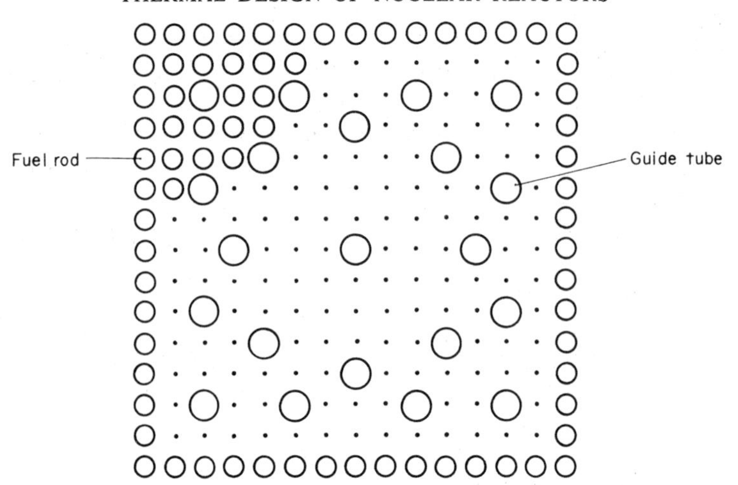

Fig. 2.3. Cross-section through a PWR fuel assembly. Not all of the fuel rods are shown.

Refuelling requires the reactor to be shut down for about a month each year. The top of the pressure vessel is unbolted and the head lifted out of the way. The core is covered with a sufficient depth of water to reduce the radiation to a safe level, and some of the fuel assemblies are replaced.

Other types of pressurized water reactor

Since ordinary water absorbs neutrons strongly and requires enriched uranium there are advantages in using heavy water instead.

In the CANDU type of reactor (CANadian Deuterium Uranium) heavy water is used as both moderator and coolant. Since heavy water is less effective at slowing down the neutrons it is necessary to use considerably more heavy water to achieve the same moderating effect. The core is consequently larger and it is difficult to design a single pressure vessel to enclose it. Instead the individual fuel channels are placed in pressure tubes, with several assemblies of short fuel rods placed one after another inside the tube, and heavy water flowing past. More moderator is needed in the spaces between the pressure tubes, but since this heavy water has no cooling function there is no reason for it to be at high temperature or pressure, and it is convenient to have it at essentially atmospheric pressure. This part of the moderator is therefore contained in a large tank, the callandria tank, which does not have to take a significant pressure difference.

Although the CANDU type of reactor requires a supply of heavy water this is largely offset by the fact that it uses natural uranium fuel (in the form of UO_2). Natural uranium reactors require frequent refuelling, because the amount of U^{235} in the fuel rapidly drops below the minimum required for criticality. By having a horizontal cylinder for the core and horizontal fuel channels access is gained to both ends of the channels. Refuelling is on load, with a new fuel assembly being inserted at one end of the channel and an old one being removed at the other end. A single assembly therefore moves along the channel during the course of its life in the reactor.

THE BOILING WATER REACTOR

The boiling water reactor (or BWR) is a fairly obvious alternative to the PWR. If the water is allowed to boil within the core, and the steam passed directly to the turbine, then there is no need for a separate steam generator. This of course implies radioactive steam in the turbine, but there are other disadvantages as well. The space between the fuel rods is taken up with a mixture of water and steam, and since the steam contributes very little to the moderation of the neutrons the rod spacing must be made larger than in a PWR. Also, the water–steam mixture is not quite such a good heat-transfer medium, and the maximum value of the heat flux from the surface of the rods is slightly lower. Consequently, the power density in a BWR core is lower, and the core must be larger for a given power output. However, the pressure in BWRs, at about 70 bar, is only half the value for PWRs, so there is no difficulty in containing the larger core in a single pressure vessel.

The two light water-moderated and cooled reactor systems, the PWR and the BWR, account for the great majority of power reactors built or under construction around the world. No other system is established on a world-wide basis.

The BWR pressure vessel is again of steel, protected on the inside by a layer of stainless steel, with typical dimensions of 5.5 m i.d. and 140 mm wall thickness. As shown in Fig. 2.4 the upward flow of water through the core is achieved with the aid of a large number of jet pumps. The main centrifugal pumps are located outside the pressure vessel, and produce a high-velocity jet of water at the throat of the jet pump. The high-velocity flow causes a fall in pressure and more water is sucked in. The advantage of this system is that only about a third of the recirculating water required through the core has to leave the main vessel, and the pipes penetrating the vessel wall can be made that much smaller. The efficiency of the jet pumps is low however.

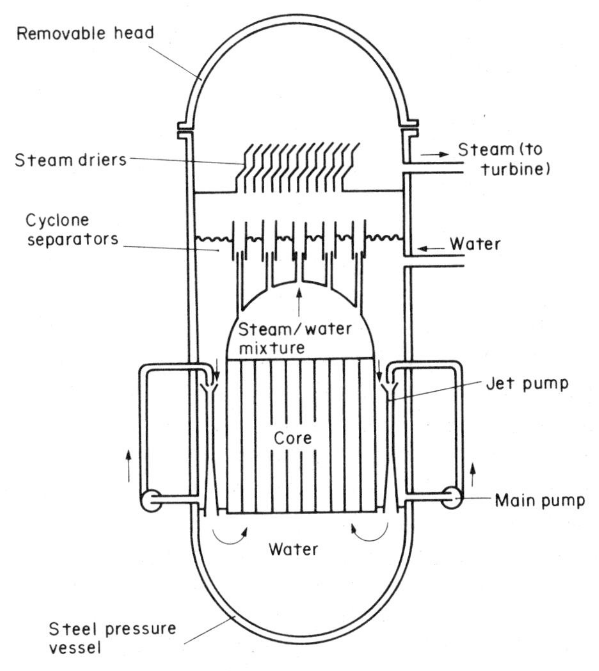

Fig. 2.4. BWR pressure vessel.

On leaving the core the steam is separated from the water by passing the mixture through cyclone separators. These contain fixed vanes that impart a rotary motion to the flow. The water drops are thrown to the sides by centrifugal force and drain back down, to be circulated again through the core. The steam goes on to the steam driers, where any remaining water drops are removed by passing the steam along tortuous paths between corrugated metal sheets. The steam can follow the rapid changes of direction, but the inertia of the water drops carries them to the sides. The water then drains away down the surfaces of the metal sheets. The dry saturated steam goes on to the turbine.

The primary circuit, i.e. the pressure vessel and the main centrifugal pumps, is surrounded by a reinforced concrete containment building. To reduce the volume of the containment building the pressure-suppression principle is often used. In the event of a break in a pipe much of the steam released would be condensed by leading it below the surface of water in a large vapour-suppression pool.

In order to make the description more precise we will now give details of the core and fuel elements used in the Brunswick plant designed by the General Electric Company [4]. The plant is located in North Carolina, U.S.A., and has two reactors, each producing a net electrical power of 821 MW. It has been in operation since 1975. The fuel assemblies are similar to those used in PWRs in that they are square in cross-section, the fuel rods themselves are on a square lattice and contain slightly enriched UO_2. However, the rods are larger, 14.3 mm diameter, and more widely spaced, 18.8 mm pitch. There are only 49 rods to a fuel assembly, in a 7 by 7 array, and the assembly is surrounded by a square Zircaloy wrapper, so there is no possibility of coolant flowing sideways from one assembly to the next. The water enters the core about 10°C subcooled and the water–steam mixture leaves at 285°C. The steam conditions are not very different to those in the PWR and give a similar net efficiency of 0.337.

More recent designs of BWR tend to have smaller fuel rods in order to increase the power output from a given size of core. For example, 12.5 mm diameter rods in an 8 by 8 array that will fit into the same size of channel that previously took the 7 by 7 assemblies [5].

Since it is not feasible to dissolve a neutron absorber in a boiling coolant, the control of the BWR relies largely on control rods. These are of cruciform section, and fit into the space between four neighbouring fuel assemblies. The neutrons are absorbed by boron carbide granules within the rods. The control system is unusual in that the rods enter from the bottom of the core, a consequence of the space above the core being taken up by the steam-separation equipment. It does have the advantage of counteracting the extra moderator present in the lower part of the core, and so giving a more uniform power distribution. During normal operation the power level can be increased simply by increasing the coolant flow rate. The immediate result of an increased coolant flow is a smaller proportion of steam in the core, giving greater moderation and a higher thermal neutron flux. The increased heat output causes more steam to be produced, and the reactor settles down to a new, higher, power level.

Refuelling is done by unbolting the top of the pressure vessel when the reactor is shut down, much as in the PWR, but with the additional complication that the devices for separating the steam and water must also be removed.

THE GAS-COOLED REACTOR—THE AGR

The first gas-cooled reactors were built to produce plutonium for weapons manufacture rather than to produce power. They used natural uranium fuel and graphite moderator, and were air cooled. When the first reactors for electricity production were planned in the U.K. it was decided to take advantage of the experience already gained with the gas–graphite plutonium production reactors. Also the materials required for the other reactor types (enriched uranium or heavy water) were not available in the U.K. at that time. For electricity production much higher temperatures are required, and air is unsuitable as a coolant because it reacts chemically with the graphite. Also it is necessary to use a closed circuit with the gas under high pressure to reduce losses of radioactivity and improve the heat transfer, so there would be little advantage in using air anyway. The gas chosen was carbon dioxide, since it was cheap, compatible with graphite at moderate temperatures, and has a high heat capacity.

As an example of a gas-cooled reactor we will describe in detail not the early natural uranium type but instead the enriched uranium AGR (Advanced Gas-cooled Reactor), since this is the type currently being built in the U.K. One of the aims behind the design of the AGR was to obtain steam conditions similar to those used in conventional coal- and oil-fired power stations. This is something that cannot be done with water-cooled reactors because water is by its very nature not a high-temperature material. With higher steam temperatures and pressures it is, of course, possible to turn a higher proportion of the heat produced by the reactor into electricity. A gas temperature at the core outlet of around 650°C is needed, but the graphite cannot withstand a temperature as high as this for the whole of the life of the plant, so the moderator must be cooled (graphite reacts with the carbon dioxide to form carbon monoxide).

The core and boilers of one type of AGR are shown in Fig. 2.5. The whole of the primary circuit is contained within a single prestressed concrete pressure vessel. There are no ducts as such to lead the hot gas from the core to the boilers, the gas is simply drawn down through the boilers by the pumps. The cool gas is then pumped out, to follow a number of different paths, some of them rather circuitous, before finally reaching the inlet to the fuel channels. About half of the gas discharged from the pumps goes directly to the bottom of the core; the other half goes up the annular gap between the boiler shield wall and the gas baffle and then divides again, part going down through the graphite moderator to cool it, and part cooling the boiler shield wall. The function of the boiler shield wall is to reduce the radiation dose received by the boilers, giving access to the boilers when the reactor is shut down. The gas baffle is a steel vessel separating the hot gas from the cool gas.

The gas flowing up the fuel channels past the fuel rods is separated from the rest of the core by a continuous graphite sleeve surrounding the channel. When the hot gas reaches the top of the core it is ducted through the region of cool gas and comes out above the gas baffle.

The cylindrical prestressed concrete pressure vessel is about 20 m i.d. with side walls 5 m thick. The top and bottom concrete slabs are rather thicker. Since the concrete is considered to have no strength in tension this enormous wall thickness is not needed to withstand the normal internal gas pressure of about 40 bars; the outward force is resisted by the steel prestressing cables running in channels on the outside of the concrete, and the concrete simply transmits the force from gas to cables. The tension in the cables is preset, and can only be altered one cable at a time, so the same tension is present if the reactor is shut down and depressurized. The full force of the cables is now taken by the concrete, and the thickness of the concrete has to be sufficient to prevent the concrete being crushed when there is no internal gas pressure. This concrete wall also serves as an effective biological shield.

The large size of the pressure vessel follows from the large size of the core, which in turn follows from the large quantity of graphite needed to moderate the neutrons and the somewhat low energy generation rates that are possible with gas cooling. It is difficult to design steel pressure vessels in these very large sizes, so the prestressed concrete vessel is preferred. It has the further advantages that it is possible to include the boilers in the main vessel as well,

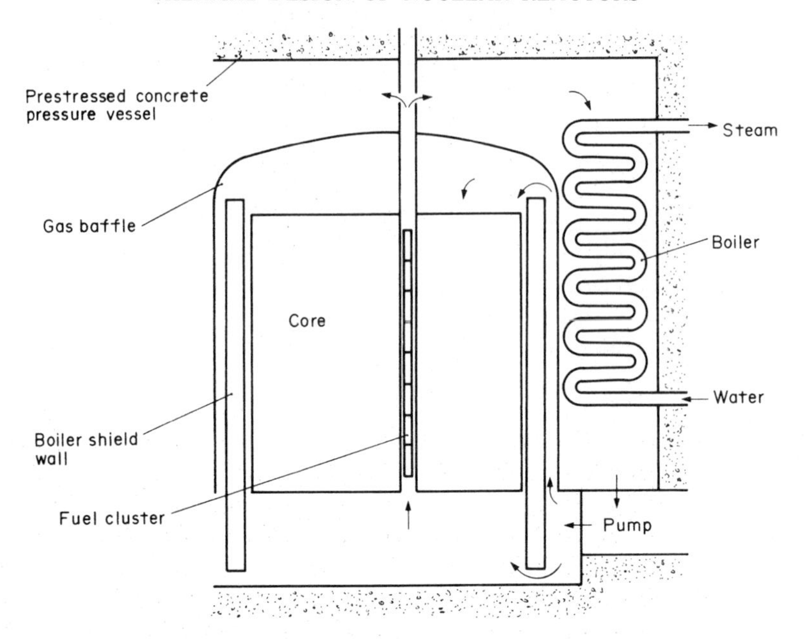

Fig. 2.5. Layout of an AGR within the prestressed concrete pressure vessel. Only one out of a couple of hundred fuel channels is shown.

and that sudden failure due to propagation of a crack is inconceivable: a failure in one prestressing cable cannot propagate to neighbouring cables.

Since the main vessel is already a containment in the sense that it contains the primary circuit it is not usual to provide a separate reinforced containment building.

The design of the AGRs varies a little from station to station. Some have the boilers in vertical channels within the concrete walls. The general description above and detailed information to follow apply to the Hinkley Point "B" plant in Somerset, U.K., designed by the Nuclear Power Company [6,7]. There are two reactors on the site, each designed for a net electrical output of 621 MW. Power production started in 1976.

As shown in Fig. 2.5 there are eight fuel clusters stacked vertically on top of each other in each fuel channel. The core is built up (Fig. 2.6) of sixteen sided graphite bricks, linked by smaller, square, interstitial bricks. Each of the main bricks contains a fuel channel. Some of the interstitial bricks have a central hole for a control rod. The downward flow of carbon dioxide that is used to cool the graphite goes partly through the gaps between the bricks, partly through the holes in the interstitial bricks and partly through the annular gap between the graphite sleeve of the fuel assembly and the moderator bricks. The graphite bricks are connected by keys, but free to slide past one another in the vertical direction. In this way differential thermal expansion is allowed for, and the channels remain vertical and under their respective control rod or fuel standpipe positions.

An individual fuel cluster (shown in cross-section in Fig. 2.7) consists of thirty-six fuel rods, 15.25 mm o.d., inside a 190-mm i.d. graphite sleeve. Eight fuel clusters, each just over 1 m long, together with a plug unit to lead the hot gas out above the core, are joined together by a central tie rod and comprise one fuel assembly. This is loaded into the fuel channel and subsequently removed as one unit. The graphite sleeve is an integral part of the assembly and is

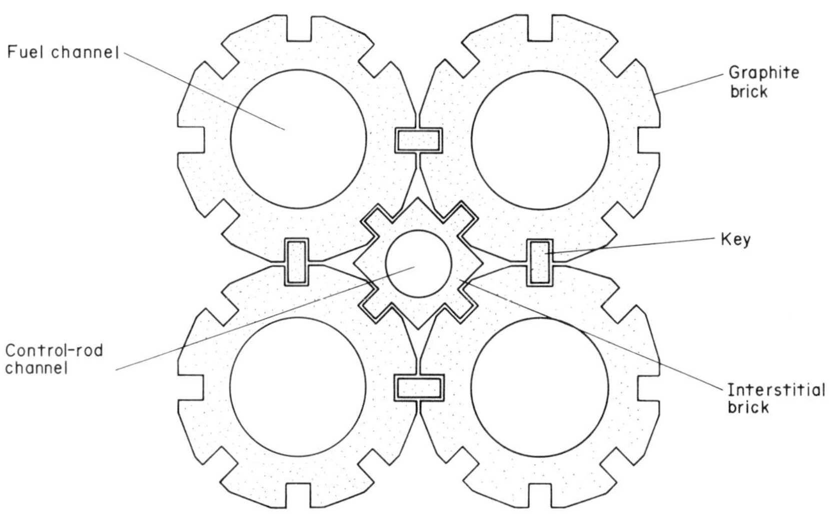

Fig. 2.6. Cross-section through part of AGR core.

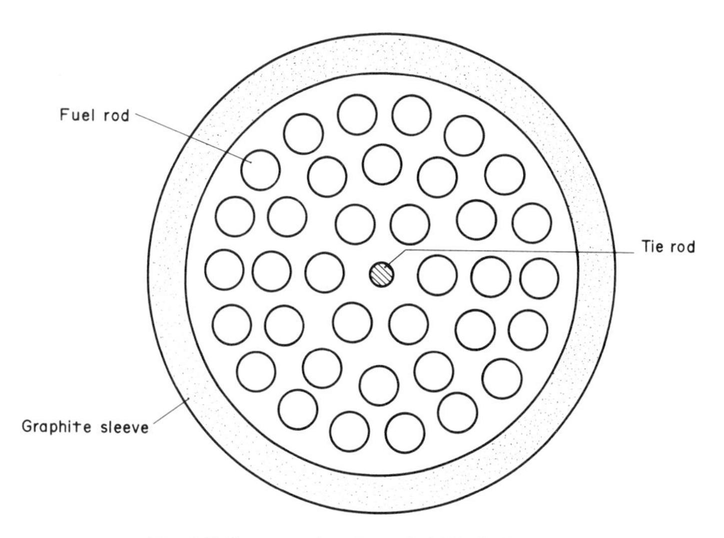

Fig. 2.7. Cross-section through AGR fuel assembly.

replaced when the fuel is replaced, since it has been in direct contact with the hot gas. The fuel cans have small circumferential ribs at 2-mm intervals to improve the heat transfer. The fuel consists of 14.4-mm o.d. pellets of enriched UO_2.

The carbon dioxide enters the core at 294°C and leaves at 645°C. Its velocity increases significantly along the channel as the gas expands, but the mean value is about 20 m s^{-1}. In this way the surface temperature of the stainless-steel cans is kept below 825°C. The high core outlet temperature enables steam to be produced in the boilers at 541°C and 170 bars pressure, giving a net plant efficiency of 0.412.

Other types of gas-cooled reactor—the Magnox reactor

The early carbon-dioxide-cooled power reactors, built in the U.K. and France, use natural uranium fuel, which is restricting because it is difficult to get the reactor to go critical. With graphite moderator the minimum size of core for criticality is large. Also the fuel rods have to be quite large, in order to reduce the number of neutrons absorbed in the U^{238} resonance region. One design uses uranium metal fuel in the form of 28-mm diameter rods. Only materials of very low neutron absorption may be used in the core, leading to the use of magnesium or magnesium alloys for the cans. The name of this reactor type in the U.K. is Magnox, after the name of the particular alloy chosen for the cans. One advantage of the Magnox type of material is a high thermal conductivity, so the heat transfer may be improved by adding fins to the cans. Since uranium metal and Magnox alloy are both limited to rather low temperatures (uranium metal undergoes a phase change at 660°C and Magnox melts at 640°C), the heat-generation rates and power densities are low.

The finned fuel rods are stacked vertically on top of one another in individual vertical channels in the graphite. Since the fuel rods are loaded and unloaded one at a time, and anyway with natural uranium the fuel must be replaced frequently, refuelling is a continuous process and carried out on load. The later reactors of this type have prestressed concrete pressure vessels, the earlier ones steel vessels. Typically the inside diameter is about 20 m.

Although this type of reactor in now considered to have been superseded, in the U.K. by the AGR and in France by the decision in 1969 to switch to light-water-moderated and cooled reactors, it is interesting to note that for several years now it has produced electricity more cheaply than coal- or oil-fired power stations.

Other types of gas-cooled reactor—the HTR

An important feature of the AGR is the high core outlet temperature. However, the temperature cannot be increased much further with the AGR concept since oxidation of the graphite and stainless-steel cans by the carbon dioxide would become excessive. Most metals in fact are unsuitable for high temperature use in the core. The next stage in the evolution of the gas-cooled reactor is to replace the carbon dioxide by inert helium gas as the coolant, and to do away with metal cans completely. The fuel is now in the form of tiny spheres, a fraction of a mm in diameter, coated with a dense layer of pyrolytic carbon. This coating contains the fission products and performs much the same function as the fuel can. Large numbers of these spheres are incorporated in a graphite matrix to make the fuel elements. This type of reactor is called the high-temperature gas-cooled reactor, variously abbreviated to HTR or HTGR. The main interest in the HTR lies in the possibility of using the heat from the core directly in various industrial processes, such as steel-making. However, the core outlet temperature would have to be raised considerably above the 750°C that has been obtained in prototype reactors.

Two large prototype HTRs have been built. The Fort St Vrain plant [8] in the U.S. has a net electrical output of 330 MW, and has been in operation since 1976. The fuel spheres in the graphite matrix are made up in the form of rods and inserted in holes in graphite blocks. Separate channels through the blocks are provided for the flow of coolant. The German prototype HTR [9] is of similar size and is expected to produce power in 1982. This plant is of the "pebble bed" type, that is the fuel is made up into graphite spheres, 60 mm diameter. The core consists of a bed of these spheres, which are free to move about. There is a continuous, on-load, process of removing individual spheres and checking whether they need to be replaced. In each of these reactors the fuel assembly combines fuel and moderator.

THE SODIUM-COOLED FAST BREEDER REACTOR

The fast reactor has no moderator to thermalise the neutrons, and it can only go critical if its fuel contains a high proportion of fissile atoms, for example 20 to 30% plutonium and the rest natural uranium. The reactor breeds new fuel because the U^{238} captures neutrons to turn in due course into more plutonium. Compared to a thermal reactor where the fissile atoms (normally U^{235}) are at a concentration of only a couple of a per cent in the fuel, the fast reactor fuel is very concentrated and expensive. If the fissile atoms are to be burnt up at a similar rate in each case then the energy generation rates in the fast reactor will be much higher. Consequently fast reactors have smaller fuel rods and require very effective cooling. Water is unsuitable as a coolant since it is a moderator. The usual coolant is liquid sodium since it has very good heat-transfer properties. Also it is cheap and compatible with structural materials, in particular, stainless steel.

The correct timing for the introduction of the fast breeder reactor on a commercial scale is a little uncertain. It will not have a significant economic advantage until the price of uranium rises considerably above the present level in real terms. At the moment very little of the cost of electricity generated from nuclear power stations is due to the cost of the original uranium. However, most of the world's known uranium reserves are required for the future supply of the thermal nuclear reactors that are already in operation or under construction. A significant expansion of the nuclear power programme will require the discovery of new uranium deposits, the working of lower-grade ores, or the introduction of the fast breeder reactor. It is interesting to note that countries that have had a large number of thermal reactors operating for some years must have large stockpiles of U^{238}, either in the form of spent fuel elements or from the enrichment plants. Since U^{238} is the raw fuel material for the fast reactor these countries would not need to import more uranium to fuel any fast reactors they might build.

Large prototype fast breeder reactors, all sodium cooled, are in operation in France, the U.K. and the U.S.S.R. The first commercial sized plant, of 1200 MW electrical output, is under construction at Creys-Malville in France [10]. Most of these plants are of the pool type, with the whole of the primary coolant circuit immersed in a pool of liquid sodium. The description that follows is for a pool type of reactor, and where specific values are quoted they are for the Prototype Fast Reactor at Dounreay in Scotland [11,12], which has been in operation since 1975.

The boiling point of liquid sodium at atmospheric pressure is 880°C, so there is no need to pressurize the coolant to prevent boiling, and there is no pressure vessel. The tank containing the pool of sodium and the primary circuit is shown in Fig. 2.8. It is not possible to fill a closed vessel completely with liquid, there must be some allowance for thermal expansion, so the space between the top of the tank and the sodium surface is filled with an inert gas (argon). The argon is maintained at just slightly over atmospheric pressure to ensure that any leaks are out of the system rather than in. The primary tank is surrounded by a leak jacket, so that in the event of a leak the sodium level would not fall so far as to expose the core. Even with the reactor shut down the core must be immersed in sodium to remove the decay heat.

Sodium at about 400°C is drawn into the pump and then forced upwards past the fuel pins

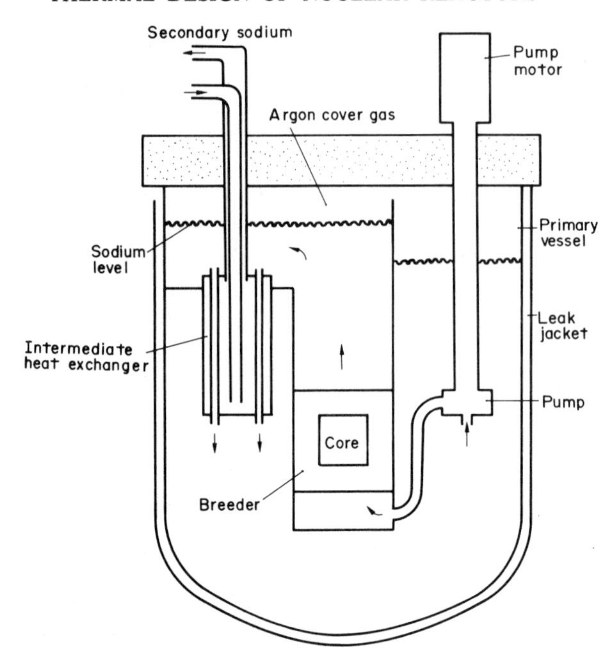

Fig. 2.8. Primary coolant circuit in a fast breeder reactor.

in the core. The core is surrounded by breeder regions containing depleted uranium. The hot sodium at 562°C from the core then flows down through tubes in the intermediate heat exchangers, and transfers heat to a secondary sodium flow on the shell side of the heat exchanger. The secondary sodium then goes to the steam generator. The complete separation of the primary and steam circuits by means of this intermediate sodium circuit is done partly to avoid having radioactive sodium in the boiler and partly to prevent any possibility of steam or water leaking into the primary tank. In addition to the vigorous chemical reaction between water and sodium there is the danger of hydrogen in some form or another being swept through the core and causing a sudden increase in reactivity.

The core (of the Prototype Fast Reactor) is only 1.45 m diameter by 0.91 m high, very small for the heat output of 600 MW. The fuel is mixed uranium and plutonium dioxide, in stainless-steel cans 5.84 mm o.d. The fuel rods are arranged on a triangular lattice with a pitch of 7.4 mm, 325 fuel rods to a fuel assembly. The hexagonal fuel assemblies are surrounded by wrappers.

The core outlet temperature is sufficient to give steam conditions similar to those in conventional plant, and the net plant efficiency is 0.423.

References

1. *Directory of Nuclear Reactors*, International Atomic Energy Agency, Vienna. The volumes containing details of power reactors are 4, 7, 9 and 10.
2. *Nucl. Engng Int.*, **16**, 845–859 (1971).
3. Reference 1, Vol. 10, pp. 179–184.

4. Reference 1, Vol. 10, pp. 253–258.
5. *Nucl. Engng Int.*, **17**, 414 (1972).
6. Reference 1, Vol. 10, pp. 313–318.
7. Hinkley Point B Nuclear Power Station, Nuclear Power Company, Whetstone, England.
8. *Nucl. Engng Int.*, **14**, 1069 (1969).
9. Reference 1, Vol. 10, pp. 305–312.
10. *Nucl. Engng Int.*, June 1978, p. 43.
11. The Prototype Fast Reactor, United Kingdom Atomic Energy Authority, Risley, England.
12. Reference 1, Vol. 9, pp. 219–226.

CHAPTER 3

Fuel-Rod Design

INTRODUCTION

Fuel for nuclear power reactors is usually made in the form of rods. The fuel must be contained in a sealed can to prevent escape of the gaseous fission products, and cylindrical cans loaded with fuel are stronger and easier to fabricate the rectangular plate fuel elements. Although in some reactors the fuel rods are loaded into the core and removed one at a time, operations which have to be performed while the reactor is producing power to avoid lengthy shutdowns, the usual practice is to combine tens or even hundreds of rods into an assembly which is put into the core and comes out again as one unit.

The internal energy produced in the fuel by fission causes heat to flow to the surface of the can by conduction. The heat is then removed by the flow of coolant past the can surface. A knowledge of the temperature distribution in the fuel rod is needed in order to be able to predict its performance, in particular the highest fuel temperature, which occurs in the middle of the fuel region, will be limited by the need to avoid undesirable changes in the material. Melting of the fuel must be avoided, and in practice there are usually other effects which are even more restricting.

When the rods are manufactured there is a small clearance between the fuel pellets and the can. At power in the reactor the fuel is at a higher temperature than the can, expands more, and the gap is largely closed, but normally the design has a very small gap even at power. Heat transfer across the gap will be by conduction through the gas present, since there is no room for convection currents to set up. So the analysis of temperature distribution concerns three conduction processes, through the fuel, gap and cladding.

This chapter is concerned only with the steady-state situation, where the temperature distribution does not change with time. Some transient cases of interest in the loss of coolant accident are examined in Chapter 7.

TEMPERATURE DISTRIBUTION IN A CYLINDRICAL FUEL PELLET

To a first approximation the neutron flux will be uniform throughout the fuel pellet and the rate of internal energy generation will be uniform. In a typical fuel rod of a little over 10 mm diameter and a couple of metres long the radial variation of temperature is very much greater than the axial variation and axial conduction may be neglected. For the moment we will assume that the thermal conductivity of the fuel is independent of temperature.

The problem then is that of radial conduction of heat out of the cylindrical region inner

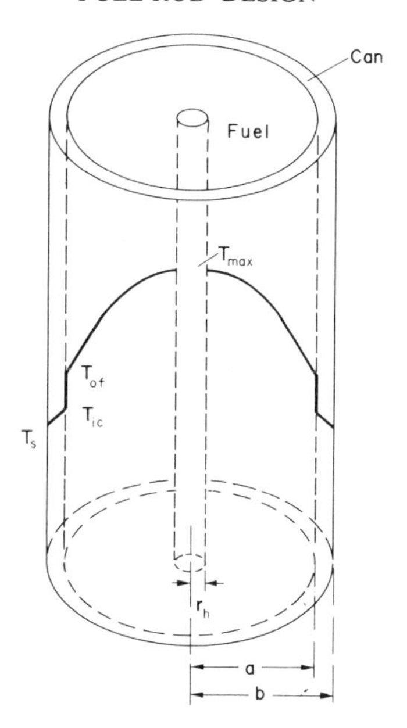

Fig. 3.1. Section of a typical fuel rod with the temperature distribution superimposed. The gap between the fuel and the can is too small to be shown on this scale, but it is responsible for a significant temperature rise.

radius r_h, outer radius a, as shown in Fig. 3.1, with uniform power generation and properties, and with the boundary condition of known temperature on the outside of the fuel T_{of} (T_{of} is not known at the moment but it can be found from the heat transfer processes outside of the fuel region).

Suppose that the rating of the fuel rod, i.e. the total rate at which energy is produced per metre length of the rod, is R watts/metre. Then the rate of energy production within a radius r is

$$\frac{r^2 - r_h^2}{a^2 - r_h^2} R$$

since the power produced is in proportion to the volume of fuel.

Now in equilibrium this rate of internal energy production must equal the rate at which heat is conducted out through the cylindrical surface at r, i.e.

$$-k 2\pi r \frac{\mathrm{d}T}{\mathrm{d}r}$$

where k is the thermal conductivity and T the temperature.

So

$$-k\mathrm{d}T = \frac{R}{2\pi(a^2 - r_h^2)}(r - r_h^2/r)\,\mathrm{d}r, \tag{3.1}$$

so the temperature at a radius r is given by

$$T_r = T_{of} + \frac{R}{2\pi k\,(a^2 - r_h^2)} \left[\frac{a^2 - r^2}{2} - r_h^2 \ln \frac{a}{r} \right] \tag{3.2}$$

and the maximum fuel temperature is

$$T_{\max} = T_{of} + \frac{R}{2\pi k\,(a^2 - r_h^2)} \left[\frac{a^2 - r_h^2}{2} - r_h^2 \ln \frac{a}{r_h} \right]. \tag{3.3}$$

For a solid rod $r_h = 0$ and the temperatures are

$$T_r = T_{of} + \frac{R}{4\pi k}(1 - r^2/a^2) \tag{3.4}$$

and

$$T_{\max} = T_{of} + \frac{R}{4\pi k} \tag{3.5}$$

since the r_h^2 term in equation (3.3) tends to zero much faster than the $\ln(a/r_h)$ term tends to infinity.

So for a solid rod with the heat output expressed as a linear rating the centre to edge temperature difference is independent of rod size.

Alternatively, this analysis could have started from the standard differential heat conduction equation in cylindrical coordinates. For purely radial variation it reduces to

$$k\nabla^2 T = k\left[\frac{d^2T}{dr^2} + \frac{1}{r}\frac{dT}{dr}\right] = -H \tag{3.6}$$

where H is the rate of energy production per unit volume.

Using the relation

$$\frac{1}{r}\frac{d}{dr}\left[r\frac{dT}{dr}\right] = \frac{d^2T}{dr^2} + \frac{1}{r}\frac{dT}{dr}$$

the equation becomes

$$k\frac{d}{dr}\left[r\frac{dT}{dr}\right] = -Hr$$

which integrated between r_h and r gives

$$k\left[r\left(\frac{dT}{dr}\right)_{r=r} - r_h\left(\frac{dT}{dr}\right)_{r=r_h}\right] = -\frac{H}{2}(r^2 - r_h^2)$$

and since, from symmetry, there is no heat flow at $r = r_h$, $(\mathrm{d}T/\mathrm{d}r)_{r=r_h} = 0$ and

$$k \frac{\mathrm{d}T}{\mathrm{d}r} = -\frac{H}{2}(r - r_h^2/r)$$

which is equation (3.1) because

$$R = H\pi(a^2 - r_h^2). \tag{3.7}$$

Although it is true that for a solid pellet the temperature rise in the fuel depends only on the linear rating R, and is independent of pellet radius, it does not follow that the size of the fuel rod is irrelevant. The linear rating is a useful and widely used concept, and it has the advantage of having the same dimensions as the quantity $\int k\mathrm{d}T$ which is introduced below, but it is not particularly fundamental. Because of the high capital cost of the core of a nuclear reactor it is important to get the maximum output for a given size and weight, that is, the volumetric energy production rate H must be high. Equation (3.7) shows that this requires small rods, and in fact by the end of Chapter 8 it will be clear that all the heat transfer processes require small-diameter rods. Since the cost of fabricating the rods increases roughly in proportion to the total number of rods the diameter chosen is a compromise. An exception to this is provided by the Magnox reactors in the U.K. where large-diameter rods are needed to increase the resonance escape probability. With natural uranium fuel the design is dominated by the difficulty of making the reactor go critical.

Allowance for variations in conductivity and heat generation

In practice the thermal conductivity of the fuel varies with temperature and the heat-generation rate is reduced in the centre of the fuel because the thermal neutron flux is lower there. Since the thermal neutrons can be considered as arising in the moderator, they enter the fuel rods from outside, some are absorbed in the outer part of the fuel, and the flux is lower in the centre.

Since all the energy produced within a radius r must still in the steady state be conducted out through the cylindrical surface at r as heat, it is again possible to write

$$-k2\pi r \frac{\mathrm{d}T}{\mathrm{d}r} = \text{rate of energy production within radius } r$$

and if the rate of energy production is known as a function of radius then

$$\int k\mathrm{d}T = \text{function of space coordinates,} \tag{3.8}$$

i.e. it is possible to separate the conductivity which depends on temperature and the energy generation rate which depends on radius, and in principle each side of the equation can be integrated.

Consider first the right-hand side of equation (3.8). For thermal reactors the neutron flux depression has been calculated [1] and the centre to edge temperature difference for a solid rod is given by

$$\int_{T_{of}}^{T_{max}} k\mathrm{d}T = \frac{R}{4\pi}\left[\frac{I_0(a/\lambda)-1}{(a/2\lambda)\,I_1(a/\lambda)}\right] = \frac{R}{4\pi}F \tag{3.9}$$

where I_0 and I_1 are the modified Bessel functions of zero and first order respectively, and λ is the fuel diffusion length. λ depends on how strongly the thermal neutrons are absorbed in the fuel, i.e. upon the enrichment since U^{235} absorbs thermal neutrons much more strongly than U^{238}. Consequently the factor F will depend upon the enrichment and size of the fuel pellet, and the most serious deviations from the simple analysis of equation (3.5) will occur for large rods heavily enriched in U^{235}. This combination of parameters does not occur in power reactors and the correction factor F is normally close to unity. Fast reactor fuel is enriched to about 20% but the fast neutrons are less easily absorbed and the assumption of uniform energy generation throughout the fuel is again a good one.

Considering now the left-hand side of equation (3.8), if k is a known function of temperature this should present no problems. However, in practice it is not easy to measure k under the conditions of temperature and irradiation that exist inside a reactor. Instead equation (3.9) is used as a method of measuring $\int k\mathrm{d}T$. A temperature in the centre of the fuel is established using a thermocouple or more commonly a change in the material which is known to occur at a certain temperature, such as melting, and the fuel surface temperature is calculated from the coolant temperature. If now the right-hand side of the equation is known from the local power produced in the fuel rod and its geometry then the value of $\int k\mathrm{d}T$ between the two temperatures can be calculated. By making measurements at other temperatures a chart can be constructed of $\int k\mathrm{d}T$ as a function of temperature. Since the main use that this information will be put to is to evaluate fuel-rod temperatures in other reactor designs, there is no reason to turn $\int k\mathrm{d}T$ values into values of k, and frequently therefore $\int k\mathrm{d}T$ is used as a parameter in its own right.

Example. Calculate the centre temperature of a solid uranium dioxide fuel pellet that has a linear heat rating of 45 kW m^{-1} and a surface temperature of 600°C,

(a) for uniform heat generation and $k = 2.7$ W m^{-1} K^{-1};

(b) with k constant at 2.7 W m^{-1} K^{-1} again but allowing for flux depression, assuming an enrichment of 3% giving $F = 0.97$;

(c) for uniform heat generation but using Fig. 3.2 for $\int k\mathrm{d}T$;

(a) is just a question of substituting in equation (3.5), which gives the centre temperature as 1926°C;
(b) including the factor F gives

$$T_{max} = T_{of} + \frac{R}{4\pi k}F = 1887°\mathrm{C};$$

(c) equation (3.9) gives

$$\int_{600}^{T_{max}} k\mathrm{d}T = \frac{R}{4\pi}$$

or

$$\int_{500}^{T_{max}} k\mathrm{d}T - \int_{500}^{600} k\mathrm{d}T = \frac{R}{4\pi} = 3581.$$

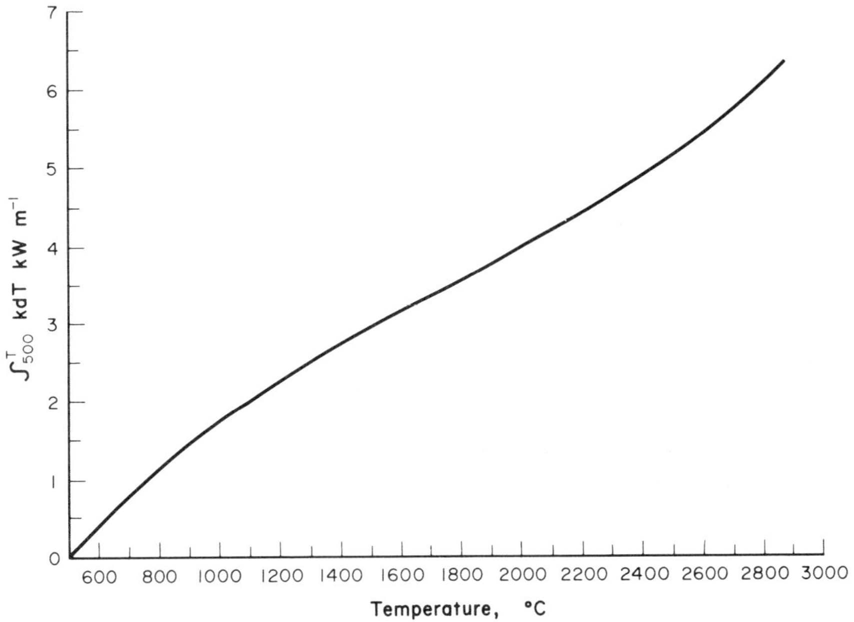

Fig. 3.2. $\int_{500}^{T}$ for sintered uranium dioxide with 95% of maximum density.
For convenience in reading accurate values a larger scale graph is presented in Appendix 5.

By inspection of Fig. 3.2 $\int_{500}^{600} k\mathrm{d}T$ is found to be 400 W m^{-1} and so

$$\int_{500}^{T_{\max}} k\mathrm{d}T = 3981 \text{ W m}^{-1}.$$

Reading 3981 W m^{-1} off the $\int_{500}^{T} k\mathrm{d}T$ axis on Fig. 3.2 gives $T_{\max} = 2000°\text{C}$ approximately.

The effect of the flux depression in the centre of the fuel is small, and often neglected. The variation of UO_2 thermal conductivity with temperature is significant and must be allowed for. The example could be criticised on the grounds that 2.7 W m^{-1} K^{-1} was a poor choice for the conductivity, but it is below the average of the conductivities at 600 and 2000°C.

Effect of porosity on UO_2 *thermal conductivity*

The main fuel material is uranium dioxide, UO_2. The starting-point for uranium dioxide manufacture is uranium hexafluoride since both the diffusion and centrifuge enrichment processes require gaseous uranium hexafluoride and rely on the very slight difference in molecular weight between $U^{235}F_6$ and $U^{238}F_6$. After a series of reactions with different gases UO_2 is left in the form of a fine powder. The powder is sintered at about 1700°C to make the fuel pellets which inevitably have a residual porosity. A porosity of around 5% is used for reactor work, that is, about 5% of the pellet volume is occupied by spaces. To produce 100% dense material by melting the UO_2 would be difficult since the melting-point is 2865°C [2,3]. Also the fuel tends to swell under irradiation and a small amount of porosity is helpful in accommodating this swelling. The extremely high melting point of this ceramic fuel is the reason that it can be used, because, as was seen in the example above, the thermal conductivity is very low.

The presence of these voids in the fuel naturally reduces the thermal conductivity. For the idealised case of porosity P that consists of isolated spheres of zero conductivity in a matrix of conductivity k_0, the expression derived by Maxwell [4] reduces to

$$k = K_0 \frac{1 - P}{1 + 0.5P}. \tag{3.10}$$

In practice the voids cannot be taken to be isolated and spherical, and they may well vary in shape from one sample to another. To allow for this various empirical expressions have been suggested, such as

$$k = k_0 \frac{1 - P}{1 + \alpha P} \tag{3.11}$$

and

$$k = k_0 (1 - \beta P) \tag{3.12}$$

where the values of the geometrical factors α and β have to be determined experimentally. Concentrating on equation (3.12) which for small values of P is essentially the same as equation (3.11) anyway, and comparing it with equation (3.10), the value of β for isolated spherical pores is seen to be 1.5. Experimental values of β show a wide scatter but average to around 2.5 [5,6]. $\int k \mathrm{d}T$ values can also be corrected using equation (3.12).

A number of more sophisticated methods of allowing for the effect of porosity have been proposed, including theoretical ones that require an accurate knowledge of the shape of the pores and whether or not they are interconnected [7], and empirical ones based on experimental results that have a temperature dependent porosity correction [8].

Measurements of UO_2 *thermal conductivity*

A good review of conductivity measurements was provided by the IAEA in 1966 [6], and for temperatures up to 1300°C, for unirradiated, sintered, 95% dense UO_2 they recommend

$$k = \frac{100}{5.33 + 0.0235T} \text{ W m}^{-1} \text{ K}^{-1} \tag{3.13}$$

where T is in K. This is based on the work of six laboratories working with samples ranging from 92 to 97% dense, and correcting to 95% using equation (3.12) with $\beta = 2.5$. The recommended values are considered to be correct to within $\pm$ 3% at a 95% probability level. Measurements made in reactors at fairly modest levels of irradiation are less accurate, but they are consistent with equation (3.13) for temperatures above 500°C. Below 500°C the effect of irradiation is to quickly reduce the conductivity to the value at 500°C, suggesting that the damage produced by irradiation cannot be annealed out at these low temperatures. Above 1300°C the very few experimental measurements are in poor agreement and no recommendation is made.

It is very difficult to make measurements in the reactor. The insertion of a number of thermocouples at different radial positions in the fuel is not feasible because of its low thermal conductivity and the very high temperature gradients that would exist across them. Instead it is more usual to have one measurement of temperature in the centre of the fuel pellet where the temperature gradient is low, and a temperature in the cladding is either measured or calculated from the coolant temperature and the local heat-generation rate. The measurement is therefore of $\int k\mathrm{d}T$ rather than of k, and is subject to some uncertainty because the clad inner surface temperature is not the same as the fuel outer surface temperature due to the poor contact between them. Thermocouples have been used up to 1800°C with a few measurements using special high-temperature thermocouples up to 2150°C, and gas bulb thermometers have been used at still higher temperatures, but the number of high-temperature measurements is small. Much more work has been based on an indirect determination of the centre fuel temperature, using a change in the UO_2 structure that is visible in post-irradiation examination.

Above about 1500°C the UO_2 recrystallises, the new grains being equiaxed, and above about 1800°C columnar grains grow, radiating out from the centre of the fuel pellet. However, the best indirect temperature indication is the melting-point at 2865°C. Even here there is uncertainty since the fuel is observed after it has resolidified, and the boundary is not quite sharp.

One review of this subject [2] recommends

$$\int_{500}^{2865} k\mathrm{d}T = 6.3\ \mathrm{kW\ m^{-1}}. \tag{3.14}$$

500°C is a convenient starting point for $\int k\mathrm{d}T$ values since the conductivity is not affected by irradiation above 500°C and in practice all the fuel in a reactor is likely to be at temperatures over 500°C.

Armed with no more information than equations (3.13) and (3.14) it is possible to make a reasonably accurate estimate of k and $\int k\mathrm{d}T$ throughout the temperature range. Since the thermal conductivity is presumably a smooth, continuous function of temperature any equation for it must join on smoothly to equation (3.13) at 1300°C and give the required $\int k\mathrm{d}T$ of 6.3 kW m^{-1}. Suppose that the thermal conductivity is given by

$$k = a + bT + cT^2$$

The values of a, b and c can be found from the three boundary conditions, that is, from the value of the integral conductivity to melting, and the requirement that k and $\mathrm{d}k/\mathrm{d}T$ are continuous at 1300°C.

The equation obtained in this way for temperatures above 1573 K, with T in K, is

$$k = 7.73 - 0.005\,51T + 1.333 \times 10^{-6}\,T^2\ \mathrm{W\ m^{-1}\ K^{-1}}. \tag{3.15}$$

The error that is likely in values of k calculated from equation (3.15) increases as the temperature increases, from 3% at 1300°C to probably around 10% at the melting-point. Schmidt [9] reported the results of a large number of laboratory measurements of conductivity, from different laboratories but using 98% dense UO_2 pellets from a common source. The average of these measurements, corrected to 95% density, is in good agreement with equations (3.13) and (3.15) up to 2000°C, but at 2500°C is some 10% higher than the value predicted by equation (3.15). On the other hand, another set of results [2] are in equally good agreement up to 2000°C but at 2500°C are some 10% lower than the value predicted by equation (3.15).

For convenience in performing calculations $\int k\mathrm{d}T$ values based on equations (3.13) and (3.15) are plotted in Fig. 3.2.

The thermal conductivity of mixed uranium and plutonium dioxide, such as is used in fast reactors, is very similar to that of UO_2.

As mentioned before, conductivity values after short irradiations are consistent with laboratory measurements, which is a little surprising in view of the changes that take place in the UO_2 structure. In addition to the recrystallisation, the high temperature gradients and low strength of UO_2 inevitably result in cracks. At high irradiations the conductivity does appear to fall. Apart from anything else the material is no longer stoichiometric UO_2; in a fast reactor 10% of the heavy metal atoms could have been burnt up.

HEAT TRANSFER IN THE GAP BETWEEN FUEL AND CLADDING

When the fuel rods are manufactured a radial gap of about 0.1 mm is allowed between the outer surface of the fuel and the inner surface of the can. A clearance of this order is required if the fuel pellets are to slip easily into the cans. When the rods are put into the reactor and the reactor is taken up to full power the fuel reaches a much higher average temperature than the can and so expands more, and the gap is nearly closed. It would be possible to design for complete closure of the gap, but because of the roughness of the two surfaces they would only come into contact at high points on the surfaces and over much of the interface there would still be a gap of approaching 0.01 mm, so it is more usual to design for a gap in operation of around 0.01 mm to avoid any danger of straining the can unnecessarily.

The cans are filled at atmospheric pressure, but in an atmosphere of helium rather than of air, which avoids corrosion and gives good initial heat transfer. Because the gap between the two surfaces is so small it is not possible for convection currents to set up in the gas, and heat transfer can be regarded as taking place by conduction through the gas, assisted by direct contact between the surfaces at local high spots. Initially the gas in the gap is helium, but as time goes on more and more fission product gases will be released from the fuel, and towards the end of its life in the reactor the gas will consist almost entirely of xenon and krypton. Thermal conductivity measurements on fission product gas, which is about 15% Kr and 85% Xe, as well as on other inert gases and mixtures, are available [10].

The gap heat transfer is usually expressed in terms of a gap heat transfer coefficient or conductance h_g. If the temperatures of the outside of the fuel and the inside of the cladding are T_{of} and T_{ic} respectively then the heat flux across the gap is

$$\frac{R}{2\pi a} = h_g\,(T_{of} - T_{ic})\ \mathrm{W\ m^{-2}} \tag{3.16}$$

and if the heat transfer is purely by conduction through the gas across a uniform gap of width l, then

$$h_g = k_g/l\ \mathrm{W\ m^{-2}\ K^{-1}} \tag{3.17}$$

where k_g is the thermal conductivity of the gas.

The thermal conductivities of helium and of fission product gas, at 520°C, are 0.30 and 0.014 W m^{-1} K^{-1} respectively, so for a gap of 0.01 mm the heat transfer coefficients would be 30,000 and 1400 W m^{-2} K^{-1} respectively. Some recent experimental work suggests that this simple model of the heat transfer in the gap is a good one. The size of the gap during power operation in the reactor was not measured directly, but calculated from the measured fuel centre temperature [11]. Since the rods were only in the reactor a short time the effect of fission product gas was simulated by filling some rods with xenon. However, other workers have failed to find the dramatic difference between helium and xenon filling that one would expect from the thermal conductivities [12].

The estimates of h_g above suggest that the heat transfer in the gap deteriorates markedly with irradiation. However, this is for a constant gap width. In practice, the fuel swells due to the build-up of fission products and the can creeps down on to the fuel because the coolant pressure is normally much higher than the pressure inside the can. So the contact between fuel and can tends to improve with time, to some extent offsetting the lower conductivity. The degree of contact between the surfaces depends on the surface roughness, the hardness of the materials, and the pressure that is pushing them together. Various analyses are available that include the effect of direct solid to solid contact on the heat transfer [13,14].

HEAT TRANSFER THROUGH CYLINDRICAL CLADDING

The final conduction heat transfer process before the energy reaches the coolant is through the cladding.

The total rate of heat flow through any cylindrical surface of radius r in the cladding will be constant at R W m^{-1}, so

$$R = k_c \, 2\pi r \frac{dT}{dr}$$

and when this is integrated between the inner radius of the cladding a and the outer radius b, then

$$T_{ic} - T_s = \frac{R}{2\pi k_c} \ln (b/a). \tag{3.18}$$

The cladding thickness is usually sufficiently small for the heat transfer through the cladding to be treated as conduction through a plane wall with negligible error.

Bringing equations (3.3), (3.16) and (3.18) together the overall fuel-rod temperature difference, from the centre of the fuel to the outer edge of the cladding is

$$T_{\max} - T_s = \frac{R}{4\pi k}\left[1 - \frac{2r_h^2}{(a^2 - r_h^2)} \ln \frac{a}{r_h}\right] + \frac{R}{2\pi a h_g} + \frac{R}{2\pi k_c} \ln (b/a) \tag{3.19}$$

The principal cladding material in water reactors is Zircaloy, zirconium with about 1% tin and very small amounts of other metals. Stainless steel has been used in PWRs but is being replaced by Zircaloy which has a lower neutron absorption. Stainless steel is suitable for higher temperatures than Zircaloy and is used in some gas-cooled reactors and the sodium-cooled fast reactor. The cans for the AGRs in the U.K. are made of steel containing 20% Cr and 25% Ni, while type 316 stainless steel was used for the first charge of the U.K. Prototype Fast Reactor. Thermal properties of various fuel and cladding materials are given in Table 3.1, together with limiting temperatures of the materials and the nature of the limitation.

TABLE 3.1. THERMAL PROPERTIES OF FUEL AND CLADDING MATERIALS

Material	Density (kg m^{-3})	Conductivity {W m^{-1} K^{-1} (at °C)}	Specific heat {J kg^{-1} K^{-1} (at °C)}	Melting-point (°C)	Limiting temp. (°C)
Uranium	19,000	30.5 (400) 33.4 (600)	155 (400) 188 (600)	1130	660 α–β phase change
Uranium dioxide *95% dense	10,400*	4.2* (500) 2.8* (1000) 2.2* (1500) 2.1* (2000)	309 (500) 324 (1000) 342 (1500) 432 (2000)	2865	M.p., also fission gas release
Magnesium	1740	163 (200) 157 (300)	1170 (400) 1254 (600)	650	M.p.
Zircaloy 2	6570	12.7 (300) 13.1 (400)	328 (300) 357 (650)	1850	400 reaction with UO_2
Stainless steel 20/25	7900	16 (400) 19 (600) 21 (800)	530 (200) 580 (400)	1400	815 oxidation in CO_2
Stainless steel 18/12/1 also 304, 347	7900	20 (400) 24 (600) 26 (800)	530 (200) 580 (400)	1400	

FISSION GAS RELEASE

The real limitation on UO_2 fuel temperatures is not the possibility of fuel melting but the high pressure exerted by the fission product gases, the release of which increases rapidly with temperature. About 15% of the fission products consist of the inert gases xenon and krypton. Initially they are present in enforced solution in the lattice of the UO_2 crystals, but gradually they come out of solution and start to exert the normal gas pressure. At low temperatures virtually all the xenon and krypton is held inside the fuel, but as the temperature increases more and more comes out of the solid solution. The details of this process are very complicated, but various empirical models have been suggested relating the proportion of the gas that is released to the temperature. For example a pessimistic design model that has been used by the General Electric Company assumes 4% release up to 1649°C (3000°F) and 100% above 1649°C [2]. Usually the release is related to the changes that are observed in the UO_2 structure, e.g. [15].

Temperature	UO_2 structure	% Release
700–1500°C	Unchanged	0
1500–1800°C	Equiaxed grain growth	25–50
Above 1800°C	Columnar grain growth	100

An internal pressure due to fission gas as high as the external coolant pressure is normally allowed. Higher fission gas pressures would tend to make the can expand away from the fuel, the fuel to can heat transfer would worsen and the fuel temperature rise, releasing more fission gas and thus causing further deterioration. Since in liquid-metal-cooled fast reactors the coolant is not pressurised a much stronger can is required.

DETAILS OF FUEL-ROD CONSTRUCTION

The individual fuel pellets are approximately cylindrical with a length equal to or larger than the diameter. The flat faces are in fact slightly concave, so that the stack of pellets inside the can are in contact with one another only at their outside diameter, and axial expansion of the column is limited to the fuel surface temperature.

Difficulties can arise due to the fact that the pellets are not positively located within the can, and at times are able to move axially relative to the can. At full power the fuel is likely to be in good contact with the can, to the extent that it may grip it and stretch it. At low power the fuel may contract and come away from the can sufficiently for the pellets to slump, i.e. drop under gravity so that each is standing on the one below. A small space is left at the top of the stack. In the next cycle the process is repeated and the space becomes larger. This phenomenon is known as ratchetting. If a sufficiently large void appears the can may collapse into it under the pressure of the coolant. Such collapses have been observed, but they were probably caused by fuel of rather low density becoming more dense and shrinking, allowing the pellets to slump. To limit the effects of ratchetting grooves are sometimes put round the fuel pellets and the can pressed into them during manufacture. For example, the AGR fuel has a groove in every fifth pellet. These anti-stacking grooves limit the number of pellets that can stack on top of one another to five.

The ends of the can are sealed by welded end caps and checked for leak-tightness by mass spectrometry. To prevent the end caps coming into contact with the high temperatures of the fuel alumina insulating pellets are often used. It is interesting to note that the thermal conductivity of the alumina "insulator" is higher than that of the UO_2 fuel.

While the proportion of the fission product gases that actually appears in gaseous form depends on the temperature in the fuel, what really matters is the pressure they exert, and this can be reduced by providing a volume for them to expand into. Normally a space is provided at one end of the fuel rod, the fission gas plenum. If there is a significant variation of coolant temperature along the length of the fuel rod as in a fast reactor it is best to have the space at the coolant inlet end, since a lower gas temperature will result in a lower gas pressure.

References

1. Robertson, J. A. L. *$\int kd\theta$ in fuel irradiations*, AECL Report No. 807, 1959.
2. Lyons, M. F., Boyle, R. F., Davies, J. H., Hazel, V. E. and Rowland, T. C. UO_2 properties affecting performance. *Nucl. Engng Design* **21**, 167–199 (1972).
3. Latta, R. E. and Fryxell, R. E. Determination of solidus-liquidus temperatures in the UO_{2+x} system. *J. Nucl. Mat.* **35**, 195–200 (1970).

4. MAXWELL, J. C. *Treatise on electricity and magnetism*, Oxford University Press, 1873 (page 440 of Third Edition in 1904).
5. GOLDSMITH, L. A. and DOUGLAS, J. A. M. Measurement of thermal conductivity of UO_2 670–1270 K. *J. Nucl. Mat.* **47,** 31–42 (1973).
6. IAEA, Vienna, *Thermal conductivity of* UO_2, Technical Report Series No. 59, 1966.
7. ONDRACEK, G. and SCHULZ, E. The porosity dependence of thermal conductivity for nuclear fuels. *J. Nucl. Mat.* **46,** 253–258 (1973).
8. ASAMOTO, R. R. *et al.* The effect of density on the thermal conductivity of UO_2, GEAP 5493, 1968.
9. SCHMIDT, H. E. Some considerations on the thermal conductivity of stoichiometric UO_2 at high temperatures. *J. Nucl. Mat.* **39,** 234–237 (1971).
10. MASON, E. A. and VON UBISH, H. Thermal conductivity of rare gas mixtures. *Phys. Fluids* **3,** 355–361 (1960).
11. WILLIFORD, R. E. and HANN, C. R. Effects of fill gas composition and eccentric gap geometry on gap conductance of UO_2 fuel rods. *Trans. Am. Nucl. Soc.* **26,** 324–325 (1977).
12. LAWRENCE, L. A., HORN, G. R. and CHRISTENSEN, J. A. Fuel-clad gap conductance in fast reactor oxide fuels. *Trans.Am. Nucl. Soc.* **13,** 572–573 (1970).
13. CETINKALE, J. N. and FISHENDEN, M. Thermal conductivity of metal surfaces in contact. *Proc. General Discussion on Heat Transfer*, Inst. Mech. Engrs, London, 1951, p. 271.
14. FENECH, H. and ROHSENOW, W. M. A prediction of thermal conduction of metallic surfaces in contact. *J. Heat Transfer*, Trans. ASME Series C, **85,** 15 (1963).
15. FROST, B. R. T. Theories of swelling and gas retention in ceramic fuels. *Nucl. Appl. Techn.* **9,** 128–140 (1970).

Problems

1. A fuel rod in a BWR consists of solid 12.4-mm o.d. pellets of UO_2 in a 14.3-mm o.d. Zircaloy can. The maximum linear rating anywhere in the reactor is 55 kW m^{-1}, and at the position where this maximum rating occurs the outer surface of the can is at 290°C. Calculate the temperatures at all the interfaces in the rod and in the centre of the fuel.

   The thermal conductivity of Zircaloy is 14 W m^{-1} K^{-1}, the gap conductance is 5000 W m^{-2} K^{-1} and the UO_2 density 95%. Assume purely radial heat conduction and uniform heat generation in the fuel.
2. How would the maximum fuel temperature in question 1 be altered if
   (a) heat transfer in the cladding was treated as conduction through a plane wall?
   (b) if the reactor power was reduced to 50% and the gap conductance fell to 2000 W m^{-2} K^{-1}?
3. A solid cylindrical fuel element of radius r_0 has a radial thermal neutron flux profile that is given approximately by $\theta = a + br^2$. Show that the temperature at radius r is given by

$$\int_{T_0}^{T} k\mathrm{d}T = \frac{\Sigma_f \alpha}{4} \{a\,(r_0^2 - r^2) + b\,(r_0^4 - r^4)/4\}$$

   where T_0 is the fuel surface temperature, Σ_f the macroscopic fission cross-section, α the heat produced per fission, and k the thermal conductivity.

   Why is θ reduced in the centre of the fuel rod?
4. At a certain position in an advanced gas-cooled reactor the outer surface of the stainless-steel cans is at 815°C and the heat flux is 40 W cm^{-2}. The cans are 0.38 mm thick and contain 95% dense UO_2 pellets, 14.5 mm o.d. If the gap conductance is 5000 W m^{-2} K^{-1}, find the maximum fuel temperature for
   (a) solid UO_2 pellets,
   (b) pellets with a 1-mm diameter hole in the centre,
   (c) pellets with an 8-mm diameter hole.
   What disadvantages are there in increasing the size of the hole?
5. In the "pebble bed" type of reactor spherical fuel elements are used, consisting of a heat-producing core of radius r_1 and conductivity k_1 and an outer cladding of radius r_2 and conductivity k_2. Assuming uniform heat generation, constant conductivities, and negligible contact resistance between the two regions, derive equations for the temperature distribution and show that the maximum temperature is given by

$$T_{\max} = T_s + \frac{R}{8\pi r_1 k_1} + \frac{R}{4\pi k_2}\left(\frac{1}{r_1} - \frac{1}{r_2}\right)$$

where T_s is the surface temperature and R is now the total rate of heat production by the element.

6. The fuel pellets in a certain reactor are at effectively constant surface temperature T_0, and consist of solid cylinders, radius a, of ceramic fuel, porosity ε. Heat is produced uniformly throughout the fuel and the linear rating is R W/m. Show that the pressure exerted by the fission gases, released to the extent of N moles/m is

$$P = \frac{NGA}{\varepsilon\pi\log_e[(T_0 + Aa^2)/T_0]} \quad \text{where } A = R/4\pi ka^2.$$

Assume constant thermal conductivity k, and that all the pores are interconnected. The perfect gas law is $PV = nGT$, where n moles occupy volume V.

7. Use the following information to estimate the pressure exerted by the fission product gases inside a PWR fuel element towards the end of its life in the reactor. The Zircaloy is 10.7 mm o.d. and contains 9.7-mm o.d. solid fuel pellets over a 3-m length, plus a 0.3-m-long fission gas plenum. Only in the central 1.5 m of the rod are temperatures high enough to cause release of gas, and in this region the average rating is 40 kW m^{-1} and the average burnup is 50,000 MWd per tonne of metal fuel; 100% of the fission product gases are released from fuel over 1600°C, but none at lower temperatures; 0.15 fission gas atoms are produced per fission.

   Assume that the behaviour of the fuel element can be adequately represented by the average quantities, that the outer surface of the cladding and the fission gas plenum are at 320°C, the cladding conductivity is 14 W m^{-1}, and the gap conductance is 4000 W m^{-2} K^{-1}.

   The density of the UO_2 fuel is 10,400 kg m^{-3} (i.e. 95% dense, but you may assume that none of the fission gas is present in the pores). The heat produced per fission is 3.2×10^{-11} J and the atomic mass unit is 1.66×10^{-27} kg.

CHAPTER 4

Forced-Convection Heat Transfer

INTRODUCTION

The previous chapter was concerned with conduction of heat out of the fuel to the surface of the can; this chapter is concerned with heat transfer from can to coolant. Because of the high capital cost of the core it is essential to convert energy at a high rate, and the only way this energy can be transported fast enough is by pumping coolant through the core at a high velocity. So the heat transfer from can to coolant is by forced convection, and in most reactor types the coolant remains in the same phase throughout. Boiling heat transfer is considered in the next chapter.

With high coolant velocities the flow is necessarily turbulent, and turbulent flow is not amenable to simple theoretical analysis starting from first principles. While it is possible to discover the dimensionless groups of variables that are important in forced-convection heat transfer, the equations for the heat-transfer coefficient must be found by experiment. For non-metallic coolants such as water or gases the main barrier to heat transfer lies in a thin layer of slow-moving fluid close to the surface of the fuel can. The flow in this layer is laminar and heat transfer across it is by conduction. Heat is transferred to the rest of the flow by the much more effective process of turbulent mixing.

Liquid metals have a very high thermal conductivity so the laminar layer of liquid next to the can surface does not present a significant barrier to heat transfer, and even at quite high velocities the predominant heat-transfer mechanism throughout the flow cross-section is conduction.

Because primarily of the low density of gases the heat-transfer coefficients that are obtained with them are lower than those obtained with liquids, and if a gaseous coolant is to be used the can to coolant heat transfer must be improved. This can be done either by providing fins to increase the surface area of the cans, or by roughening the surface to increase the heat-transfer coefficient.

HEAT-TRANSFER COEFFICIENT AND DIMENSIONAL ANALYSIS

If the temperature at the outer surface of the can is T_s and the bulk or mixed mean temperature of the coolant is T_b then the heat-transfer coefficient is defined by

$$h = \frac{\text{heat flux}}{T_s - T_b} \tag{4.1}$$

where the heat flux is the rate at which heat flows across unit area of the heat-transfer surface, in this case the surface of the fuel can. This definition is just a statement of Newton's law of cooling, which is closely obeyed in forced convection.

The coolant flowing past a given point of the heat transfer surface is not all at the same temperature, as shown in Fig. 4.1 the coolant temperature falls from T_s is contact with the surface to below T_b in the centre of the channel. The bulk temperature T_b may be worked out by considering the temperature of the coolant at the inlet to the core T_1 and the total heat added up to the point of interest.

$$T_b = T_1 + \frac{\text{rate of heat addition}}{mc} \tag{4.2}$$

where m is the mass flow rate and c the specific heat of the coolant at constant pressure.

While the heat-transfer coefficient cannot be worked out from first principles, any equation for it must satisfy the condition that all the terms in it have the same units and dimensions, and this can be used to find the dimensionless groups of variables that must appear in the equation. However, before the process of dimensional analysis can be started, it is necessary to know all the variables that influence the phenomenon under consideration.

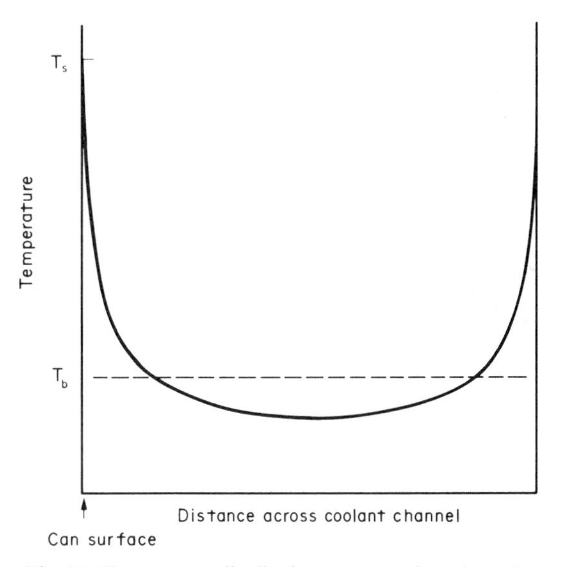

Fig. 4.1. Temperature distribution across coolant channel.

Suppose, as is in fact found by experiment, that the value of the heat-transfer coefficient h is determined by the following variables: the coolant viscosity μ, density ρ, thermal conductivity k, specific heat (at constant pressure) c, the flow velocity u, and some characteristic dimension of the flow channel d. The geometry of the flow channel will also influence the heat-transfer coefficient, so the argument is confined to one particular geometry which can be completely defined by a single linear dimension d.

Whether or not h turns out to be expressible as a simple analytical function of these variables it must be possible to write it as an infinite series

$$h = B_1 \mu^{\alpha} \rho^{\beta} k^{\gamma} c^{\delta} u^{\varepsilon} d^{\zeta} + B_2 \mu^{\alpha'} \rho^{\beta'} k^{\gamma'} c^{\delta'} u^{\varepsilon'} d^{\zeta'} + \text{, etc.,} \tag{4.3}$$

where B_1, B_2, etc., are dimensionless constants, and each term of the series must have the dimensions of heat-transfer coefficient.

The dimensions of the variables, in terms of mass M, length L, time t, and temperature T, are:

h	$Mt^{-3}T^{-1}$	c	$L^2t^{-2}T^{-1}$
μ	$ML^{-1}t^{-1}$	u	Lt^{-1}
ρ	ML^{-3}	d	L
k	$MLt^{-3}T^{-1}$		

Considering the first term on the right of equation (4.3) and applying the condition that it must have the same dimensions as h to each of the fundamental quantities in turn:

equating dimensions of M $\quad 1 = \alpha + \beta + \gamma,$ (4.4)

equating dimensions of L $\quad 0 = -\alpha - 3\beta + \gamma + 2\delta + \varepsilon + \zeta,$ (4.5)

equating dimensions of t $\quad -3 = -\alpha - 3\gamma - 2\delta - \varepsilon,$ (4.6)

equating dimensions of T $\quad -1 = -\gamma - \delta.$ (4.7)

With six unknowns and four equations it is not possible to solve for α, β, etc., all that can be done is to reduce the number of unknowns by 4. Arbitrarily choosing α and γ as the quantities to keep, and expressing all the others in terms of these two:

equation (4.4) gives $\quad \beta = 1 - \alpha - \gamma,$ (4.8)

equation (4.7) gives $\quad \delta = 1 - \gamma,$ (4.9)

substituting into (4.6) gives $\quad \varepsilon = 1 - \alpha - \gamma,$ (4.10)

substituting into (4.5) gives $\quad \zeta = -\alpha - \gamma,$ (4.11)

and using these expressions in equation (4.3) gives

$$h = B_1 \mu^{\alpha} \rho^{1-\alpha-\gamma} k^{\gamma} c^{1-\gamma} u^{1-\alpha-\gamma} d^{-\alpha-\gamma} + \text{similar terms}$$

or

$$\frac{h}{\rho u c} = B_1 \left(\frac{\mu}{\rho u d}\right)^{\alpha+\gamma} \left(\frac{k}{\mu c}\right)^{\gamma} + \text{similar terms.} \tag{4.12}$$

Now $h/\rho uc$ is a dimensionless group called the Stanton number, St, $\rho ud/\mu$ is the Reynolds number, Re, and $\mu c/k$ is the Prandtl number, Pr, so it must be possible to express the heat transfer by

$$St = f(Re, Pr). \tag{4.13}$$

However, the process of dimensional analysis reveals nothing about the form of the function f

since in principle there may be an infinite number of terms in equation (4.12) and each one may have different values of α and γ.

With practice in performing this kind of analysis it becomes clear that the number of dimensionless groups formed is normally equal to the number of the original variables minus the number of fundamental quantities that are used, also that by solving the equations in a different order it is possible to arrive at different dimensionless groups as solutions to the same problem. For example, if the Stanton number is multiplied by $RePr$ a new dimensionless number, the Nusselt number hd/k, is formed, and equation (4.13) shows that

$$Nu = StRePr = RePrf(Re,Pr) = g(Re,Pr). \tag{4.14}$$

In the above analysis heat was not treated as one of the fundamental quantities, instead where it appeared it was given the dimensions of energy, ML^2t^{-2}. Often heat is treated as a fundamental quantity, and this would apparently lead to one fewer dimensionless group. However, in this case heat only appears as heat/temperature and the new equation is the same as equation (4.7) and gives no new information. If in addition to regarding heat as a fundamental unit it is also assumed that temperature is one of the variables that influence the value of the heat-transfer coefficient, then an additional equation is obtained. This can be used to show that the power of the temperature in the extended version of equation (4.3) is zero, so temperature as such does not affect the heat-transfer coefficient.

Physical significance of the dimensionless groups

Since each of the groups is dimensionless it is possible to think of it as the ratio of similar quantities.

The Stanton number contains the heat-transfer information, and can be thought of as a ratio of temperature differences and areas. Consider the overall heat balance in any heat exchanger, such as the core of a reactor. The heat coming out of the heat-transfer surface can be regarded in two ways. If the area of the fuel can surface in the channel is Ls, where L is the length of the fuel rods and s their perimeter, then the total heat input to the channel is at a rate $h\Delta TLs$, where ΔT is the average can to coolant temperature difference. Also this rate of supply of heat raises the temperature of the coolant from T_1 at the inlet to T_2 at the outlet, i.e. it equals $mc\,(T_2 - T_1)$, where m is the mass flow rate of coolant through the channel.

So

$$h\Delta TLs = mc\,(T_2 - T_1) = \rho uAc\,(T_2 - T_1) \tag{4.15}$$

where A is the cross-sectional area of the flow channel.

Rearranging (4.15) gives

$$St = h/\rho uc = \frac{A}{Ls}\,\frac{(T_2 - T_1)}{\Delta T}. \tag{4.16}$$

The Reynolds number controls the nature of the flow in the channel, i.e. the degree of turbulence and the flow pattern. It is the ratio of the inertial forces tending to push the flow forwards, ρu^2 per unit area, to the viscous forces tending to slow it down, which are proportional to viscosity times velocity gradient, or roughly to $\mu u/d$ per unit area.

The Prandtl number determines the effect of the fluid properties on the heat transfer. It is the ratio of the molecular diffusivities of momentum and heat. In transient heat-conduction problems the quantity $k/\rho c$ appears, the thermal diffusivity. It has the units $m^2\ s^{-1}$ and determines how far the heat can diffuse in a certain time. Equally the quantity μ/ρ, which also has the units $m^2\ s^{-1}$, controls the diffusion of momentum.

HEAT-TRANSFER CORRELATIONS FOR NON-METALS

Experimental measurements on heat transfer are always presented in terms of the dimensionless groups, since this greatly reduces the volume of data. Over a limited range of Reynolds and Prandtl numbers it is normally possible to correlate the results with adequate accuracy by a simple equation. This equation can then be used to predict the heat-transfer coefficient for another situation, which might involve a different coolant or a different size of channel, provided the Reynolds and Prandtl numbers are within the range for which the correlation has been tested.

The behaviour of liquid metals, with high values of k, and hence low Prandtl numbers, is so different to that of non-metals that they are considered separately.

Circular tubes

For fully developed turbulent flow of a gas or non-metallic liquid in a smooth tube the most widely quoted equation is that of Dittus and Boelter [1]

$$St = 0.023Re^{-0.2}\ Pr^{-0.6}. \tag{4.17}$$

The fluid properties are calculated at the bulk coolant temperature. The equation should not be used if there are large variations of temperature and hence properties between the bulk coolant and the heated surface.

A comparison of equation (4.17) with the experimental results of a dozen different groups of workers, over a wide range of Reynolds and Prandtl numbers, showed an overall root mean square error between the individual experimental points and the predictions of the equation of 13% [2]. For very high Prandtl numbers (over 100) the predictions of the equation were badly in error. However, for reactor coolants Prandtl numbers are normally a little under 1. This is true for water at reactor temperatures, and Prandtl numbers for all gases are around 0.7. In this range equation (4.17) fits the experimental data with an accuracy of about 10%.

Example 4.1. Water at 280°C flows through a 15 mm i.d. circular tube at 5 m s^{-1}. Calculate the heat-transfer coefficient (the pressure is sufficient to prevent boiling).

If heat is supplied to the tube at the rate of 20 kW per metre length, what is the temperature of the inside surface of the tube?

In order to use the dimensionless equation for the heat-transfer coefficient we must first work out the Reynolds and Prandtl numbers. Although the water is subcooled values of the properties of saturated water at 280°C may be used since the properties of liquid water are only slightly affected by pressure.

$$Re = \frac{\rho d u}{\mu} = \frac{750.8 \times 0.015 \times 5}{96 \times 10^{-6}} = 5.87 \times 10^5,$$

$$Pr = \frac{\mu c}{k} = \frac{96 \times 10^{-6} \times 5.24 \times 10^3}{0.574} = 0.876.$$

Substituting in equation (4.17) gives $St = 0.001\ 75$, and from the definition of Stanton number

$$h = St\rho uc = 0.001\ 75 \times 750.8 \times 5 \times 5.24 \times 10^3 = 3.44 \times 10^4\ \mathrm{W\ m^{-2}\ K^{-1}}.$$

So the heat-transfer coefficient is $3.4 \times 10^4\ \mathrm{W\ m^{-2}\ K^{-1}}$.

The heat flux on the inner surface of the tube is

$$\frac{20}{\pi \times 0.015} = 424\ \mathrm{kW\ m^{-2}}$$

and the surface to bulk temperature difference is

$$\frac{424 \times 10^3}{3.44 \times 10^4} = 12.3°\mathrm{C}$$

giving a temperature on the inside of the tube of 292.3°C.

Simple model to interpret the heat-transfer equation

Equation (4.17) is quite straightforward to use for calculating heat-transfer coefficients, but since it is not based on any theory, it does not provide any insight into what is happening in the heat transfer process. Although the equation cannot be proved from first principles it can be justified provided considerable information about the nature of turbulent flow is accepted as a starting-point. In particular, the velocity profile is needed. Detailed analysis is quite consistent with the equation [3], but the simple model to be developed here only accounts for the main trends of the equation (it is worth noting that much more sophisticated models of turbulence are available, of considerable predictive value in single-phase flows [4]; these models will not be discussed further here since the complex three-dimensional computer programs used in nuclear analysis mostly have a quite different basis, which will be explained in Chapter 8).

The flow in the tube is considered to be divided into two regions (see Fig. 4.2): a narrow laminar sublayer close to the wall where the flow is streamlined and the velocity increases linearly from zero at the wall to u_1 at the boundary; and a turbulent core where the velocity is everywhere comparable with the mean flow velocity u, but superimposed on the forward movement of the flow are turbulent eddies having velocities v of around $u/20$. The velocity at the boundary, u_1, is about $u/2$, and for coolants with $Pr \sim 1$ the velocity and temperature profiles are similar, so the temperature at the boundary is half-way between the wall and bulk temperatures also. This sharp division into two distinct layers is of course an oversimplification. As will be explained later there is a transition region or buffer layer between the laminar sublayer and the turbulent core of the flow, but for the purpose of the simple model the buffer layer may be ignored.

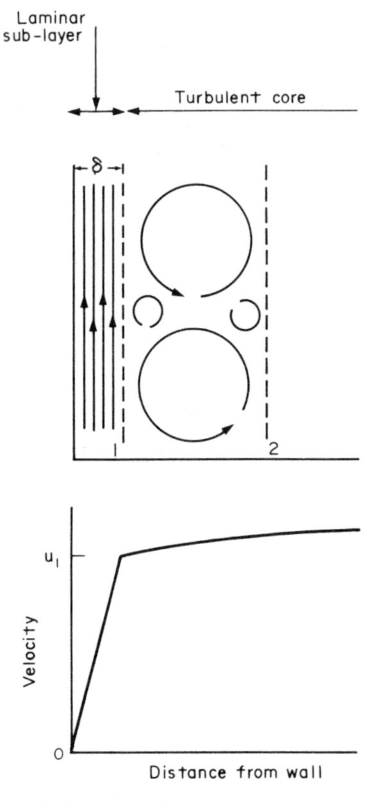

Fig. 4.2. Simplified model of the flow close to the heated surface.

Heat transfer through the laminar layer is by conduction, since there is no mixing of the adjacent layers of fluid, so the heat flux from the wall is

$$h\,(T_s - T_b) = k\,\frac{(T_s - T_b)/2}{\delta}$$

where δ is the thickness of the laminar layer.

So

$$h = k/2\delta. \tag{4.18}$$

The value of δ is determined by the shearing forces in the flow, that is by the rate at which momentum is transferred from one layer parallel to the surface to the next. In developing this model we are only interested in the parts of the flow that lie close to the wall of the tube, and it is possible to show that the shear stress in the flow is nearly constant. Consider a cylinder of the fluid, radius r, concentric with the tube. If there is a difference in pressure Δp per unit length between the two ends of the cylinder then there will be an axial force $\pi r^2 \Delta p$ acting on the cylinder. This is balanced by the shear force acting on the sides of the cylinder, $2\pi r \tau$ per unit length, where τ is the shear stress. So close to the wall where r is virtually constant τ will be constant also. A similar argument could be applied to the average shear stress in a non-circular channel.

Within the laminar sublayer the shear stress is given by Newton's law of viscosity:

$$\tau = \mu \frac{\mathrm{d}u}{\mathrm{d}y} = \mu \frac{u_1}{\delta}. \tag{4.19}$$

Just inside the turbulent core the shear stress is the same, but now it is determined by the turbulent eddies rather than by the molecular viscosity. Consider the transfer of momentum between the edge of the laminar layer, point 1, and point 2 which is one turbulent eddy width inside the turbulent core. The axial momentum of the flow at point 2 is ρu_2 per unit volume, and if all of this flow were carried sideways towards the wall with a turbulent velocity υ then the rate of transfer momentum, per unit area parallel to the wall, would be $\upsilon \rho u_2$. However, only half of the flow will be travelling towards the wall rather than away from it, so the rate of momentum transfer is $\frac{1}{2}\upsilon \rho u_2$. Similarly, the half of the flow travelling the other way will bring a rate of momentum change of $-\frac{1}{2}\upsilon \rho u_1$.

So the net rate of momentum transfer per unit area is

$$\tau = \tfrac{1}{2}\upsilon \rho (u_2 - u_1) \tag{4.20}$$

but $u_2 - u_1$ itself is roughly 2υ, since as shown in Fig. 4.2 the turbulent eddies will tend to increase the velocity at point 2 but subtract from it at point 1.

So equating (4.20) and (4.19), and replacing υ by $u/20$ and u_1 by $u/2$,

$$\delta = \mu u_1/\tau = \mu u_1/\rho \upsilon^2 = 200\mu/\rho u$$

and substituting in (4.18) gives

$$h = 0.0025 \frac{k \rho u}{\mu}$$

or

$$St = 0.0025\, Pr^{-1}. \tag{4.21}$$

For Reynolds numbers of around 10^5 and Prandtl numbers of around 1 the agreement between this equation and equation (4.17) is quite close.

With Prandtl numbers not close to one the simplifying assumption of similar velocity and temperature profiles is not valid, and this accounts for the factor of $Pr^{0.4}$ difference between the equations. It is not quite correct to say that the turbulent velocities are a fixed fraction of the mean flow velocity, the ratio decreases slightly with increasing Reynolds number, and this introduces the $Re^{-0.2}$ factor.

However agreement between the simple analysis and the correct equation is sufficient to allow the following conclusions:

(a) The main barrier to forced convection heat transfer of non-metals is presented by a narrow boundary layer close to the wall. Heat transfer across the laminar part of this layer is by conduction.

(b) Since the thickness of this layer is roughly inversely proportional to the flow velocity the heat-transfer coefficient increases roughly in direct proportion.

(c) If the level of turbulence could be increased, that is if the velocity of the turbulent eddies could be raised for a given mean flow velocity, the heat transfer would be improved.

(d) A similar argument could be developed for other channel shapes, leading to the same Stanton number equation, suggesting that the accurate correlation, equation (4.17), can be applied to other shapes of channel as a first approximation.

Equivalent diameter

In the case of a circular tube it is fairly obvious what distance should be taken as the characteristic linear dimension for the Reynolds number, but for other shapes it is convenient to have a simple rule, and the convention is to use the equivalent diameter defined by

$$d_e = \frac{4 \times \text{flow cross-sectional area}}{\text{perimeter of channel}} \tag{4.22}$$

This definition gives the actual diameter for a circular tube. For a number of simple geometries the equivalent diameter can be used in equation (4.17) to give heat-transfer coefficients within 10 or 20%. The success of this procedure is probably due to the fact that the heat-transfer coefficient is not strongly influenced by channel size or shape, rather than to the inherent correctness of the equivalent diameter concept.

Even when correlations have been specifically developed for a particular channel shape the Reynolds number (and Nusselt number if used) are still worked out using d_e.

Entrance effects

The correlation of experimental results, equation (4.17), is for fully developed turbulent flow. It applies therefore to the flow some distance from the inlet to the channel where the boundary layer has built up to its equilibrium thickness. At the entrance to the channel, or following a sharp bend or sudden change in cross-section, the boundary layer will be thinner and the heat-transfer coefficient as much as two or three times the equilibrium value. This high value only persists for about one channel diameter downstream and by 20 diameters it is difficult to detect any effect. With turbulent velocities of the order of 1/20 of the mean flow velocity it is reasonable that the flow should take around 20 channel diameters to settle down.

Non-isothermal flow

The dimensional analysis indicated that the heat-transfer coefficient does not depend on temperature as such, but it was assumed that the properties of the fluid, such as viscosity, are well-defined, constant quantities. In fact these properties are temperature dependent, and when there is a large variation of temperature between the wall and the bulk it is not sufficient just to take the value of the properties at the average, i.e. bulk, temperature. Because of the importance of the laminar sublayer it is the value of the properties in this layer that seems to matter, and better results are obtained if the properties are evaluated at the film temperature T_f which is the average of the wall and bulk temperatures, i.e. $T_f = (T_s + T_b)/2$.

This procedure can be used with equation (4.17), though it is more logical to use an equation that has been developed for use with the properties evaluated at the film temperature, that is the Colburn equation [5]:

$$St = 0.023 Re^{-0.2} Pr^{-2/3}. \tag{4.23}$$

However, neither of these equations is satisfactory for large temperature drops across the film.

In practice it is the variation of viscosity with temperature that matters, and for liquids equation (4.17) should be multiplied by the Sieder–Tate correction [6], $(\mu/\mu_s)^{0.14}$, so the equation becomes

$$St = 0.023 Re^{-0.2} Pr^{-0.6} (\mu/\mu_s)^{0.14} \tag{4.24}$$

where all the properties are evaluated at the bulk temperature apart from μ_s which is evaluated at T_s, the temperature of the wall. Since T_s is not known in advance a first estimate of T_s must be made using (4.17).

With gases it is usual to adopt a different approach. Since gas properties are often a function of the absolute temperature all the property variations can be brought together in a $(T_s/T_b)^n$ factor, so the Stanton number is now given by

$$St = 0.023 Re^{-0.2} Pr^{-0.6} (T_s/T_b)^n \tag{4.25}$$

where T_s and T_b are both absolute temperatures. Again everything is evaluated at the bulk temperature, apart from T_s.

Theoretical predictions of n for air and hydrogen are almost the same for the two gases, and given with good accuracy by [7]

$$n = -0.3 \log_{10} (T_s/T_b) - 0.36.$$

Experimental results for these two gases, and a number of others (helium, nitrogen, argon and carbon dioxide), are in reasonable agreement with this equation; the experimental values tend to be slightly more negative, but the difference may not be significant.

Correlation for water flow parallel to rod bundles

A correlation for this specific case, which can be applied to the flow of water past fuel rods in a reactor, has been derived by Weisman [8]:

$$St = C\, Re^{-0.2} Pr^{-2/3} \tag{4.26}$$

for a triangular array $C = 0.026P/D - 0.006$ valid for $1.1 \leqslant P/D \leqslant 1.3$,

for a square array $C = 0.042P/D - 0.024$ valid for $1.1 \leqslant P/D \leqslant 1.5$,

where P/D is the pitch to diameter ratio.

The higher heat-transfer coefficients in the square lattice appear to be due to the more open nature of the lattice (for a given P/D). If the heat-transfer coefficients are plotted against the proportion of the total cross-sectional area occupied by water, then the points for the triangular and square arrays lie on the same line.

LIQUID-METAL HEAT TRANSFER

Constant heat flux to slug flow in a circular tube

In this case it is possible to get a usable result from first principles with a very simple model. Since in turbulent flow the velocity is nearly constant over the bulk of the flow it is not a bad approximation to say that the velocity is constant everywhere. In other words the liquid behaves like a solid slug of metal as it moves through the tube, and heat transfer into it is purely by conduction.

At some distance from the inlet to the channel the temperature profile in the metal slug or rod will have settled down to an equilibrium shape. The temperature is still rising in the rod but at every radius it is rising at the same rate, and the centre to edge temperature difference stays constant. With the temperature rising at the same rate at all radial positions the heat supplied to each region of the liquid metal must be in proportion to the volume of metal. If the heat flux is q then the total rate of heat supply per unit length of the channel is $2\pi aq$, and the heat flowing into the region of the liquid metal bounded by the cylindrical surface radius r is

$$2\pi aq \frac{\pi r^2}{\pi a^2}$$

where a is the radius of the tube.

This heat must be conducted through the surface at r, so

$$2\pi q \frac{r^2}{a} = k\,2\pi r \frac{\mathrm{d}T}{\mathrm{d}r} \tag{4.27}$$

or

$$\frac{q}{ka} \int_r^a r\mathrm{d}r = \int_{T_r}^{T_s} \mathrm{d}T$$

so

$$\frac{q}{ka} [\,(a^2 - r^2)/2] = T_s - T_r.$$

The bulk temperature of the flow is the volumetric average temperature

$$T_b = \frac{1}{\pi a^2}\int_0^a T_r\, 2\pi r \mathrm{d}r = T_s - \frac{q}{ka^3}\int_0^a (a^2 - r^2) r \mathrm{d}r$$

so

$$T_s - T_b = \frac{q}{ka^3}[a^4/2 - a^4/4] = \frac{qa}{4k}.$$

The heat-transfer coefficient is

$$h = \frac{q}{T_s - T_b} = \frac{4k}{a}$$

and the Nusselt number is

$$Nu = \frac{hd}{k} = \frac{4k}{a}\frac{2a}{k} = 8. \tag{4.28}$$

For liquid-metal heat transfer the Nusselt number, expressing as it does the conduction resistance of the whole flow cross-section, is obviously preferable to the Stanton number.

Mathematically the above analysis is very similar to that for the temperature distribution in a cylindrical fuel pellet given in the previous chapter. There the heat flow out of a region in the fuel was in proportion to its volume, here the flow into a region of the coolant is in proportion to its volume.

The Lyon–Martinelli equation

On the basis of a numerical analysis which included the effect of both convection and conduction in the liquid metal, Lyon proposed the following equation for fully developed turbulent flow in a circular tube, with constant heat flux at the surface [9]:

$$Nu = 7 + 0.025 Pe^{0.8} \tag{4.29}$$

where Pe is the Peclet number ($= RePr$).

Earlier Martinelli had performed a similar analysis and obtained similar results [3]. Both of these analyses were based on the known velocity profiles in turbulent flow, and had to make assumptions about the relative efficiencies of the turbulent eddies in carrying heat and momentum. Equation (4.29) results if it is assumed that the ratio of the eddy diffusivities of heat and momentum, ψ, is unity. If ψ is assumed constant, that is independent of radial position in the flow, then

$$Nu = 7 + 0.025(\psi Pe)^{0.8}. \tag{4.30}$$

For low Peclet numbers, when the effect of forced convection on the heat transfer is negligible, the Nusselt number tends to 7 rather than the value of 8 that was calculated for slug flow. This is the result of using the actual turbulent velocity profile instead of assuming a constant velocity, and since in the real flow more of the heat has to go to the central regions to balance the higher flow velocity, the average distance the heat is conducted is higher and the heat-transfer coefficient lower.

Note that in liquid-metal heat transfer the temperature boundary condition has to be specified, since it affects the temperature distribution throughout the flow and hence the heat-transfer coefficient. In the core of a reactor operating at constant power the heat output is fixed, an example of the constant heat-flux boundary condition. In other circumstances, however, perhaps in a heat exchanger, the wall temperature may be fixed. For a constant wall temperature the constant in equation (4.29) is 5 instead of 7 [10].

There is no general agreement, either experimental or theoretical, on what the values of ψ should be. At low velocities an eddy in the liquid metal is likely to come quickly into temperature equilibrium with its surroundings as it moves about in the flow, because of its high molecular conductivity. It is less effective at carrying heat than momentum because it loses its heat before it ceases to exist as an eddy. So the value of ψ is likely to be below 1 at low velocities and tend to 1 at high velocities.

One equation for ψ [11] is:

$$\psi = 1 - 1.82 Pr^{-1} (\varepsilon_m/\nu)^{-1.4} \tag{4.31}$$

and values of ε_m/ν as a function of Reynolds number are given in [12] (for various flow geometries). ε_m is the eddy diffusivity of momentum and ν the kinematic viscosity, μ/ρ. For high conductivity, low Prandtl number liquids like sodium the values of ψ are low (even zero if equation (4.31) predicts negative values) and this reduces the forced-convection term in equation (4.30), with the result that heat is transferred almost entirely by conduction even at quite high velocities.

Measurements of liquid-metal heat transfer have often yielded Nusselt numbers well below these theoretical predictions, some as low as half the values obtained from equation (4.29). The discrepancy persists over a wide range of Peclet numbers, though there is some tendency for better agreement at higher values of Pe. Most of this disagreement is due to the difficulty of obtaining valid experimental results. Because liquid-metal heat transfer is so good the temperature differences involved are small and a small amount of contamination of the heat-transfer surface will provide a contact resistance high enough to mask the inherently good heat transfer of the liquid metal. Measurements under carefully controlled conditions, with provision for measuring temperature profiles within the liquid-metal flow as well as in the tube wall so that any contact resistance can be detected, show good agreement with (4.29) [13]. The results cover the Peclet number range of 90 to 20,000, using mercury in nickel and stainless-steel tubes for $Pe > 600$ and sodium–potassium alloy in copper tubes for $90 < Pe < 1500$. The only significant deviation from equation (4.29) occurs for $Pe < 300$ where the average of the experimental values is some 12% below the prediction. Equation (4.30) with ψ calculated from (4.31) would give better agreement.

The contact resistance that is so often experienced in practice in liquid-metal systems may, in the case of the alkali metals such as sodium, be due to a layer of the metal oxide deposited on the surface. The solubility of the oxide increases with temperature, and the level in solution may build up to the point where the oxide starts to precipitate on surfaces in the cooler parts of the circuit. To prevent this a cold trap is normally provided, that is a subsidiary circuit that is deliberately maintained at a lower temperature than everywhere else in the system. The effectiveness of this depends on maintaining a large difference in temperature between the cold trap and the rest of the circuit, something that is not always easy to do in an experimental system that might have, compared to a reactor, a rather low maximum temperature. Certainly it has proved possible to halve the measured Nusselt number by providing conditions under which the oxide would be expected to precipitate [14]. At low flow velocities a similar reduction in Nusselt number could result from the surface being covered with gas bubbles. [15].

Flow parallel to rod bundles

The technique of calculating Nusselt numbers numerically, assuming suitable velocity profiles, has been extended to a number of different geometries, and the results expressed by equations of the form of equation (4.30), but with different constants [11].

The flow velocity past a fuel rod which is part of an infinite triangular lattice increases from zero in contact with the rod to a maximum at a point half-way between the rod and its nearest neighbour. Thus there is a hexagonal flow zone associated with the rod, and the hexagonal boundary is a surface of maximum velocity and zero heat flow. If this hexagon is approximated by a circle then it could be regarded as the inner part of an annulus, and the heat transfer from the rod is equivalent to that from the inner surface in an annulus, which can be predicted theoretically using data on the velocity profile in an annulus.

For the triangular lattice Dwyer and Lyon [11] recommend:

$$Nu = 6.66 + 3.126\frac{P}{D} + 1.184\left(\frac{P}{D}\right)^2 + 0.0155\,(\psi Pe)^{0.86} \tag{4.32}$$

valid for $1.3 < P/D < 3$.

ψ can be worked out from equation (4.31) and the results given in [12] (for $P/D > 1.4$) and in [16] (for $P/D < 1.4$). However, under reactor conditions the calculated value of ψ is frequently zero, so equation (4.32) can be used without the last term. For sodium with $P/D = 1.3$ this is a good approximation provided the Peclet number is less than about 400. For other liquid metals and higher pitch to diameter ratios ψ is zero over an even larger range of Peclet numbers.

Often the fuel rods in a sodium-cooled fast reactor are closely spaced with $P/D < 1.3$, and it is not reasonable to pretend that each rod is surrounded by an annular flow channel. Temperatures and heat-transfer coefficients tend to vary around the circumference of the rod, and even the average Nusselt number depends on the boundary conditions. The lowest, most pessimistic, values of Nu are obtained with a constant heat-flux boundary condition. This is because the heat is forced to flow into the poorly cooled regions where the rods are nearly touching, whereas in practice some of it would be redistributed by conduction within the fuel and cladding. Numerical calculation is still possible, and results for Prandtl numbers corresponding to liquid sodium have been presented graphically (e.g. [16], [17]).

An alternative approach is to fit empirical equations to experimental results. Graber and Rieger [18] measured Nusselt numbers for tubes on triangular lattices, with sodium–potassium alloy (NaK) flowing inside and outside the tubes, for P/D ratios of 1.25,

1.60 and 1.95. The equation they derived is in good agreement with their own experimental results and in reasonable agreement with the measurements of other workers on other liquid metals, including some results for $P/D = 1.2$. The equation is:

$$Nu = 0.25 + 6.2P/D + (0.032P/D - 0.007)\, Pe^{(0.8 - 0.024P/D)} \tag{4.33}$$

valid for constant heat flux from rod bundles on a triangular lattice for $150 < Pe < 3000$ and $1.2 < P/D < 2$.

This equation is in quite good agreement with equations (4.32) and (4.31), also with the numerical results of [16] and [17], and is probably the simplest to use for most purposes, since it is valid over an important range and does not require calculation of ψ, the ratio of the eddy diffusivities of heat and momentum.

Because liquid-metal heat-transfer coefficients are so high there is no need to calculate them with great accuracy, and in any case the predictions of the numerical analyses all depend on ψ, which is not accurately known. There is both experimental [19] and theoretical [20] evidence that the variation of ψ with Pe is not as abrupt as equation (4.31) implies.

Example 4.2. Use the following data for the core of a prototype fast reactor to calculate the maximum can to coolant temperature difference.

The 5.8 mm o.d. fuel rods are on an equilateral triangular lattice with a pitch of 7.4 mm. The liquid sodium enters the core at 400°C and leaves at 560°C. In the most highly rated channel the coolant flows (parallel to the fuel rods) at 6.4 m s^{-1} and the maximum heat flux is 2500 kW m^{-2}.

The pitch to diameter ratio is $7.4/5.8 = 1.28$, so we are within the range of validity of equation (4.33), though the value of the Peclet number Pe will have to be checked in due course. Since both Nu and Pe depend on the equivalent diameter the next step is to calculate this, using equation (4.22),

$$d_e = \frac{4 \times \text{flow cross-sectional area}}{\text{perimeter of channel}}.$$

To evaluate this consider Fig. 4.3, which shows a cross-section of part of the coolant channel. Joining the centres of neighbouring fuel rods by imaginary lines we see that the whole cross-section may be built up by multiples of this basic triangular unit, and that the ratio of

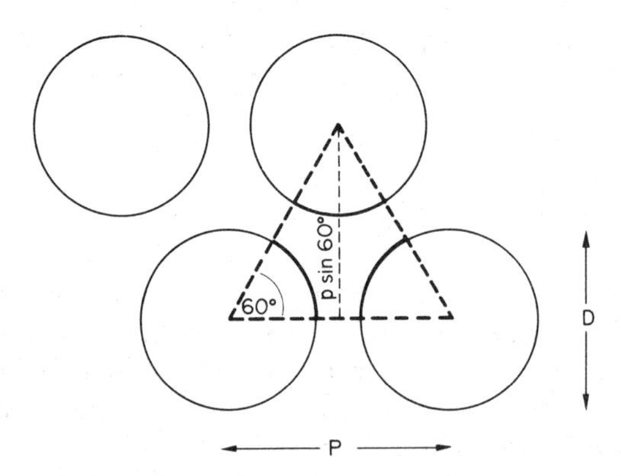

Fig. 4.3. The flow cross-section in an infinite array may be considered to be made up of multiples of this basic triangular unit.

flow cross-sectional area to channel perimeter is the same for this unit as for an infinite array (there are 325 fuel rods in a channel, so few of them will be affected by the presence of the channel wall).

So

$$d_e = \frac{4 \times [\frac{1}{2}PP \sin 60 - \frac{1}{2}(\pi/4)D^2]}{\frac{1}{2}\pi D} = 4.61 \text{ mm}.$$

Note that only the solid–liquid boundary is included in the perimeter.

Taking liquid sodium properties at 500°C we have

$$Re = \frac{\rho d_e u}{\mu} = \frac{833 \times 0.004\,61 \times 6.4}{0.239 \times 10^{-3}} = 1.03 \times 10^5,$$

$$Pr = \frac{c\mu}{k} = \frac{1260 \times 0.239 \times 10^{-3}}{66.5} = 0.004\,53,$$

$$Pe = RePr = 466.$$

So the Reynolds number is well into the turbulent region and the Peclet number is within the range for which equation (4.33) was derived.

Substituting into that equation gives

$$Nu = 12.0.$$

The heat-transfer coefficient is given by

$$h = kNu/d_e = \underline{1.73 \times 10^5 \text{ W m}^{-2} \text{ K}^{-1}}$$

and the maximum can to coolant temperature difference is

$$\frac{2500 \times 10^3}{1.73 \times 10^5} = \underline{14.5°\text{C}.}$$

COMPARISON OF COOLANTS

Economic operation of a nuclear power station requires a high rate of energy conversion in the core, which in turn implies a high heat flux at the surface of the fuel rods, and since the heat flux is $h\Delta T$ a high heat-transfer coefficient is desirable. Only water (ordinary and heavy) and carbon dioxide gas have been used extensively as coolants in power reactors, and the only new coolants that are likely to be used in the near future are liquid sodium and helium gas. Large prototype reactors using sodium and helium are already in operation. From the heat-transfer point of view ordinary and heavy water are almost identical, and the difference between the two gases is not very great, so the comparison is for just three coolants, with one representative of each of the three possible types: non-metallic liquid, gas, and liquid metal.

To relate the comparison closely to reactor conditions two channel sizes, 15 mm (typical of thermal reactors) and 5 mm (typical of fast reactors), are chosen. The temperature is 280°C for the water and 500°C for the carbon dioxide and the liquid sodium. The carbon dioxide pressure is 40 bar. The velocity is taken to be 5 m s^{-1} for the liquids and 12 m s^{-1} for the gas (gases are invariably circulated at a higher velocity – this is possible because of their lower density, the force the coolant exerts on components in the flow being proportional to ρu^2).

Using equations (4.17) and (4.29) for circular tubes (not that the coolant channels in the reactor are circular, but it is a convenient method of comparison) the following heat-transfer coefficients are obtained, relative to that for water in the 15-mm channel:

	Relative heat-transfer coefficient	
	$d = 15$ mm	$d = 5$ mm
Water	1	1.24
Carbon dioxide	0.029	0.036
Liquid sodium	1.83	3.87

The heat-transfer coefficient for water in the 15-mm channel is in fact 3.44×10^4 W m^{-2} K^{-1} (Example 4.1). Helium for the same conditions gives values about 20% below the carbon dioxide ones, but would in practice probably be circulated with a higher velocity.

As expected, changing the channel size has little effect for the non-metals; the way to increase their heat-transfer coefficients would be to increase the flow velocity. However, reducing the channel size increases the liquid-sodium coefficient substantially, because the heat has to be conducted a much shorter distance. Although they have similar heat-transfer coefficients liquid sodium and water are not in practice alternatives. Water cannot be used in a fast reactor because it is a moderator, sodium would not be used in a thermal reactor because it is not a moderator.

The most striking feature of the results is the poor heat transfer that is obtained with gases. However, the heat flux is the product of h and ΔT, the can to coolant temperature difference, and gas-cooled reactors use much higher values of ΔT. The heat flux in water-cooled reactors is limited, as will be explained in the next chapter, by the possibility of the surface of the fuel rods becoming blanketed with steam. There is no comparable limitation with gases.

Even if we allow that the average can to coolant temperature difference in the gas-cooled reactor is probably five times what it would be in the water-cooled reactor, this does not bring the heat flux in the gas-cooled reactor up to the point where it can compete economically. It is in fact essential to improve the gas heat transfer above the levels given by equation (4.17) and this can be done, as is described in detail later, either by adding fins to the surface or by roughening the surface. In this way the effective heat transfer is increased by a factor of at least 2, and heat fluxes comparable to those used in water reactors are obtained.

Heat fluxes in water-cooled reactors are typically around 400 to 500 kW m^{-2}, in gas-cooled reactors roughly half this, and in the sodium-cooled fast reactor roughly twice this value. This has implications for the relative sizes of the fuel rods. It is desirable that the heat-transfer processes inside and outside of the fuel rod should be of comparable efficiency; there is no point in having the forced convection outside of the fuel rod at such a high level of efficiency that the heat conduction within the fuel cannot deliver a sufficient amount of heat without fuel melting. Given the very high temperatures that are attainable in the fuel, the temperature difference between the centre of the fuel and the outside of the cladding will be similar in all reactors using UO_2 fuel, which implies similar linear ratings for the fuel rods in the different reactors. The lower heat flux required at the surface of the fuel rod in the gas-cooled reactor therefore implies a larger diameter rod. Similarly the higher heat flux with sodium implies a smaller rod.

IMPROVEMENT OF HEAT TRANSFER USING FINS

One method of achieving the necessary improvement in can to coolant heat transfer in gas-cooled reactors is to extend the can surface in the form of fins. Provided the cladding material has high thermal conductivity and low neutron absorption this will be worth doing. Heat will be conducted into the fins and a larger heat-transfer area will be exposed to the coolant, which will allow a greater heat output for the same can to coolant temperature difference.

Constant cross-section fin with constant heat-transfer coefficient

The simplest fin geometry is one where the fin has a constant cross-section from root to tip, as shown in Fig. 4.4, which could, for example, be one of a number of fins running longitudinally along the can. It is usual in analysing the performance of a fin to assume that the heat-transfer coefficient is the same over the whole length of the fin, although in practice this is a poor approximation and the actual performance of the finned surface must be established by constructing it and testing it.

Let the temperature at the base of the fin at $z = 0$ be T_0, the length and thickness of the fin L and t respectively and the bulk gas temperature T_b (also assumed constant).

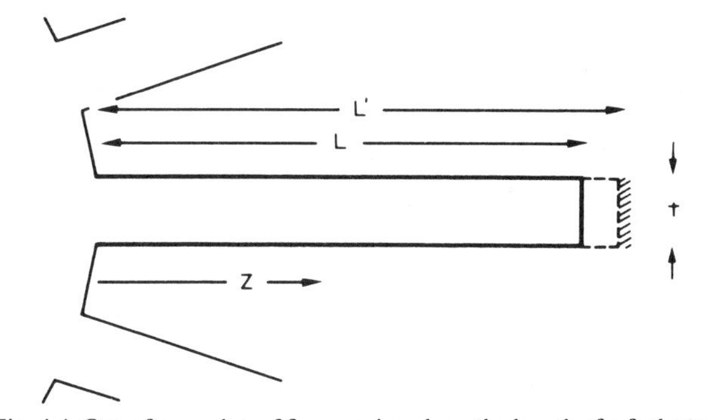

Fig. 4.4. One of a number of fins running along the length of a fuel can.

Considering unit width of the fin (perpendicular to the plane of Fig. 4.4) the heat flowing at z is

$$-k_c t \frac{dT}{dz}$$

where k_c is the thermal conductivity of the material of the fin, and the decrease in heat flow over a distance dz is:

$$-k_c t\frac{\mathrm{d}T}{\mathrm{d}z} - \left\{- k_c t\left[\frac{\mathrm{d}T}{\mathrm{d}z} + \frac{\mathrm{d}^2T}{\mathrm{d}z^2}\mathrm{d}z\right]\right\} = k_c t\frac{\mathrm{d}^2T}{\mathrm{d}z^2}\mathrm{d}z.$$

This equals the heat lost by convection from the fin surface which is

$$2\mathrm{d}zh\,(T - T_b).$$

Equating the last two expressions and putting $\theta = T - T_b$ gives

$$k_c t\frac{\mathrm{d}^2\theta}{\mathrm{d}z^2} = 2h\theta. \qquad (4.34)$$

This type of differential equation is satisfied by solutions of the form $\theta = Be^{mz}$ and substituting this back into the equation gives

$$m^2 = \frac{2h}{k_c t}, \qquad (4.35)$$

i.e. m can be either positive or negative, so a general solution is

$$\theta = Be^{mz} + Ce^{-mz}. \qquad (4.36)$$

The values of B and C come from the boundary conditions. At $z = 0$, $\theta = \theta_0 = T_0 - T_b$ so

$$\theta_0 = B + C. \qquad (4.37)$$

The second boundary condition is adjusted in order to simplify the solution. The end of the fin is imagined to be extended slightly, to a new total length L' with $t = 2(L' - L)$, and the new tip is considered to be insulated, as shown in Fig. 4.4. Exactly the same surface area is exposed to the coolant, but we now have the simple boundary condition of no heat flow and hence zero temperature gradient at $z = L'$.

So at $z = L'$

$$\frac{\mathrm{d}\theta}{\mathrm{d}z} = Bme^{mL'} - Cme^{-mL'} = 0$$

substituting for C from (4.37) gives

$$B = \theta_0 e^{-mL'}/(e^{mL'} + e^{-mL'}) \qquad (4.38)$$

and hence

$$C = \theta_0 e^{mL'}/(e^{mL'} + e^{-mL'}). \qquad (4.39)$$

Using the last two equations with equation (4.36) gives the temperature distribution along the fin, but what we are mainly interested in is the total rate at which heat is dissipated by the fin, and this equals the heat conducted in at the root,

$$-k_c t\left(\frac{d\theta}{dz}\right)_{z=0} = -k_c t\,(Bm - Cm) = k_c t\, m\theta_0 \frac{e^{mL'} - e^{-mL'}}{e^{mL'} + e^{-mL'}}.$$

So the total heat is dissipated by the fin is

$$k_c t\, m\theta_0 \tanh mL'. \tag{4.40}$$

A quantity that is sometimes used as a measure of fin performance is the fin efficiency defined as the ratio of the heat actually dissipated by the fin to the heat that would be conveyed to the coolant if the whole of the fin surface were at the root temperature T_0. In other words the actual behaviour is compared with that of an idealised fin with infinite thermal conductivity.

If the whole surface were at T_0, the heat convected away from it would be

$$2L'h\,(T_0 - T_b) = 2hL'\,\theta_0$$

and the fin efficiency is

$$\frac{\tanh mL'}{mL'}. \tag{4.41}$$

When fins are tested the importance of the parameter mL' is confirmed, as would be expected since

$$(mL')^2 = \frac{2hL'^2}{k_c t} = \frac{\text{resistance to heat conduction along fin}}{\text{resistance to convection from the surface}}.$$

Returning to equation (4.40) for the total heat dissipated by the fin, we see that the performance apparently improves continuously as the length of the fin is increased. However, tanh mL' increases very little for values of mL' much over 1, as the following table shows:

mL'	0	1	2	∞
tanh mL'	0	0.76	0.96	1

In practice doubling mL' to 2 might not improve the heat transfer at all since the flow will find it more difficult to get between the longer fins and the effective heat-transfer coefficient might fall enough to offset the increased heat transfer area.

To see whether fins are worthwhile, and if they are what benefit they bring, we have to compare (4.40) with the heat that would be lost by a fuel can without fins. Before we can do this we need to know the number of fins that can be put on the can, and this depends not only on the thickness of the fins, but also on their spacing. The fins cannot be too close together or the boundary layers associated with the two surfaces will meet and the main flow will skim over the tops of the fins instead of penetrating down between them, causing a drastic fall in heat transfer coefficient.

If the minimum gap between the fins consistent with the main flow being able to penetrate between them is l, then the number of fins that may be fitted round the circumference of a can radius b, assuming that the fins are longitudinal or helical, is

$$2\pi b/(t + l)$$

and the total heat lost per unit length of the can is

$$\frac{2\pi b}{(t + l)} k_c t\, m\theta_0 \tanh mL' \tag{4.42}$$

where the contribution from the small part of the can surface between the roots of the fins has been ignored.

The rate at which heat is lost from unit length of the plain, unfinned can is

$$2\pi b h\theta_0 \tag{4.43}$$

so the ratio of heat-dissipation rates for the finned and plain cans is

$$\frac{t^{1/2}}{(t + l)} \left(\frac{2k_c}{h}\right)^{1/2} \tanh mL' \tag{4.44}$$

Assuming that l is constant for a given coolant and flow conditions then the value of t could be chosen to make $t^{1/2}/(t + l)$ a maximum, which would require $t = l$, as shown in Fig. 4.5. The value of $t^{1/2}/(t + l)$ does not vary much with t over the range $\frac{1}{3}l < t < 3l$ though, and for a reactor application fins of width $\frac{1}{3}l$, requiring only half the volume of material, might be preferred. The value of $t^{1/2}/(t + l)$ is only 14% below the maximum possible.

With $t = \frac{1}{3}l$ the performance ratio becomes

$$0.433 \left(\frac{2k_c}{hl}\right)^{1/2} \tanh mL'$$

and since in practice L' will be increased until tanh mL' reaches about 0.8, beyond which point there is little if anything further to be gained, we can write the ratio as

$$0.346 \left(\frac{2k_c}{hl}\right)^{1/2}.$$

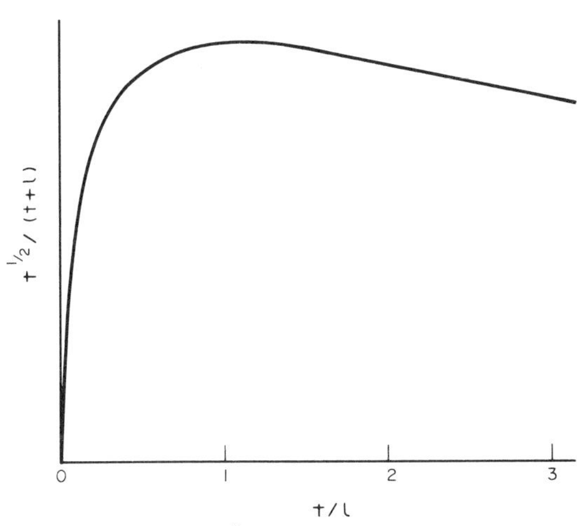

Fig. 4.5. Relative values of the parameter $t^{1/2}/(t + l)$ as a function of the fin thickness/spacing ratio.

The value of l is going to be connected with the thickness of the laminar sublayer δ. Clearly l must be greater than δ, and in fact it must be very much larger. The division of the flow into just two regions, laminar and turbulent, is an oversimplification. A closer description is obtained with three regions: laminar by the wall; an intermediate or buffer layer; then the turbulent core. In terms of the estimate of the laminar layer thickness δ given by equation (4.18) the combined thickness of laminar and buffer layers is 2 or 3 times δ. If there is to be anything like the normal turbulent flow in the spaces between the fins, then the turbulent core itself should occupy much more room, perhaps a further 25δ. So with a thickness of about 30δ associated with each surface the spacing l of the fins must be at least 60δ.

A major simplification of the performance ratio is now possible, since the heat-transfer coefficient also depends on δ, in fact it is roughly equal to $k/2\delta$, where k is the gas thermal conductivity (equation (4.18)).

With $h = k/2\delta$ and $l = 60\delta$ the ratio of the heat dissipated by the finned can to that dissipated by the plain can is

$$0.089\,(k_c/k)^{1/2}. \tag{4.45}$$

A direct comparison of this equation with experimental results is difficult because when measurements are made with different can materials giving different values of k_c it is usual to keep the geometry fixed, whereas equation (4.45) incorporates the assumption that tanh $mL' = 0.8$, requiring a different fin height for each material. If the experimental results of [21], which cover a sixteen-fold range of k_c, are corrected for the varying values of tanh mL', then equation (4.45) is confirmed to within 30% (and the power of k_c/k to within 10%).

Applying equation (4.45) to the two types of gas-cooled reactors in commercial use in the U.K., firstly for stainless-steel cans cooled by CO_2 at 500°C and 40 bar (typical AGR conditions) the ratio comes to 1.7, so it is marginal whether fins would be worth while from the heat-transfer point of view, and anyway they are ruled out by the high neutron absorption of steel. For Magnox cans cooled by CO_2 at 300°C and 20 bar the ratio is 5.7, suggesting that a very useful economic gain may be made by using fins.

The spacing of the fins, and hence their thickness, depends on the thickness of the boundary layer, and this in turn can be estimated from the heat-transfer coefficient given by equation (4.17).

So we have

$$\delta = k/2h = k/(2\rho uc 0.023 Re^{-0.2}\, Pr^{-0.6}). \tag{4.46}$$

For carbon dioxide under reactor conditions, for example, at 300°C, 20 bar and 12 m s^{-1}, and taking $Re = 2 \times 10^5$, δ is 0.034 mm. This suggests a fin spacing of around 2 mm (60δ) and a fin thickness of a little under 1 mm. The length of the fins then follows from the practical compromise that the value of tanh mL' should be around 0.8, so $mL' = L'(2h/k_c t)^{1/2}$ should be around 1.

In practice the heat-transfer coefficient is not independent of fin geometry, so the analysis of this section can only be regarded as the starting-point for a programme of experimental tests.

The herringbone design of finned can that is used in the U.K. Magnox reactors is shown in Fig. 4.6. The finned surface is divided by longitudinal splitters, with the fins running in opposite senses in adjacent quadrants. This arrangement promotes good mixing between the hotter gas in contact with the surface and the cooler gas in the main stream.

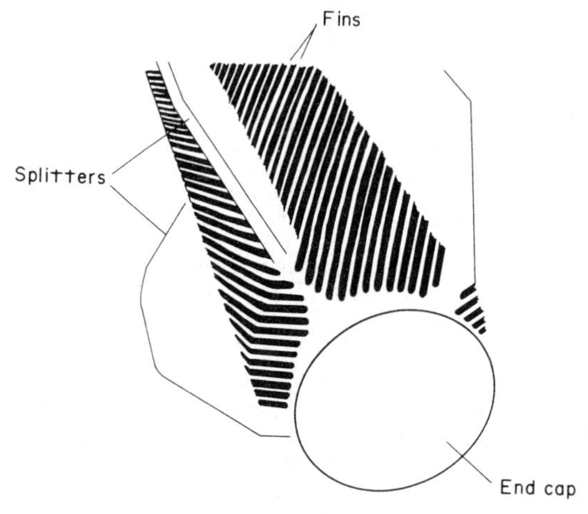

Fig. 4.6. End view of a Magnox fuel can with a herringbone pattern of fins.

IMPROVEMENT OF HEAT TRANSFER BY ROUGHENING THE SURFACE

The dual requirements of high thermal conductivity and low neutron absorption make it impossible to extend most cladding materials into fins, but in gas-cooled reactors it is still desirable to increase the heat output above the smooth surface value. This may be done by roughening the surface, by which is meant not a random effect, but small projections at regular intervals. For example, the fuel cans used in AGRs, shown in Fig. 4.7, have ribs, roughly square in section, running circumferentially round the cans at intervals of 2 mm.

The improvement in performance may be explained from two equivalent points of view.

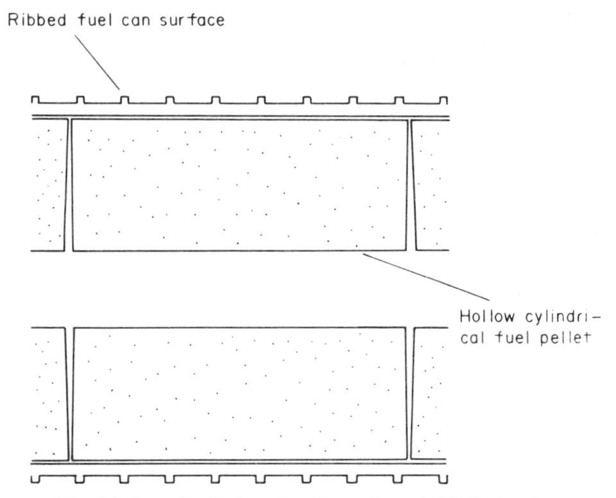

Fig. 4.7. Longitudinal section through an AGR fuel rod.

Firstly, the simple model of turbulent forced-convection heat transfer emphasises the importance of the laminar layer of fluid next to the surface as the main barrier to heat transfer, and the thickness of this layer depends on the rate at which the turbulent eddies transport momentum from the main flow to the boundary layer. Any projections sticking out into the flow will cause stronger eddies to form, increase the turbulent velocities and the transport of momentum to the surface, thus breaking up the laminar sublayer and improving the heat transfer. Alternatively, the effect of the ribs could be considered similar to that of a change of cross-section in the flow. The boundary layer does not build up again to its equilibrium thickness until some distance downstream. Just as the heat-transfer coefficient following a bend or abrupt change of cross-section may be 2 or 3 times the equilibrium value, a similar improvement may be achieved by roughening the surface, even though the projections are small in comparison with the channel size.

Clearly a first requirement is that the ribs or turbulence promoters should project beyond the laminar sublayer and come into contact with the main turbulent flow. Using equation (4.46) the thickness of the laminar layer for CO_2 at 500°C, 40 bar, and 12 m s^{-1} is roughly 0.028 mm, and to reach beyond the buffer layer into the turbulent core of the flow one would expect a rib height of at least 3 times this, or about 0.1 mm. In fact, the ribs on the AGR cans are 0.3 mm high, showing that the best results are obtained with quite small projections that only just protrude into the main turbulent flow.

The effect of higher ribs is to improve the heat transfer only slightly at the expense of a quite disproportionate increase in flow resistance and pumping power (it appears that surface roughening always increases the flow resistance more than it increases the heat-transfer coefficient).

The spacing of the ribs or other roughness elements can be estimated from the distance the flow needs to recover from a disturbance. With turbulent velocities of the order of 1/20 of the mean forward velocity then at a distance equal to roughly 20 rib heights downstream of the rib the flow will largely have recovered, and the laminar layer on the surface will have built up to close to its equilibrium thickness again. So the next rib should follow at a distance of appreciably less than 20 rib heights. A survey of a large number of roughened surfaces showed an optimum pitch to height ratio of 7 [22]. The local Stanton number shows considerable variation over the length of the fuel rod, being high immediately by the rib itself and low behind the rib where there is a recirculating region in the flow, with the main flow not in contact with the surface. Between 4 and 5 rib heights downstream from the rib the main flow reattaches to the surface and the Stanton number is high again.

Transformation of results in channels with mixed rough and smooth surfaces

The interpretation of roughened surface heat transfer would be straightforward if all the surfaces in a reactor coolant channel or a laboratory test rig were roughened and heated. However, neither is the case. In the reactor some of the fuel pins are surrounded by other fuel pins, but others are next to the smooth unheated channel wall. The majority of laboratory measurements are made on one heated rough rod inside a smooth circular unheated channel. In each case the velocity and temperature distributions, and the heat-transfer coefficients, are influenced by the presence of the smooth, unheated surface.

The effect on the Stanton number is not usually more than about 10%, but the effect on the flow resistance and pressure drop can be much more. The basic method of transforming the data was given by Hall [23]. Consider the particularly simple case of a flow channel with parallel sides, one rough and heated, one smooth and unheated, as shown in Fig. 4.8. The velocity profile is not symmetrical and the maximum velocity is displaced towards the smooth surface. If pressure-drop measurements are made along the channel it is not clear how much of the frictional resistance is associated with the rough surface and how much with the smooth. Suppose now that the part of the flow channel to the right-hand side of the position of maximum velocity is removed and replaced by the mirror image of the left-hand side. If the surface of maximum velocity is the surface of zero shearing force, then the flow will not be affected by this change since there is no shearing force or exchange of momentum across the boundary. We now have the pressure-drop measurements for an all-rough channel of known flow area, $2A_r$.

With a rough fuel rod inside a smooth circular channel the procedure is more difficult to visualise, but assuming that the equivalent diameter concept holds, then the pressure-drop measurements are interpreted as applying to an all-rough channel of flow area $2A_r$ and equivalent diameter $4(2A_r/2s_r) = 4A_r/s_r$, where s_r is the perimeter of the rough surface. Also the mean velocity for the part of the channel associated with the rough surface must be worked out from the velocity profile.

The transformation of the heat-transfer measurements is complicated by the fact that the smooth wall is unheated, and the temperature profile is as shown in Fig. 4.8, horizontal where it intersects the smooth wall, whereas if both walls were the same and both heated then the temperature would be a minimum in the centre of the channel.

The temperature distribution for an all-rough, all-heated channel can be calculated since the effective thermal conductivity of the flow, depending as it does on the unchanged turbulent eddies, is the same in the real and transformed flows, and can be found from the measured velocity and temperature profiles. Once the transformed temperature distribution is known the new bulk temperature and wall to bulk temperature difference and hence heat-transfer coefficient can be worked out.

There are a number of difficulties in using this transformation procedure. Ideally the velocity and temperature profiles should be measured, but a method that does not require this

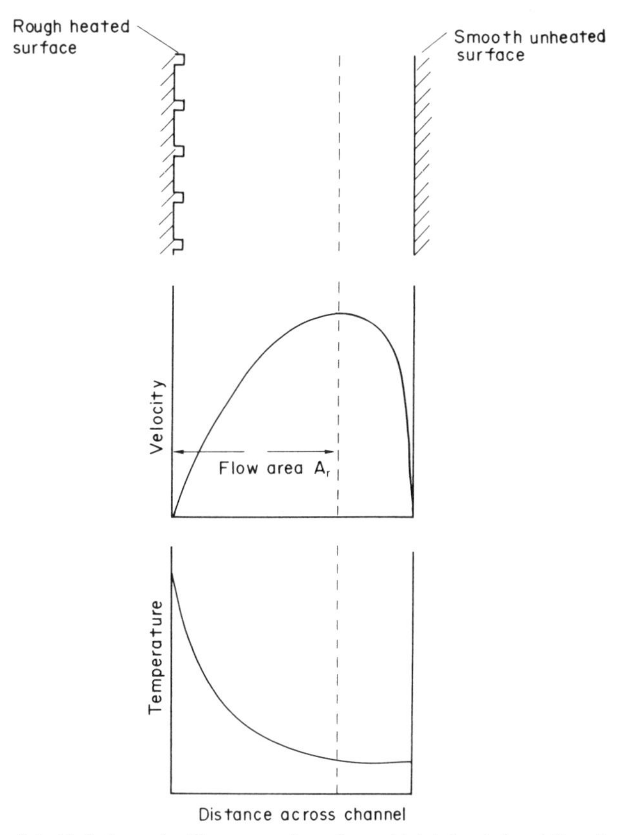

Fig. 4.8. Flow in a parallel-sided channel with one rough surface which is heated and the other surface smooth and unheated. The flow area associated with the rough surface is A_r.

information has been developed. An empirical correction has been found necessary to allow for the fact that the transformed flow resistance of the smooth surface is not the same as in an all-smooth channel. Also the surface of zero shear is not quite coincident with that of maximum velocity. A recent list of references may be found in [24].

Heat-transfer correlations for rough surfaces

A study [25] of a number of surfaces roughened by transverse ribs showed Stanton numbers between 1.5 and 3 times the value for a smooth surface, and for Reynolds numbers in the range of reactor interest, that is over 10^5, the variation with Reynolds number was approximately the same as for smooth surfaces, $Re^{-0.2}$. The friction factor, which is a measure of the frictional resistance to flow through the channel, was between 2 and 10 times the smooth surface value.

Results for the roughened surfaces used in AGRs are given in Fig. 9 of reference [26], and the predictions for the reactor can be expressed by

$$St = 0.054 Re^{-0.2} Pr^{-0.6}. \tag{4.47}$$

Comparing this equation with equation (4.17) for a smooth surface we see that the effect of roughening the AGR cans is to increase the Stanton number to 2.35 times the smooth surface value. The equation gives the transformed Stanton number for a channel composed entirely of rough surfaces, and would apply to a fuel rod surrounded by other fuel rods. For a fuel rod facing the smooth wall the transformation procedure would have to be used.

The $Pr^{-0.6}$ dependence in equation (4.47) is based purely on analogy with the equation for smooth surfaces. It is not possible working only with gases, with an almost constant Prandtl number of 0.7, to establish the Prandtl number exponent with accuracy.

Equation (4.47) applies specifically to CO_2 at reactor temperature and stainless-steel cans. The ribs on the surface behave to a small extent as fins, and their fin efficiency depends on $L'(2h/k_c t)^{1/2}$, so with a different heat-transfer coefficient h or cladding conductivity k_c the performance of the roughened surface will be slightly different [27]. Going from stainless-steel cans in the laboratory to stainless-steel cans in the reactor, with CO_2 coolant in each case, the correction is small, but laboratory measurements on aluminium cans yield Stanton numbers some 5% high.

This small correction underlines the point that the distinction between finned and roughened surfaces is not sharp. The projections on rough surfaces behave to a small extent as fins, and a good finned surface requires the same sort of regular disturbance and mixing of the flow that is provided by ribs.

References

1. DITTUS, F. W. and BOELTER, L. M. K. University of California, Berkeley, *Publ. Eng.* **2,** 443 (1930).
2. ENGINEERING SCIENCES DATA, *Heat transfer*, Vol. 1, Item 67016, 1967.
3. MARTINELLI, R. C. Heat transfer to molten metals. *Trans. ASME* **69,** 947–959 (1947).
4. LAUNDER, B. E. and SPALDING, D. B. *Mathematical models of turbulence*, Academic Press, 1972.
5. COLBURN, A. P. A method of correlating forced convection heat transfer data and a comparison with fluid friction. *Trans. Amer. Inst. Chem. Engrs* **29,** 174 (1933).
6. SIEDER, E. N. and TATE, G. E. *Ind. Eng. Chem.* **28,** 1429–1435 (1936).
7. PETUKHOV, B. S. Heat transfer and friction in turbulent pipe flow with variable properties. *Advances in Heat Transfer* **6,** 504–561 (1970).
8. WEISMAN, J. Heat transfer to water flowing parallel to tube bundles. *Nucl. Sci. Eng.* **6,** 78–79 (1959).
9. LYON, R. N. Liquid metal heat transfer coefficients. *Chem. Engng Prog.* **47,** 75 (1951, Feb. issue).
10. SEBAN, R. A. and SHIMAZAKI, T. Heat transfer to a fluid flowing turbulently in a smooth pipe with walls at constant temperature. *Trans. ASME* **73,** 803 (1951).
11. DWYER, O. E. and LYON, R. N. Liquid metal heat transfer. *Proc. 3rd U.N. Int. Conf. Peaceful Uses of Atomic Energy, Geneva* **8,** 182–191 (1965).
12. DWYER, O. E. Eddy transport in liquid metal heat transfer. *Am. Inst. Chem. Eng. J.* **9,** 261–268 (1963).
13. KIRILLOV, P. L., SUBBOTIN, V. I., SUVOROV, M. Y. and TROYANOV, M. F. Heat transfer in pipes to a sodium–potassium alloy and to mercury. *J. Nucl. Energy Part B, Reactor Technology* **1,** 123–129 (1959).
14. SUBBOTIN, V. I., KOZLOV, F. A. and IVANOVSKII, N. N. Heat transfer to sodium under conditions of free and forced convection and when oxides are deposited on the surface. *High Temperature* **1,** 368–372 (1963).
15. WINTERTON, R. H. S. Effect of gas bubbles on liquid metal heat transfer. *Int. J. Heat Mass Transfer* **17,** 549–554 (1974).
16. DWYER, O. E. and BERRY, H. C. Heat transfer to liquid metal flowing turbulently and longitudinally through closely spaced rod bundles. *Nucl. Engng Design* **23,** 273–294 (1972).
17. PFANN, J. Turbulent heat transfer to longitudinal flow through a triangular array of circular rods. *Nucl. Engng Design* **34,** 203–219 (1975).
18. GRABER, H. and RIEGER, M. Experimental study of heat transfer to liquid metals flowing in line through tube bundles. *Progress in Heat and Mass Transfer* **7,** 151–166 (1973).
19. FUCHS, H. and FAESCH, S. Measurement of eddy conductivity in sodium. *Ibid.*, pp. 39–43.
20. RAMM, H. and JOHANNSEN, K. Radial and tangential turbulent diffusivities of heat and momentum in liquid metals. *Ibid.*, pp. 45–48 (1973).
21. CUNNINGHAM, C. and SLACK, M. R. Heat transfer and pressure drop performance of spiral polyzonal heat transfer surfaces for gas cooled reactors. *J. Brit. Nucl. Energy Conf.* **6,** 348–367 (1961).

22. WALKER, V. and WILKIE, D. The wider applications of roughened heat transfer surfaces as developed for advanced gas-cooled reactors. Symposium on high pressure gas as a heat transfer medium. Inst. Mech. Engngs, London, 1967, Paper 26.
23. HALL, W. B. Heat transfer in a channel having rough and smooth surfaces. *J. Mech. Engng Sci.* **4,** 287 (1962).
24. LYALL, H. G. Comments on 'Turbulent convective heat transfer from rough surfaces'. *Int. J. Heat Mass Transfer* **21,** 523 (1978).
25. WILKIE, D. Forced convection heat transfer from surfaces roughened by transverse ribs. *Proc. Third Int. Heat Transfer Conf., Chicago*, Vol. 1, pp. 1–19.
26. KIMPTON, A. D. and LYALL, H. G. The heat transfer and pressure drop performance of a surface roughened by small square ribs. *J. Brit. Nucl. Energy Soc.* **11,** 271–277 (1972).
27. MANTLE, P. L., FREEMAN, A. R. and WATTS, J. Conductivity effects on ribbed surface heat transfer. *Int. J. Heat Mass Transfer* **14,** 1825–1834 (1971).

Problems

1. Non-boiling water at 300°C flows through a 10-mm i.d. circular pipe at a rate of 0.3 kg s^{-1}. There is a heat flux of 400 kW m^{-2} at the surface. What is the temperature of the inside of the pipe?
2. Liquid sodium is used as the coolant, but otherwise conditions are as in question 1. What is the temperature of the inside of the pipe now?
3. In a proposed design for a High Temperature Reactor the channels for the helium coolant consist of smooth circular holes, 12 mm diameter, running through the graphite blocks. If the flow of helium through a particular channel is 0.01 kg s^{-1}, and its pressure and bulk temperature are 40 bar and 600°C, calculate the temperature of the graphite wall for a heat flux of 500 kW m^{-2}.
4. A PWR has 10.7-mm o.d. fuel cans on a square lattice with a 14.3-mm pitch. In the most highly rated channel the water flows at 4.57 m s^{-1}, and half-way along the channel the water temperature is 297°C. Calculate the pressure required to prevent boiling at this point if the local rating is 44.7 kW m^{-1} from each can.
   Do you think this pressure will be sufficient to prevent boiling everywhere in the core?
5. In order to test the burst-can detection system in a CO_2-cooled reactor it is proposed to place a thin 55-mm square natural uranium plate parallel to the flow in the centre of one of the coolant channels. The plate is to be supported by a bolt through its centre but may be considered completely exposed to the flow on both sides. The CO_2 flows at 0.7 kg s^{-1} and 250°C and the channel diameter is 100 mm. The pressure is 20 bar.
   Check that the plate will not become dangerously hot (rapid oxidation of the bare uranium surface will occur at temperatures over 550°C). The mass of the plate is 100 g and the thermal neutron flux 1.5×10^{17} neutrons s^{-1} m^{-2}. Assume the flow over the plate is fully developed thermally, but comment on whether this is likely to over- or underestimate the cooling.
   The following standard information is also needed. Avogadro's number is 6.023×10^{26} atoms per kg atom, the fission cross-section of U^{235} is 5.77×10^{-26} m^2, and the heat produced per fission is 3.2×10^{-11} J.
6. An AGR has its fuel rods assembled in clusters of 36 rods, and 8 clusters are stacked vertically on top of one another in each fuel channel. Carbon dioxide coolant enters at the bottom of the channel and leaves at the top. The fuel cans are roughened to improve the heat transfer. In a particular design the maximum can temperatures in each cluster, and the corresponding bulk gas temperatures, are as follows:

Cluster No.	1	2	3	4	5	6	7	8
Can temp. °C	407	451	556	626	670	694	689	683
Gas temp. °C	336	340	419	476	533	582	616	620

Because of doubts about the ability of the pumps to maintain the desired mass flow rate it is proposed to reduce the frictional resistance by replacing some of the clusters by ones with smooth cans.

If the design is limited by a maximum permitted can temperature, how many clusters can be replaced? The heat-transfer correlation for the rough surface is

$$St = 0.054\, Re^{-0.2}\, Pr^{-0.6}.$$

7. For each of the following pairs of heat-transfer surface material and coolant estimate the improvement in heat transfer that might result from extending the surface in the form of fins.

   It may be assumed that the flow is fully turbulent. The CO_2 pressure is 40 bar. The numbers in brackets are the respective thermal conductivities in W m^{-1} K^{-1}.

   (a) Mild steel (45) and carbon dioxide at 200°C.
   (b) Stainless steel (18.0) and carbon dioxide at 500°C.
   (c) Beryllium alloy (120) and carbon dioxide at 500°C.
   (d) Zircaloy (12.7) and water at 300°C.

   For (a) suggest a suitable width and length of fins as a starting-point for a programme of experimental tests. Assume $Re = 2 \times 10^5$ and $u = 5$ m s^{-1}.

CHAPTER 5

Boiling Heat Transfer

INTRODUCTION

Under suitable conditions a boiling liquid is a very good heat-transfer medium. Energy is conveyed by evaporation of the liquid rather than by increasing its temperature, with the result that high heat fluxes are possible with low can to coolant temperature differences. If boiling water is used in the core of a reactor then there is the additional advantage that the steam can be passed directly to the turbine and the secondary circuit can be dispensed with.

The main problem with using a liquid at or near its boiling-point is that the normally very good heat transfer may suddenly break down, and the heat-transfer surface become covered in vapour. This possibility is a limiting factor in the design of both BWRs and PWRs.

The first step in boiling is the nucleation of the phase change. This is not a significant barrier in water-cooled reactors, but is often found to be important in experimental work on liquid metals.

NUCLEATION

To start a liquid boiling it is not sufficient just to raise its temperature to the boiling-point. Nucleation sites are needed as well.

That boiling cannot start spontaneously within the bulk of a pure liquid at its saturation temperature is clear if we consider the mechanical equilibrium of a small vapour bubble. The vapour region must start as a very small bubble, radius r. Within the bubble the pressure is p_v, the vapour pressure, outside the external pressure is p. The condition for mechanical equilibrium is

$$p_v = p + 2\sigma/r \tag{5.1}$$

where σ is the surface tension, and the condition for the bubble to grow is

$$p_v > p + 2\sigma/r. \tag{5.2}$$

Since the definition of saturation temperature is that $p_v = p$, equations (5.1) and (5.2) cannot be satisfied, and the embryonic vapour bubble would collapse.

So to initiate the phase change nucleation sites are required. A nucleation site must provide a pre-existing region of gas or vapour which at the moment of nucleation has an interface of radius r to satisfy equation (5.2). Even with a nucleation site p_v will be greater than p, and the temperature of the liquid will be above the saturation temperature. Only with $r = \infty$ would boiling take place at the saturation temperature, and apparatus for the determination of saturation temperatures is designed to achieve this.

Before boiling starts there are two main types of nucleation site that are likely to be present: free gas bubbles suspended in the flow, which may be important in flowing systems; and cavities in solid surfaces in contact with the liquid that have not been filled with liquid, which are likely to be the only sites in a stagnant system. The assumption of nucleation by free gas bubbles entrained in the flow has been used to explain the inception of boiling in experiments with flowing liquid metals [1].

A cavity or crack in a solid surface can only act as a nucleation site if it is not filled with liquid. With low temperatures and low dissolved gas content in the liquid the vapour and gas partial pressures in the cavity can be made negligibly small, and at first sight it appears that the imposition of a small external pressure should be sufficient to fill the cavity with liquid and deactivate it. If now the boiling experiment is performed the cavity should remain inactive, because to form a vapour embryo from nothing in contact with a solid surface is not very different to the problem of creating one within the bulk liquid. In practice it is not possible to deactivate surface nucleation sites even by imposing large pressures, and the explanation was given by Harvey in 1944 [2]. Provided the sides of the cavity are sufficiently steep, and the advancing contact angle sufficiently large, then the shape of the liquid meniscus advancing into the cavity will be as shown in Fig. 5.1(a), i.e. concave on the liquid side. The surface tension forces now oppose the entry of the liquid into the cavity, and if the cavity is small enough the excess pressure due to surface tension can balance indefinitely large external pressures.

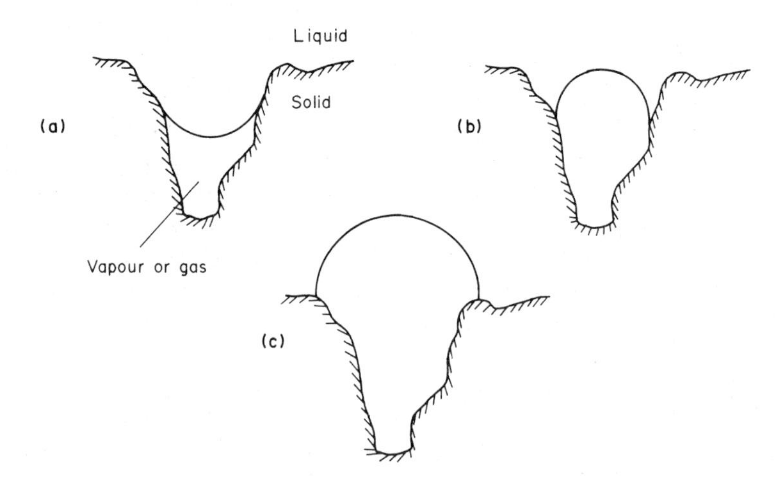

Fig. 5.1. A surface cavity nucleation site. (a) Position of liquid–solid interface before boiling. (b) Position of interface at nucleation of boiling; position is determined by pre-boiling conditions. (c) Nucleation at cavity mouth independent of pre-boiling conditions.

A number of investigators, e.g. [3], [4], have studied boiling on surfaces that had artificial cavities drilled into them, and found agreement with theoretical predictions. It is important to be able to predict the behaviour of ordinary surfaces, however, and various workers have suggested that this can be done by a pressurisation theory, e.g. [5], whereby the radius of the meniscus at nucleation, as shown in Fig. 5.1(b), can be predicted from the radius it assumed during prior pressurisation (Fig. 5.1(a)). However, experimental results for the initiation of boiling in water show that cavities can recover from pressurisation, and the actual behaviour is often closer to that shown in Fig. 5.1(c) [6].

Assuming that surface cavities giving values of r of around 1 μm are present on the heating surfaces we can compare the boiling of water and sodium under reactor conditions using equation (5.1) (boiling of sodium could only occur during an accident in current reactor designs). For sodium the excess pressure $p_v - p$ needed to nucleate boiling is about 3 bar, for water it is about 0.3 bar because of the lower surface tension. However, the big difference comes when we consider the temperature increase above saturation, that is the liquid superheat, required to achieve these increases in vapour pressure. For sodium it is about 100°C, while for water it is less than 1°C. Consequently sodium boiling tends to be more irregular and violent, with a large superheat building up before boiling starts, followed by very rapid vapour growth until the excess heat has been dissipated by evaporation.

Once boiling has started there is vapour present that may be trapped in other cavities and nucleation of subsequent bubbles may well be easier. It is common to find a fall in superheat once boiling has started. However, the basic need for nucleation sites remains, and this type of boiling, with bubbles growing from cavities and then being swept off into the flow, is called nucleate boiling.

TYPES OF BOILING

For given conditions, such as pressure and mass flow rate, the effect of steadily increasing the power input to a heated surface immersed in the liquid coolant is to produce a curve such as that in Fig. 5.2, where heat flux is plotted against wall to bulk temperature difference on log scales. The curve drawn is strictly for pool boiling, but similar behaviour is exhibited in flow boiling.

At low heat inputs the temperature of the heated surface is insufficient to cause boiling and heat is transferred by convection of the single-phase liquid. At some point such as b a few nucleation sites become active, but it is not until c that there are enough sites for boiling to be in evidence all over the surface.

From c to d is the nucleate boiling region, characterised by very good heat transfer. This good heat transfer is due partly to the breaking up of the laminar layer of liquid next to the wall by the turbulence associated with the growth and departure of the bubbles, and partly to the evaporation of liquid underneath the growing bubble in contact with the wall, which takes away latent heat.

As point e is approached the bubbles become larger, making it difficult for fresh liquid to reach the surface. At point e the *critical heat flux* is reached and the heat-transfer coefficient starts to fall, because much of the surface is covered with a blanket of vapour. If the power to the heater is further increased then the situation rapidly becomes much worse. The whole surface becomes blanketed with vapour and the temperature rapidly rises to that at point f, since this is the only point on the curve corresponding to a heat flux greater than the critical

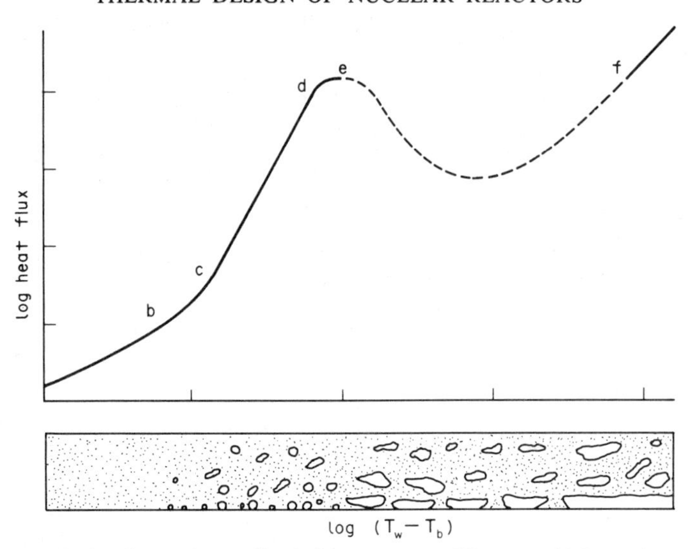

Fig. 5.2. Heat flux against wall to bulk temperature difference, with log scales.

heat flux. The part of the curve between *e* and *f*, corresponding to first unstable film boiling and then to stable film boiling as the heat flux rises again, is of limited interest so far as the steady-state operation of the core of a nuclear reactor is concerned. It can be investigated experimentally by controlling the temperature of the surface rather than the power input.

The seriousness of exceeding the critical heat flux depends on the conditions. In pool boiling, with no forced convection of the coolant, the only way that the heat can escape from a surface blanketed with poorly conducting vapour is by radiation. The sudden jump from the very good heat transfer of the nucleate boiling region, where high heat fluxes can be dissipated by quite small can to coolant temperature differences, to the film boiling region, is accompanied by an increase in the temperature difference of approaching two orders of magnitude. This rise in temperature is often enough to destroy the heating element, hence an alternative name for the critical heat flux phenomenon of *burnout*. However, in forced convection there may be sufficient cooling by the flow of vapour, aided by the occasional drop of liquid striking the surface, for the heating surface to survive. For this reason a better alternative description is *departure from nucleate boiling*, often abbreviated to DNB.

Channels in prototype boiling water reactors have been deliberately starved of coolant and operated without water in contact with the fuel cans for short periods [7,8]. The fuel cans were undamaged.

Nonetheless, for normal operation the heat fluxes in water reactors must be well below the critical heat flux, and this is one of the main limitations on heat output in both BWRs and PWRs.

FLOW REGIMES IN FORCED-CONVECTION BOILING

The detailed flow pattern in a turbulent flow containing both liquid and vapour is very complicated, and often not easy to determine even in experimental channels with transparent walls. Experimental work on steam–water mixtures in heated channels under reactor conditions of pressure and mass flow rate (e.g. [9], [10]) shows that three main flow regimes exist, depending on the amount of steam in the flow. The first, as shown in Fig. 5.3, is subcooled flow, where the bulk liquid has not reached its saturation temperature. Bubbles that have nucleated and grown by the hot wall move out into the flow until they encounter subcooled liquid and then they collapse. Once the bulk liquid reaches the saturation temperature bubbles start to move throughout the flow cross-section and the bubbly flow regime starts. As more water is evaporated and more steam generated the steam tends to form larger bubbles in the centre of the channel, and these join together to form a core of vapour surrounded by an annulus of liquid. This is the annular flow regime. The segregation of the phases is not complete, there are still small bubbles in the water film and drops of liquid in the core.

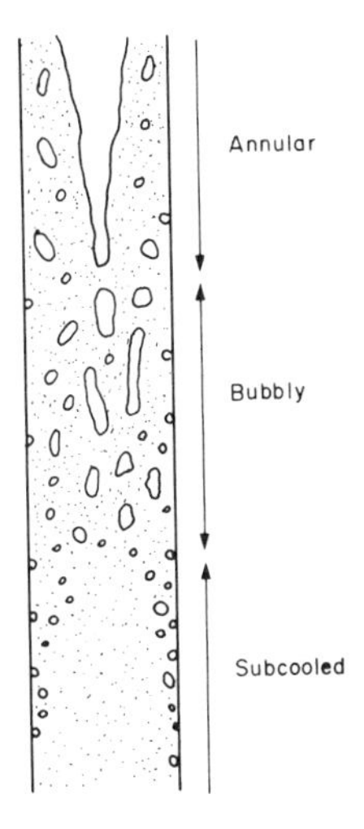

Fig. 5.3. Flow regimes in high-velocity forced-convection boiling.

At lower mass flow rates than normally encountered in reactors there is a distinct additional flow regime, between bubbly and annular. This is the slug flow regime where large bubbles almost filling the cross-section persist over a longer length of the channel and are associated with undesirable fluctuations in the flow rate.

The reason that the two phases tend to separate out, once there is a high proportion of vapour present, may be connected with the different densities of the phases. In an accelerating flow (accelerating because the total mass flow rate is constant along the channel, and the average density of the mixture is continuously falling), the pressure gradient is the same for both phases, but the lighter vapour is accelerated more and travels faster. It therefore moves to the centre of the flow where the retarding effect of the walls is less, and may travel at several times the speed of the liquid.

Presumably the flow pattern in the reactor is similar, with the water clinging to the sides of the fuel cans, and it is fortunate that this is so, because the boiling-water reactor relies on it for the efficient cooling of the cans.

Quality, void fraction and slip ratio

Two different parameters are used to specify the amount of vapour in the two-phase flow. From the point of view of the reactor physics of the core what matters is the relative volume of steam present at a given point in the channel, since this gives the amount of moderator that is missing. Accordingly the void fraction is defined as

$$\text{void fraction} = \alpha = \frac{\text{volume of vapour}}{\text{total volume}}. \tag{5.3}$$

From the point of view of heat transfer the steam-flow rate is important, so we have

$$\text{vapour quality} = x = \frac{\text{mass flow rate of steam}}{\text{total mass flow rate}}. \tag{5.4}$$

These two parameters are related by the

$$\text{Slip ratio} = S = \frac{\text{velocity of vapour}}{\text{velocity of liquid}}. \tag{5.5}$$

Suppose the flow area occupied by the vapour is A_v, that occupied by the liquid is A_l, and the total area $A_v + A_l = A$, then

$$\alpha = \frac{A_v}{A}.$$

If the vapour and liquid velocities and specific volumes are respectively u_v, u_l and v_v, v_l then

$$x = \frac{u_v A_v / v_v}{u_v A_v / v_v + u_l A_l / v_l} = \frac{1}{1 + \dfrac{u_l A_l v_v}{u_v A_v v_l}}$$

and since $A_l/A_v = (A - A_v)/A_v = 1/\alpha - 1 = (1-\alpha)/\alpha$

$$x = \frac{1}{1 + \dfrac{(1-\alpha)}{\alpha} \dfrac{1}{S} \dfrac{v_v}{v_l}}. \tag{5.6}$$

This relation can be used to find the steam quality if the void fraction is known. For example, a minimum void fraction at the exit from the channel might be specified in order to provide adequate moderation. The value of x would in turn determine the channel power for a given total mass flow rate.

Normally though, the channel power is determined by other considerations, and values of α at different positions in the core are needed for reactor physics calculations from known values of x (there is some feedback between the reactor physics and heat-transfer calculations since a different void fraction means a changed local reactivity and a changed power distribution). If the total mass flow rate in a channel in the core is m and the total power integrated from the channel inlet up to a certain position is Q, then the rate at which the steam flows at that position is xm and

$$Q = m(xh_{lv} + h_l - h_{in}) \tag{5.7}$$

where h_{in} is the specific enthalpy of the bulk water at the inlet, h_{lv} the specific enthalpy change on evaporation and h_l the specific enthalpy of the liquid at its saturation temperature.

Rearranging equation (5.6) the void fraction is given by

$$\alpha = \frac{1}{1 + \dfrac{(1-x)}{x} S \dfrac{v_l}{v_v}}. \tag{5.8}$$

Unfortunately the slip ratio S is not constant. It is itself a function of x and v_l/v_v (i.e. pressure), also it changes with mass flow rate and flow pattern. The dependence on pressure is to be expected since it is the difference between v_v and v_l that gives rise to different vapour and liquid velocities when the flow is accelerated. As the pressure rises and the values of v_v and v_l come closer together the slip ratio would decrease, and at the critical pressure with $v_v = v_l$ the slip ratio is unity.

There is no single generally accepted method of calculating S, and indeed it is arguable that the concept itself is not very useful. Since S itself varies with x and v_l/v_v it may be more convenient to correlate α with x directly, and this is frequently done. One widely used correlation, based on low-pressure results with air–liquid mixtures and extrapolated to high pressures using $S = 1$ at the critical point, is that of Martinelli and Nelson [11].

Direct measurements of void fraction, using the attenuation of a γ-ray beam, have been made on high-pressure boiling steam–water mixtures [12]. Thom [13], while recognising that the slip ratio does vary with steam quality, has worked out a constant best-fit value of S for each pressure. The values of S for each of the experimental pressures and a graph for interpolation are given in Thom's paper, but it is more convenient to have an equation.

$$S = 0.93\,(v_v/v_l)^{0.11} + 0.07\,(v_v/v_l)^{0.561} \tag{5.9}$$

fits Thom's results to well within 1%, and can be used to estimate S from atmospheric pressure right up to the critical point.

The void fraction can now be calculated from equation (5.8). For example, at a typical BWR pressure of 70 bar, equation (5.9) gives $S = 1.67$, and the values of α are shown in Fig. 5.4, with the predictions of Martinelli and Nelson for comparison.

When the bulk coolant is below its saturation temperature, i.e. subcooled, the calculation of void fraction is even more complicated. A simple approach based on an overall heat balance, such as that of equation (5.7), predicts a zero void fraction since on average the flow has not reached boiling-point. However, there are bubbles by the wall. Methods of predicting void fraction in this case have been presented by Thom and co-workers [14].

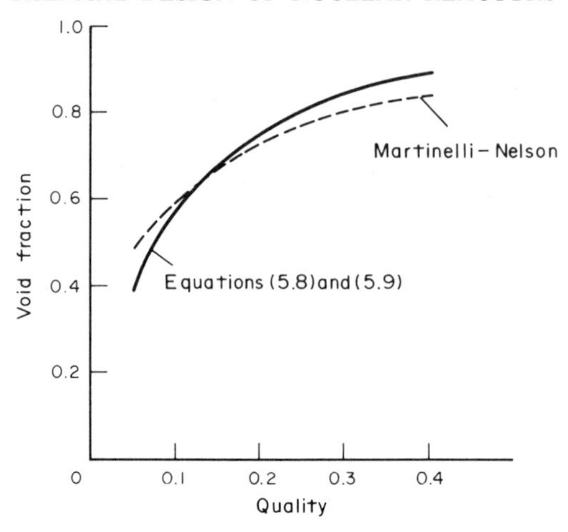

Fig. 5.4. Void fraction versus quality for steam–water mixtures at 70 bar.

Example 5.1. A BWR operates at 70 bar. Water enters a coolant channel 12°C subcooled and at 18 kg s^{-1}. It is desired to limit the void fraction at the outlet of this channel to 0.80 to ensure adequate moderation. What is the maximum channel power consistent with this objective? (Ignore any pressure drop along the channel.)

The void fraction can be turned into a steam mass flow using equation (5.6), but first we need the slip ratio S.

From steam tables (Appendix 2) the specific volumes of water and steam at 70 bar are 0.001 351 and 0.027 37 respectively; v_v/v_l equals 20.26 and substitution in equation (5.9) gives $S = 1.67$.

Equation (5.6) gives the steam quality:

$$x = \frac{1}{1 + \dfrac{(1 - 0.8)\,20.26}{0.8 \times 1.67}} = 0.248.$$

T_{sat} at 70 bar is 285.8°C, so the water enters the channel at 273.8°C, at which temperature its enthalpy is 1205 kJ kg^{-1}. The total channel power is thus

$$18\{h_l - 1205 + x\,h_{lv}\} = 18\{1267 - 1205 + 0.248 \times 1505\}\ \text{kW}$$
$$= \underline{7.83\ \text{MW}}.$$

HEAT-TRANSFER CORRELATIONS FOR FLOW BOILING

Nucleate boiling of water

The Jenns–Lottes correlation for fully developed nucleate boiling is [15]:

$$T_s - T_{sat} = 4.45\ e^{-p/62}\ q^{1/4}\ ^\circ\text{C} \tag{5.10}$$

where T_s is the temperature of the heated surface, T_{sat} the saturation temperature, p the pressure in bars, and q the heat flux in kW m^{-2}. It is valid for pressures between 34 and 138 bar, and although derived for subcooled boiling may also be used for bulk boiling. The correlation is not given in the form of a heat-transfer coefficient because, as is clear from equation (5.10), the heat-transfer coefficient is not constant. The flow velocity has no effect on the heat transfer, showing that the laminar sublayer present in a single-phase flow has been broken up by the boiling.

Thom and co-workers [14] made measurements over a similar range of pressure and recommend

$$T_s - T_{sat} = 0.71\ e^{-p/86.9}\ q^{1/2}\ ^{\circ}C. \tag{5.11}$$

Under reactor conditions there is at most a couple of degrees difference between the two equations, but there is some evidence [16] that equation (5.11) is also valid at much lower pressures (4 bar), so it is to be preferred for general use.

The point in the channel at which boiling starts may be found by working out the cladding surface temperature using both equation (5.11) and a correlation for non-boiling flow such as equation (4.17), and when both equations give the same T_s then the real heat-transfer situation will be somewhere between single phase and fully developed boiling. It will not be until further down the channel, when the bulk temperature of the coolant reaches the saturation temperature, that bulk boiling will be established.

At very high mass flow rates and void fractions the layer of liquid in contact with the surface becomes very thin, so thin that there is no room for vapour bubbles to form and high heat fluxes can be conducted directly through the liquid to the vapour core. Evaporation takes place at the liquid–vapour interface, and the wall temperature is low enough to suppress nucleation. An equation for the heat-transfer coefficient when this effect is significant has been given by Chen [17].

Film boiling

Once the heat flux is increased above the critical level there is a step increase in the wall temperature because the wall is no longer in contact with the flowing liquid. If this occurs at high mass flow rates and high qualities in the annular flow regime then it corresponds to the dryout of the liquid film, and beyond the dryout position there is no continuous liquid phase, though there are still drops of liquid entrained in the vapour.

Heat transfer is now mainly by forced convection to the vapour, assisted by the impacts of liquid drops against the wall, and, if the wall temperature is high enough, by radiation. As a first approximation it appears that in stable film boiling the direct contribution of the liquid drops can be neglected, presumably because even when thrown against the wall by the turbulent motion they do not wet it. The momentum of the vapour generated from the surface of the approaching drop is sufficient to prevent physical contact. In other words, the wall temperature is higher than the Leidenfrost temperature.

Consequently it should be possible to get a rough estimate of the heat-transfer coefficient using one of the standard forced convection correlations with the vapour physical properties and the vapour velocity.

For example, the Dittus–Boulter equation (4.17) gives

$$Nu_v = 0.023\ Re^{0.8}\ Pr_v^{0.4}.$$

We need to calculate the vapour velocity, u_v, and have used the equation in its Nusselt number form ($Nu = StRePr$) to avoid having to substitute for u_v in two places.

If the total mass flow rate is m, then the vapour mass flow rate is xm, and if the flow area occupied by vapour is A_v then

$$u_v = \frac{xm}{\rho_v A_v} = \frac{xGA}{\rho_v A_v} = \frac{xG}{\rho_v \alpha}$$

where G is the mass velocity, m/A.

Substituting for the void fraction $\alpha = A_v/A$ from equation (5.8) gives

$$u_v = \frac{G}{\rho_v}\{x + (1-x)S\, v_l/v_v\}.$$

The slip ratio, S, in this type of flow is not well known, but since normally $(1-x)S\, v_l/v_v$ is much smaller than x there is little error in assuming a homogeneous flow with $S = 1$.

The heat-transfer correlation becomes

$$Nu_v = 0.023\,[d_e\, G\{x + (1-x)\, v_l/v_v\}\,/\mu_v]^{0.8}\, Pr_v^{0.4}. \tag{5.12}$$

Before we can use this equation, however, we need to know values of x and of the bulk vapour temperature downstream of the dryout position. Because heat is transferred directly from the wall to the vapour the vapour tends to superheat above the saturation temperature, and the evaporation of the liquid drops lags behind, giving values of x below the equilibrium value calculated from a heat balance.

The analysis of the heat and mass transfer processes between liquid and vapour is complicated and uncertain. However, two extreme possibilities can be identified:

(a) With no heat or mass transfer between the phases x stays constant at the value it had at the dryout position, x_{do}, and the vapour bulk enthalpy h rises steadily according to

$$mx_{do}\,(h - h_v) = \text{power supplied after dryout} \tag{5.13}$$

where h_v is the enthalpy of saturated vapour.

This should provide an upper limit to the wall temperature, since the heat-transfer coefficient is low (low vapour velocity) and the vapour bulk temperature is the highest it could possibly be.

(b) If the phases are in equilibrium then x is the equilibrium value and the vapour bulk temperature remains at T_{sat}.

This gives a lower limit to the wall temperature, with high vapour velocities and the lowest bulk temperature.

An empirical correlation developed along these lines for mixtures of water and steam is that of Miropolskiy [18]:

$$Nu_v = 0.023[Re_v\,\{x + (1-x)v_l/v_v\}]^{0.8}\, Pr_w^{0.8} Y \tag{5.14}$$

where Y is an empirical factor, less than 1, to allow for the fact that the rest of the equation, based as it is on the equilibrium value of x and T_{sat}, tends to overestimate the heat transfer.

$$Y = 1 - 0.1\{v_v/v_l - 1\}^{0.4}\,\{1 - x\}^{0.4}, \tag{5.15}$$

$Re_v = d_e\, G/\mu_v$ and Pr_w is the value at the wall.

Groeneveld [19] took the same parameters as in equation (5.14), but then varied all the constants to obtain the best fit with the available experimental data on stable film boiling of water. His most general equation, based on tube and annulus data, is

$$Nu_v = 3.27 \times 10^{-3} \, [Re_v \, \{x + (1 - x)v_l/v_v\} \,]^{0.901} \, Pr_w^{1.32} Y^{-1.5} \tag{5.16}$$

valid for pressures 34 to 215 bar, G 700 to 5300 kg m^{-2} s^{-1} and x 0.1 to 0.9. Again x is the equilibrium value and the heat transfer coefficient is based on T_{sat}. The discrepancy between individual data points and the predictions of this equation can be quite large, so it is useful to have the method of setting upper and lower limits to the post-dryout temperatures in addition.

At lower mass velocities, such as might occur in an accident, heat-transfer correlations developed for pool boiling are often used.

Example 5.2. Tests on post-dryout heat transfer are being conducted on a uniformly heated tube, 6 mm i.d. and 3 m long. The heat flux is 900 kW m^{-2} and the pressure 70 bar. In a particular test water enters the tube at 3.7 kg per minute and dryout is detected at 2.23 m from the start of the tube, at which point the steam quality is calculated from a heat balance to be 0.46.

Make upper and lower estimates of the temperature of the inside of the tube at the exit. Also make a best estimate using the Groeneveld correlation.

(a) First we make an upper estimate by assuming that no more water evaporates. Consequently the steam quality remains equal to 0.46.

The heat supplied after the initial dryout increases the steam enthalpy to a new value h given by

$$0.46m\,(h - h_v) = 900 \times \pi \times 0.006\,(3 - 2.23)\ \text{kW}$$

and with $m = 0.0617$ kg s^{-1} and $h_v = 2772$ kJ kg^{-1} this gives

$$h = 3232\ \text{kJ kg}^{-1}.$$

Interpolation in the superheated steam tables shows that the temperature of the steam at the exit from the tube is 428.7°C.

The Nusselt number at the tube exit is given by equation (5.12) with $x = 0.46$ still and, strictly, the properties appropriate to superheated steam at 428.7°C. However, since this is only a rough estimate and the values for superheated steam are often not readily available, we will use saturation values at 70 bar.

The mass velocity G is $m/A = 0.0617 \times 4/(\pi \times 0.006^2) = 2182$ kg s^{-1} m^{-2} so

$$Nu = 0.023 \left[\frac{0.006 \times 2182}{19.1 \times 10^{-6}} \left\{0.46 + (1 - 0.46)\frac{0.001\,351}{0.027\,37}\right\}\right]^{0.8} 1.57^{0.4} = 722.$$

The heat-transfer coefficient is

$$Nuk/d_e = 722 \times 64 \times 10^{-3}/0.006 = 7703\ \text{W m}^{-1}\ \text{K}^{-1}$$

and the surface to bulk temperature difference is $900 \times 10^3/7703 = 117$°C.

So the upper estimate of the wall temperature is $429 + 117 = $ 546°C (the effect of using the correct property values for superheated steam would be to increase this temperature, but the assumption of no further evaporation of the water is so severe that 546°C would in practice be an upper limit).

(b) For the lower limit the bulk temperature remains at the saturation value, 285.8°C, throughout. The flow of steam increases, and at the exit the steam quality x is given by

$$(x - 0.46)mh_{lv} = 900 \times \pi \times 0.006\,(3 - 2.23)\ \mathrm{kW}$$

and since $m = 0.0617\ \mathrm{kg\ s^{-1}}$ as before, and $h_{lv} = 1505\ \mathrm{kJ\ kg^{-1}}$, we have

$$x = 0.60.$$

The bulk steam is now at its saturation temperature, so there is no approximation involved in using the saturation values of the properties. Substituting $x = 0.60$ in equation (5.12), with the other values as before, gives $Nu = 876$.

The corresponding surface to bulk temperature difference is 96°C, so the lower estimate of the wall temperature is 285.8 + 96 = 382°C.

(c) The values of p, G and x lie within the limits of validity of equation (5.16), so it can be used for the best estimate.

The correct value of x is the equilibrium value, 0.60, and apart from Pr_w the equation is based on the saturation temperature, so the values of the properties are the same as those used in (a) and (b). To find Pr_w we need to know the wall temperature, i.e. an iterative approach must be adopted. In this case we already have estimates of the wall temperature, so we start with a temperature of (546 + 382)/2 = 464°C, giving $Pr_w = 0.99$.

Substituting in equation (5.16) gives $Nu = 558$ and hence a wall to bulk temperature difference of 151.2°C.

So the next estimate of the wall temperature is 285.8 + 151.2 = 437°C, giving $Pr_w = 1.02$.

Repeating the calculation with this value of Pr_w gives the best estimate of the wall temperature as 431°C.

CRITICAL HEAT-FLUX CORRELATIONS FOR FORCED-CONVECTION BOILING OF WATER

Theoretical understanding of the critical heat flux phenomenon is not good enough for theoretical expressions to be used for prediction. Instead empirical correlations of experimental results are used.

Correlations for subcooled boiling

A particularly simple equation was derived by Jens and Lottes [15]:

$$q_{\mathrm{crit}} = CG^n\,(T_{\mathrm{sat}} - T_b)^{0.22}\ \mathrm{kW\ m^{-2}} \qquad (5.17)$$

where G is the coolant mass velocity in $\mathrm{kg\ m^{-2}\ s^{-1}}$ and $T_{\mathrm{sat}} - T_b$ is the subcooling in °C. The values of C and n are functions of the pressure.

Pressure bar	C	n
34.5	925	0.16
69	309	0.275
138	43.4	0.5
207	4.64	0.73

The range of validity is G between 1300 and 10,600 kg m^{-2} s^{-1} and the subcooling between 3 and 90°C.

The W-3 correlation developed by Tong [20] for the Westinghouse Corporation includes the effect of other parameters and extends to low-quality bulk boiling. It is

$$\begin{aligned} q_{crit} &= [(2.022 - 0.006\,238p) + (0.1722 - 0.001\,427p)e^{(18.177 - 0.059\,87p)x}] \\ &\times [(0.1484 - 1.596x + 0.1729x\,|x|)\,2.326G + 3271] \\ &\times [1.157 - 0.869x] \\ &\times [0.2664 + 0.8357e^{-124.1d_e}] \\ &\times [0.8258 + 0.000\,341\,3(h_{sat} - h_{in})] \end{aligned} \tag{5.18}$$

where d_e is the channel equivalent diameter, h_{sat} and h_{in} the saturation and inlet enthalpies, and x is the steam quality (negative for subcooled flow).

The limits of validity of the various parameters and their units are as follows:

q is in kW m^{-2}		G	680 to 6800 kg m^{-2} s^{-1}
p	70 to 160 bar	h_{in}	> 930 kJ kg^{-1}
x	-0.15 to 0.15	d_e	0.0051 to 0.018 m

Comparing the two correlations it seems improbable at first sight that they can be referring to the same phenomenon. They have quite different mathematical forms and appear to contain different parameters. First we need to understand what is meant by a negative quality in the Tong correlation. When the coolant is above its saturation temperature and vapour is being produced the vapour quality is given by

$$x = \text{rate of heat supply above saturation}/h_{lv}m$$

where h_{lv} is the enthalpy change on evaporation and m the mass flow rate. If the coolant is below saturation and its enthalpy is h then the rate at which heat would have to be supplied to bring it up to the saturation temperature is $m(h_{sat} - h)$, and so by analogy the subcooled quality is defined as

$$x = -(h_{sat} - h)/h_{lv}. \tag{5.19}$$

This is a way of expressing the subcooling in a non-dimensional form.

Under PWR conditions the parameter that has the greatest influence on the critical heat flux is the mass velocity G. To compare the two correlations we allow G to vary but fix the other parameters as follows:

$$p = 138 \text{ bar}, x = -0.1, d_e = 0.012 \text{ m and inlet subcooling is } 50°\text{C}.$$

The Jens–Lottes equation reduces to

$$q_{\text{crit}} = 79.3\, G^{0.5} \text{ kW m}^{-2} \tag{5.20}$$

and the Tong correlation reduces to

$$q_{\text{crit}} = 0.431G + 1979 \text{ kW m}^{-2}. \tag{5.21}$$

The predictions of the two equations are plotted in Fig. 5.5. The agreement over the range of mutual validity is quite good, in spite of the different mathematical form of the two equations. For interest the predictions have also been extended some way outside the valid ranges, giving poor agreement at both high and low mass velocities. This emphasises the danger of extrapolating empirical equations outside the range of the original experimental data. An even clearer example can be seen if the Jens–Lottes correlation is extrapolated towards zero subcooling. At $T_{\text{sat}} - T_b = 0$ it quite erroneously predicts $q_{\text{crit}} = 0$.

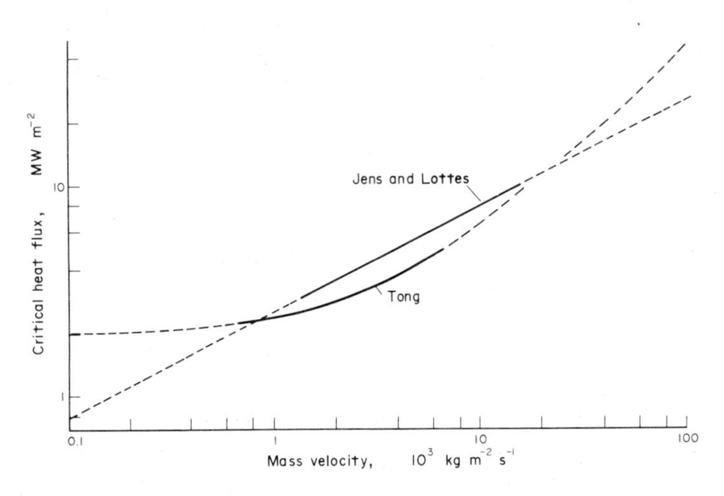

Fig. 5.5. Critical heat flux in forced-convection boiling of water. Comparison of two correlations, for the conditions described in the text. The dashed portions of the curves are invalid extrapolations.

The Tong correlation was developed from data obtained in uniformly heated single-channel test sections. A couple of minor modifications were found necessary [21] to obtain good agreement (to within about ± 20%) with measurements on rod bundles with axially varying heat flux.

To extend the correlation to non-uniformly heated channels the critical heat flux for the uniformly heated channel given by equation (5.18) is divided by a factor F, where

$$F = \frac{C \int_0^l q(z) \exp[-C(l - z)]\, dz}{q(l)\, [1 - \exp(-C l_{\text{unif}})]}. \tag{5.22}$$

q is the actual heat flux as a function of distance along the channel, l the distance from the point in the channel where nucleate boiling starts to the position of critical heat flux, l_{unif} the equivalent distance for a uniformly heated channel, and C is given by

$$C = 186\,(1-x)^{4.31}\,G^{-0.478}\ \mathrm{m}^{-1}. \tag{5.23}$$

The factor F reflects the fact that the temperature of the flow immediately by the wall and the number of bubbles in it depend on the heat flux upstream of the point in question, and consequently the critical heat flux is influenced by the upstream heat-flux distribution.

To allow for the beneficial effect that support grids, particularly those with mixing vanes, have in increasing turbulence and in separating the bubble layer from the surface of the rods, the critical heat flux given by equation (5.18) is multiplied by a factor F_s.

$$F_s = 1.0 + 2.21 \times 10^{-5}\,G\,(\mathrm{TDC}/0.019)^{0.35} \tag{5.24}$$

where TDC is an empirically determined thermal diffusion coefficient, varying, for the grid types and spacings investigated in [21], from 0.019 to 0.108.

When the correlation is used with rod bundles the values of x, G, etc., should be local values within the individual subchannels. The method of doing the subchannel analysis is outlined in Chapter 8.

Correlations for bulk boiling

Hench and Levy of the General Electric Company have proposed the following correlation for bulk boiling at 69 bar pressure [22]. Converted to SI related units (all these correlations are given in British units in the original references) the equations are:

$$q_{crit} = 3155 \quad \text{for} \quad x < x_1 \tag{5.25}$$

$$= 5994 - 10410x - 2208\,\tanh^2(G/452.2) \quad x_1 < x < x_2 \tag{5.26}$$

$$= 1893 - 2208x - 284\,\tanh^2(G/678.2) \quad x > x_2 \tag{5.27}$$

where

$$x_1 = 0.273 - 0.212\,\tanh^2(G/452.2), \tag{5.28}$$

$$x_2 = 0.5 - 0.269\,\tanh^2(G/452.2) + 0.035\,\tanh^2(G/678.2), \tag{5.29}$$

at other pressures

$$q_{crit}(p) = q_{crit}\,(69\ \mathrm{bar})\left\{1.1 - 0.1\left[\frac{p-41}{28}\right]^{1.25}\right\}. \tag{5.30}$$

The ranges of validity and the units employed are:

q_{crit} is in kW m^{-2} G 270 to 2170 kg m^{-2} s^{-1}

p 41 to 100 bar d_e 0.008 to 0.012 m.

Unlike the two correlations given for subcooled boiling, which are based on the average of the experimental results, this correlation is based on the lower envelope of the experimental results. Even with rod bundles the values of x and G are channel averages, so there is no need for a subchannel analysis.

While adequate for predicting whether the critical heat flux will be reached in a given assembly, the Hench–Levy correlation is unsuccessful in predicting some of the details of the phenomenon. For example, the axial position at which the critical heat flux first occurs as the power is raised in experimental tests is often incorrectly predicted. There appears to be an effect of upstream heat flux distribution, which is not taken into account in the correlation.

A more recent General Electric Company correlation, which gives critical quality as a function of boiling length, is in closer agreement with experiment [23], but full details do not appear to have been released.

There are a number of other critical heat-flux correlations, and it is clear that several of them successfully predict experimental results with a root mean square deviation of around 10% [24]. If applied to peculiar conditions outside their range of validity, such as very narrow (3 mm) or very long (7.1 m) tubes, the correlations can deviate from the average of the experimental results by 20% or more.

When eight different laboratories agreed to perform the same critical heat flux test (on a 2 m long, 10 mm i.d. tube), the data itself had a scatter of about 10% from the best-fit curve [24], so it is probably not reasonable to expect empirical correlations to do any better. However, with the results from two of the eight laboratories excluded the remaining data were well within 10% of the predictions of a correlation due to Becker [25].

References

1. WINTERTON, R. H. S. Liquid metal superheat in forced convection. *Int. J. Heat Mass Transfer* **18,** 205–212 (1975).
2. HARVEY, E. N. *et al. J. Cellular Comp. Physiol.* **24,** 1–34 (1944).
3. GRIFFITH, P. and WALLIS, J. D. *Chem Engng Prog. Symp. Series* **56,** No. 30, 49–63 (1960).
4. MARTO, P. J. and ROHSENOW, W. M. *Trans. ASME J. Heat Transfer* **88,** 196–244 (1966).
5. APFEL, R. C. *J. Accoust. Soc. Am.* **48,** 1179–1186 (1970).
6. WINTERTON, R. H. S. Nucleation of boiling and cavitation. *J. Phys. D: Appl. Phys.* **10,** 2041–2056 (1977).
7. KJAERHEIM, G. Heat transfer as limiting factor in water cooled nuclear reactors. *Nucl. Engng Design* **21,** 278–302 (1972).
8. REDPATH, W. Winfrith SGHWR in-reactor dryout tests. *J. Brit. Nucl. Energy Soc.* **13,** 87–97 (1974).
9. TIPPETS, F. E. Critical heat flux and flow patterns in high pressure boiling water flows. *J. Heat Transfer* **86,** 12–22 (1964).
10. BENNETT, A. W., HEWITT, G. F., KEARSEY, H. A., KEEYS, R. K. F. and LACEY, P. M. C. Flow visualisation studies of boiling at high pressures. *Proc. Inst. Mech. Engrs*, Part 3C, pp. 1–11 (1965–66).
11. MARTINELLI, R. C. and NELSON, D. B. Prediction of pressure drop during forced circulation boiling of water. *Trans. ASME* **70,** 695–702 (1948).
12. HAYWOOD, R. W., KNIGHTS, G. A., MIDDLETON, G. E. and THOM, J. R. S. An experimental study of the flow conditions and pressure drop of steam–water mixtures at high pressures in heated and unheated tubes. *Proc. Inst. Mech. Engrs* **175,** 669–748 (1961).
13. THOM, J. R. S. Prediction of pressure drop during forced circulation boiling of water. *Int. J. Heat Mass Transfer* **7,** 709–724 (1964).
14. THOM, J. R. S., WALKER, W. M., FALLON, T. A. and REISING, G. F. S. Boiling in subcooled water during flow up heated tubes or annuli. *Proc. Inst. Mech. Engrs* **180,** Part 3C, 226–246 (1966).
15. JENS, W. H. and LOTTES, D. A. Analysis of heat transfer, burnout, pressure drop and density data for high pressure water. Argonne Natl. Lab. Report ANL–4627 (1951).
16. BROWN, W. Study of flow surface boiling. Doctoral dissertation M.I.T., 1967 (quoted in *Handbook of heat transfer*, by Rohsenow, W. M. and Hartnett, J. P., McGraw Hill, 1973).
17. CHEN, J. C. A correlation for boiling heat transfer to saturated fluids in convective flow, ASME Paper 63–HT–34, 1963.

18. MIROPOLSKIY, Z. L. Heat transfer in film boiling of steam–water mixtures in steam generating tubes. *Teploenergetika* **10** (5), 49–53 (1963).
19. GROENEVELD, D. C. Post-dryout heat transfer: physical mechanisms and a survey of prediction methods. *Nucl. Engng Design* **32,** 283–294 (1975).
20. TONG, L. S. Heat transfer in water cooled nuclear reactors. *Nucl. Engng Design* **6,** 301–324 (1967).
21. ROSAL, E. R., CERMAK, J. O., TONG, L. S., CASTERLINE, J. E., KOKOLIS, S. and MATZNER, B. High pressure rod bundle DNB data with axially non-uniform heat flux. *Nucl. Engng Design* **31,** 1–20 (1974).
22. HENCH, J. E. and LEVY, S. (1966) quoted in *The thermal-hydraulics of a boiling water nuclear reactor*, by LAHEY, R. T. and MOODY, F. J., Amer. Nucl. Soc., 1977.
23. General Electric BWR thermal analysis basis: data, correlation and design applications, NEDO–10958, 1973.
24. MARINELLI, V. Critical heat flux: a review of recent publications. *Nucl. Tech.* **34,** 135–171 (1977).
25. BECKER, K. M., DJURSING, D., LINDBERG, K., EKLIND, O. and OSERDAHL, C. Burnout conditions for round tubes at elevated pressures. *Prog. Heat and Mass Transfer* **6,** 55–73 (1972).

Problems

1. A channel in a BWR has a thermal power of 6 MW. If subcooled water at 275°C enters the channel at 15 kg s^{-1}, what is the void fraction
   (a) at the channel outlet (pressure 68 bar),
   (b) half-way along the channel (pressure 70 bar)?

   Assume a symmetrical variation of heat generation along the channel.
2. An information sheet on a certain BWR states that the average and maximum heat fluxes in the core are 514 kW m^{-2} and 1337 kW m^{-2} respectively, and the pressure is 71.4 bar.

   Calculate the can to coolant temperature difference for each of these heat fluxes, and compare your answers with the stated values (6.7 and 8.7°C). What meaning can be attached to the statement in the sheet that the heat-transfer coefficient is 85.1 kW m^{-2} K^{-1}?
3. The performance of boiling water as a heat transfer medium is being investigated in tests on an 8-mm i.d. smooth-walled tube, with a uniformly heated length of 2 m. The flow is well throttled at the inlet of the tube to ensure a constant mass flow rate through it. In a particular test the pressure is 60 bar, mass flow rate 0.1 kg s^{-1}, and inlet temperature 269.9°C. By mistake the power level is not correctly matched to the mass flow rate, and set to 45 kW. Dryout of the water film in contact with the tube wall is detected at 1.43 m from the start of the heated section. If cooling beyond the dryout position is due solely to the flow of steam, calculate an upper limit to the wall temperature at the end of the heated length, assuming no further mass transfer between water drops and steam after the dryout position.
4. Make a best estimate of the wall temperature for the conditions of question 3. Prandtl numbers for superheated steam at 60 bar are:

T°C	340	360	380	400	420	440	460	480	500
Pr	1.16	1.14	1.10	1.06	1.02	1.00	0.98	0.96	0.95

5. Calculate the critical heat flux ratio at the centre of the PWR described in question 4 of Chapter 4 on forced convection given that the pressure is 138 bar.
6. The maximum heat flux in a certain BWR is 1250 kW m^{-2}. If, at the position where this maximum value occurs, the void fraction is 0.6 and the pressure 72 bar, calculate the critical heat flux ratio.

   The fuel assembly consists of 49 rods, 14.3 mm o.d., in a square wrapper of side 0.134 m. The coolant flow rate is 18 kg s^{-1}.

   Could the critical heat flux be increased significantly by increasing the flow rate (for the same void fraction)?

CHAPTER 6

Fluid Flow

INTRODUCTION

The high heat output from the core of a nuclear reactor is only possible because the coolant is circulated at a high velocity. With narrow passages between the fuel rods there is a high frictional resistance to the flow, giving rise to a large pressure drop and a large pumping-power requirement. The heat output can always be increased by increasing the coolant flow rate, but this has a number of disadvantages: it may be necessary to use smaller fuel rods; the vibration of fuel rods and other components increases; the capital cost of the pumps rises; and the power consumed by the pumps rises faster than the heat output of the core. From this point of view then the analysis of fluid flow is an important part of reactor heat transfer. Also, the detailed analysis of heat transfer that might be performed by a computer needs a knowledge of local fluid properties, which depend on the flow distribution.

In general there are three components to the pressure drop across part of a reactor circuit: frictional pressure drop due to the frictional resistance of the flow against the solid boundaries of the channel, and around any obstructions; gravitational pressure drop due to changes in vertical level; and acceleration pressure drop due to the need to accelerate the coolant to a higher velocity if its density falls (to maintain a constant mass flow rate). Frequently the frictional component is the largest, and often either the gravitational or acceleration component is negligible. In another sense though the frictional component is the most important, because the work done in overcoming the frictional resistance appears finally as increased internal energy of the coolant and cannot be recovered in full as mechanical work (some work is recovered via the steam cycle). On the other hand, the fall in gravitational pressure as the coolant rises through the core is balanced by a rise as it descends through the heat exchangers, and in fact regardless of the details of the flow circuit the net gravitational pressure drop round the circuit is zero, and does not influence the pumping power. To some extent the same is true of the acceleration pressure drop; a pressure drop required to accelerate the coolant in one part of the circuit may be partly recovered later if the coolant slows down.

The friction factor

The friction factor f is the ratio of the shear stress τ on the bounding walls of the channel to the dynamic pressure of the coolant, i.e.

$$\tau = f \tfrac{1}{2} \rho u^2 \tag{6.1}$$

where ρ is the coolant density and u its velocity (the dynamic pressure $\frac{1}{2}\rho u^2$ is the rise in pressure that ideally could be obtained if the coolant were slowed down to zero velocity).

An alternative friction factor sometimes used is the Darcy–Weisbach friction factor defined by $f' = \tau/2\rho u^2 = f/4$.

The friction factor is dimensionless, and for turbulent flow over a given type of surface it is roughly constant, being only weakly dependent on Reynolds number and channel geometry.

PRESSURE DROP WITH A LIQUID COOLANT

Consider a uniform cross-section vertical channel, as in Fig. 6.1, with turbulent, non-boiling liquid flowing up it. With a liquid coolant it is reasonable to assume constant density and hence constant velocity along the channel, so there is no acceleration pressure drop (variations in density are typically only a few per cent). If the pressure at a position z is p and the flow area is A, then an upwards force of pA is being exerted, and the net force on the coolant in a height $\mathrm{d}z$ of the channel is

$$A\,[p - (p + \mathrm{d}p)\,] = -A\mathrm{d}p = \rho g \mathrm{d}z A + \tau s \mathrm{d}z$$

where $\rho g \mathrm{d}z A$ is the weight of the liquid and $\tau s \mathrm{d}z$ the frictional resistance on the sides of the channel, perimeter s.

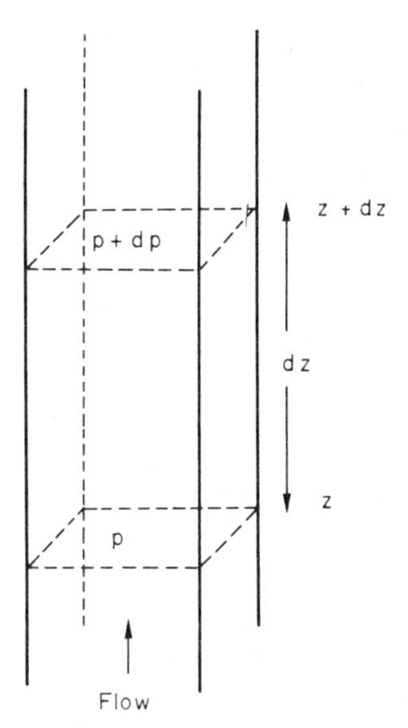

Fig. 6.1. Pressure drop along a length $\mathrm{d}z$ of coolant channel.

Substituting $\tau = \frac{1}{2}\rho u^2 f$ (from the definition of friction factor), the mass flow rate $m = \rho A u$, and the equivalent diameter $d_e = 4A/s$, gives

$$\frac{\mathrm{d}p}{\mathrm{d}z} = -\rho g - \frac{1}{\rho}\left(\frac{m}{A}\right)^2 \frac{2f}{d_e} \qquad (6.2)$$

and the pressure drop from channel inlet (1) to outlet (2) is given by

$$p_1 - p_2 = \rho g L + \frac{1}{\rho}\left(\frac{m}{A}\right)^2 \frac{2fL}{d_e} \tag{6.3}$$

where L is the channel length and ρ is the average value for the channel.

The term $\rho g L$ is, of course, just the change in hydrostatic pressure. For downward flow its sign would be reversed and for horizontal flow it would be zero.

As regards the pumping power only the frictional pressure drop need be considered (the net change in hydrostatic pressure round a complete circuit is zero), and the power required to overcome the frictional resistance at the walls of the channel is just force times velocity or

$$\tau s L u = \tfrac{1}{2}\rho u^2 f s L u = \frac{1}{\rho}\left(\frac{m}{A}\right)^2 \frac{2fL}{d_e}\frac{m}{\rho} = \frac{m}{\rho}\Delta p \tag{6.4}$$

where Δp is the frictional pressure drop from equation (6.3).

This result is, as we shall see later, quite general, and the minimum pumping power to produce a pressure rise Δp is always $m\Delta p/\rho$, regardless of what happens in the rest of the circuit.

The above analysis for the pressure drop assumed that the only significant variation in pressure was in the z direction, i.e. the analysis was one dimensional. This is a good approximation within a given coolant channel, but some detailed computer calculations allow variation in pressure at right angles to the main flow direction. The basis of such a three-dimensional calculation is outlined in the description of subchannel analysis given in Chapter 8.

Correlation for the friction factor in a smooth circular tube

For turbulent flow over smooth surfaces (Reynolds number greater than about 4000) the friction factor is given by

$$f = 0.046\, Re^{-0.2}. \tag{6.5}$$

Strictly this equation is only valid for circular channels, but it gives reasonable results for a number of other geometries provided the equivalent diameter $4A/s$ is used in calculating the Reynolds number.

The surfaces of fuel rods can normally be regarded as smooth. Other surfaces can have much higher friction factors, and if the size of the roughness projections is known then the value of f $(=f'/4)$ can be found from the Moody chart [1].

Reynolds analogy

Comparison of equation (6.5) with the equation for the Stanton number in a smooth channel (equation (4.17)) shows a certain similarity, and for a Prandtl number of 1 we have

$$St = f/2. \tag{6.6}$$

This is a simple statement of Reynolds analogy between heat and momentum transfer, and follows from the fact that in a turbulent flow both heat and momentum are transported by the same mechanism, physical movement of the turbulent eddies. Figure 6.2 shows a small particle of fluid, mass δm, initially at the bulk fluid temperature T_b and velocity u. The particle is then transported to the solid surface and brought to rest. The momentum transferred is δmu and the heat transferred is $\delta mc(T_s - T_b)$. If there are n particles of fluid per unit area and time striking the surface then the rate of momentum transfer, which equals the force on the surface, is

$$n\delta mu = \tau$$

and the rate of heat transfer is

$$n\delta mc\,(T_s - T_b) = h'\,(T_s - T_b)$$

where h' is the heat-transfer coefficient. Dividing these equations and substituting for τ results in equation (6.6).

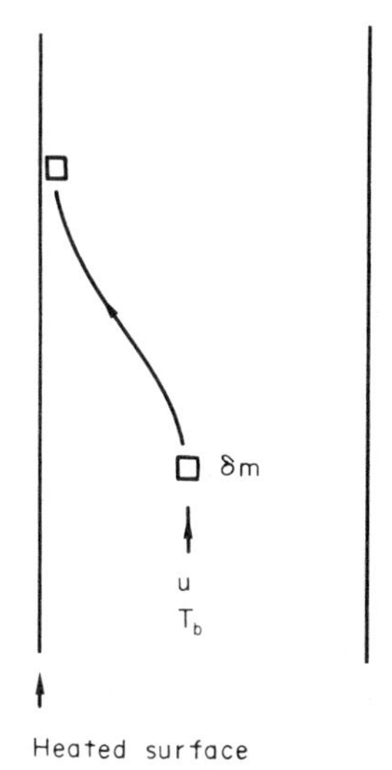

Fig. 6.2. Illustration of Reynolds analogy; in a turbulent flow particles of fluid carry both heat and momentum.

In performing this simple derivation we have ignored the laminar sublayer next to the surface. Since the Prandtl number is the ratio of the molecular diffusivity of momentum to that of heat, with $Pr = 1$ the equality of heat and momentum transfer is preserved in the laminar layer.

Note that equation (6.6) cannot be applied to the ribbed fuel-element surfaces mentioned in Chapter 4. The effect of the ribs projecting into the flow is to increase the friction factor considerably more than the Stanton number.

Other losses

In addition to the frictional resistance associated with the surface of the fuel cans there are other potential sources of pressure loss in the core: at the inlet and outlet of the coolant channels; at gags; at grids or spacers used to support the fuel cans; and at any axial gaps between the cans. All of these losses in pressure can be expressed by

$$\Delta p = k\frac{1}{2\rho}\left(\frac{m}{A}\right)^2, \tag{6.7}$$

i.e. by the dynamic pressure multiplied by a pressure-loss coefficient k.

Note that the pressure loss at one of these obstructions is not necessarily the same as the pressure drop across it, because some of the pressure drop at a change in cross-section will be recovered when the flow cross-section returns to its original value. To take the specific case of a sudden expansion in the flow area, which might be a reasonable model for the channel exit, the loss coefficient is given approximately by

$$k_e = (1 - A_1/A_2)^2 \tag{6.8}$$

where A_1/A_2 is the ratio of the flow areas, and the flow area A in equation (6.7) should be taken as A_1, the smaller area.

To find the actual change in pressure across the expansion equation (6.7) is subtracted from the pressure change predicted by Bernoulli's equation, i.e. from the pressure change in an ideal gradual expansion without losses. Bernoulli's equation gives a pressure rise of

$$\frac{m^2}{2\rho}\left[\frac{1}{A_1^2} - \frac{1}{A_2^2}\right]$$

so the actual pressure rise across the expansion is

$$\frac{m^2}{2\rho}\left[\frac{1}{A_1^2} - \frac{1}{A_2^2} - \frac{(1 - A_1/A_2)^2}{A_1^2}\right] = \frac{m^2}{\rho}\left[\frac{1}{A_1A_2} - \frac{1}{A_2^2}\right].$$

The loss coefficient for a sudden contraction is smaller, reflecting the greater stability of converging flows, and given roughly by

$$k_c = 0.4\,(1 - A_1/A_2)^2 \tag{6.9}$$

where again the flow area in equation (6.7) is A_1, the smaller area.

Generally though the loss coefficients depend so much on the detailed design that they have to be found experimentally. The pressure loss due to all the other effects in the fuel channel combined is comparable with the frictional pressure drop associated with the fuel-can surfaces.

PUMPING POWER

Although equation (6.4) for the ideal pumping power was derived for a special case it is in fact quite general, which is not surprising since it is the equation that would result if the pump were considered to be a simple piston with fluid at pressure $p + \Delta p$ on one side and pressure p on the other.

The steady-flow energy equation (e.g. [2]), which can be applied to any device that has a steady flow of fluid through it, is:

$$Q - W = m(h_2 - h_1) + \tfrac{1}{2}m(u_2^2 - u_1^2) + mg(z_2 - z_1) \qquad (6.10)$$

where Q is the rate of heat input to the fluid, W the rate at which work is done by the fluid and m the mass flow rate. This equation is just a statement of the law of conservation of energy applied to a flowing system, where allowance has to be made for the fact that work is done by fluid outside the system in pushing the fluid in at the inlet, and also work is recovered at the outlet. This is the reason that the internal energy of the fluid is replaced by the enthalpy h. In many applications, including the present one, the changes of kinetic energy and potential energy (the last two terms of (6.10)) may be neglected.

Also in a pump where no heat is exchanged with the working fluid $Q = 0$, so

$$W = -m(h_2 - h_1).$$

For an ideal pump with no internal losses due to friction of the fluid as it goes through we may assume isentropic behaviour, and the change in enthalpy may be approximated using

$$\mathrm{d}h = v\mathrm{d}p + T\mathrm{d}s = v\mathrm{d}p.$$

For reactor coolants the specific volume v is roughly constant, either because the coolant is a liquid and virtually incompressible, or in the case of gases because the absolute pressure of the gas, at for example 40 bar, is much larger than the change of pressure across the pump, which might be only 3 bar.

So the pumping power P is given by

$$P = -W = mv\Delta p \qquad (6.11)$$

which is the same as equation (6.4) since $v = 1/\rho$. The change of sign results from W in equation (6.1) being positive for work done *by* the fluid.

If the overall efficiency of the pump including both frictional losses in the working fluid and mechanical losses in the bearings, etc., is η, then the actual pumping power is

$$P' = \frac{1}{\eta} mv\Delta p \qquad (6.12)$$

and since the efficiency of the pumps used in practice is over 70%, equation (6.11) can be used to establish the effect of changes in m, v or Δp on the pumping power required with good accuracy.

Δp is the sum of the frictional pressure drops across the various components in the circuit, and each of these pressure drops is proportional to $\frac{1}{2}(m/A)^2/\rho$ (equations (6.3) or (6.7), ignoring the dependence of friction factors or loss coefficients on Reynolds number), so we can write

$$\Delta p = \frac{K}{2}\frac{1}{\rho}\left(\frac{m}{A}\right)^2 \qquad (6.13)$$

where K is an overall loss coefficient, and the ideal pumping power becomes

$$P = \frac{K}{2A^2} \frac{1}{\rho^2} m^3 . \tag{6.14}$$

From the point of view of obtaining a low pumping power this equation shows the importance of a high coolant density, i.e. a liquid rather than a gaseous coolant, and if a gas is used then it should be at as high a pressure as possible. In Chapter 8 this point is examined in more detail.

PRESSURE DROP WITH A GASEOUS COOLANT

To a first approximation gases can be treated as incompressible and all the equations of the section on pressure drop with a liquid coolant apply. Because of the much lower density of gases the change in hydrostatic pressure across the core is typically less than 1% of the total pressure drop and may be ignored.

However, because the absolute temperature of the gas leaving the core is appreciably higher than that of the gas entering there is a significant fall in density, and the velocity of the gas flow has to increase to maintain the same mass flow rate. This results in an acceleration pressure drop. Considering again flow through a constant cross-section channel, a force balance on section dz of the channel, as shown in Fig. 6.1, gives

$$-A\,dp - \tau s\,dz = m\,du,$$

i.e. net force equals rate of change of momentum.

Substituting for the wall shear stress τ from equation (6.1) and using $u = m/\rho A$ gives

$$-dp = \frac{1}{\rho}\left(\frac{m}{A}\right)^2 \left[\frac{2f\,dz}{d_e} + \rho\,d(1/\rho)\right]$$

and if the perfect gas law is assumed to apply then $1/\rho = v = RT/p$ and

$$\rho\,d(1/\rho) = dT/T - dp/p$$

so

$$-dp = \frac{1}{\rho}\left(\frac{m}{A}\right)^2 \left[\frac{2f\,dz}{d_e} + \frac{dT}{T} - \frac{dp}{p}\right]. \tag{6.15}$$

This equation cannot conveniently be integrated because ρ and T are functions of position in the channel. However, in practice the acceleration terms dT/T and dp/p are a small part of the total and an approximate treatment is acceptable. Replacing the differentials in equation

(6.15) by the differences in the properties over the whole core,

$$p_1 - p_2 = \frac{1}{\rho}\left(\frac{m}{A}\right)^2 \left[\frac{2fL}{d_e} + \frac{T_2 - T_1}{T_{av}} + \frac{p_1 - p_2}{p_{av}}\right] \tag{6.16}$$

where subscript 1 refers to the inlet and subscript 2 refers to the outlet, and ρ, T_{av} and p_{av} are core average values.

Typically the acceleration pressure drop is only a few per cent of the frictional pressure drop, so the approximate derivation of equation (6.16) is justified.

PRESSURE DROP WITH A TWO-PHASE MIXTURE

With a mixture of liquid and vapour all three contributions to the pressure drop are significant.

Gravitational pressure drop

For a coolant that is flowing vertically upwards the gravitational pressure gradient is given as before by

$$\left(\frac{dp}{dz}\right)_{grav} = \rho_m g$$

but the density of the mixture, ρ_m, depends on the void fraction α that was introduced in Chapter 5. Unit volume of the mixture contains a fraction α of vapour and a fraction $1 - \alpha$ of liquid, so

$$\left(\frac{dp}{dz}\right)_{grav} = -g\Big[\alpha\rho_v + (1-\alpha)\rho_l\Big] = -\frac{g}{v_l}\left[\alpha\frac{v_l}{v_v} + 1 - \alpha\right].$$

This equation is exact, but α has to be worked out by the inexact methods of Chapter 5, and integration of the pressure drop along the channel may require a numerical approach.

If the slip ratio S is known then we can substitute for α from equation (5.8), which gives, after some rearrangement,

$$\left(\frac{dp}{dz}\right)_{grav} = -\frac{g}{v_l}\left[\frac{1 - x(1 - 1/S)}{1 + x(B-1)}\right] \tag{6.17}$$

where $B = v_v/(v_l S)$.

For a linear increase of quality x with distance, and assuming that S is a function only of pressure (i.e. independent of x), this equation can be integrated by writing $x = Cz$, and making the substitution $y = 1 + Cz(B - 1)$ with $dy = C(B-1)dz$.

If saturated liquid with $x = 0$ enters the channel, length L, and the exit quality is x_e, then the result is

$$\Delta p_{\text{grav}} = \frac{gL}{v_l}\left[\frac{(B - 1/S)}{(B-1)^2}\frac{\log_e\left[1 + x_e(B-1)\right]}{x_e} - \frac{(1 - 1/S)}{(B-1)}\right]. \tag{6.18}$$

This equation applies for uniform heating. The exit quality is worked out from an energy balance, using equation (5.7).

For the specific case of a high-pressure steam–water flow the slip ratio is given by equation (5.9).

Acceleration pressure drop

The acceleration pressure drop may be worked out for the whole channel based on inlet and outlet conditions. It is not affected by local variations in the channel. Suppose pure liquid enters the channel with a mass flow rate m and velocity u, and a mixture of liquid and vapour leaves the channel, with mass flow rates m_l and m_v, and velocities u_l and u_v, respectively.

Then applying the momentum equation between inlet and outlet, i.e. net force equals rate of change of momentum, gives

$$A\Delta p_{\text{acc}} = m_l u_l + m_v u_v - mu$$

and if the flow area occupied by the liquid is A_l, that occupied by the vapour is A_v, and the total flow area is A, then

$$u_l = m_l/\rho_l A_l, \quad u_v = m_v/\rho_v A_v, \quad u = m/\rho_l A \quad \text{and} \quad A = A_l + A_v$$

where it has been assumed that the liquid density ρ_l is the same at both ends of the channel. Using these relationships the pressure drop becomes

$$\Delta p_{\text{acc}} = \left(\frac{m}{A}\right)^2\left[\frac{(m_l/m)^2}{\rho_l A_l/A} + \frac{(m_v/m)^2}{\rho_v A_v/A} - \frac{1}{\rho_l}\right]$$

and from the definitions of void fraction and vapour quality we have

$$A_v/A = \alpha, \quad A_l/A = 1 - \alpha, \quad m_v/m = x_e, \quad \text{and} \quad m_l/m = 1 - x_e$$

so

$$\Delta p_{\text{acc}} = \frac{1}{\rho_l}\left(\frac{m}{A}\right)^2\left[\frac{(1-x_e)^2}{1-\alpha} + \frac{x_e^2\,\rho_l}{\alpha\,\rho_v} - 1\right]. \tag{6.19}$$

Again equation (5.8) can be used to relate α to x_e, and for high-pressure steam–water flow S is given by equation (5.9).

Friction pressure drop in two-phase flow

There is no generally accepted method that may be used to calculate the frictional pressure drop in two-phase flow accurately. Probably the simplest theoretical approach is that using the homogeneous model [3], where the slip ratio is assumed to be unity and the mixture is treated as a single-phase fluid with a mean specific volume.

A common method of calculating two-phase pressure drops is to define a two-phase multiplier,

$$M = \frac{\text{actual two-phase pressure drop}}{\text{pressure drop for same mass flow rate of pure liquid}}.$$

The friction pressure gradient for pure liquid is given by equation (6.2):

$$\left(\frac{\mathrm{d}p}{\mathrm{d}z}\right)_{\text{frict}} = -\frac{1}{\rho_l}\left(\frac{m}{A}\right)^2 \frac{2f}{d_e} \tag{6.20}$$

and replacing $1/\rho_l$ by the specific volume v_l,

$$\left(\frac{\mathrm{d}p}{\mathrm{d}z}\right)_{\text{frict}} = -\left(\frac{m}{A}\right)^2 \frac{2f}{d_e} v_l. \tag{6.21}$$

The reference liquid-phase pressure gradient is calculated assuming that the mass flow rate m is the same as the total two-phase mass flow rate.

In the homogeneous model it is assumed that an equation of the form of equation (6.21) also applies to the two-phase flow, but the specific volume should be that of the mixture. With no slip between the phases unit mass of the mixture contains a fraction x of vapour and a fraction $1 - x$ of liquid. So the volume of unit mass of the mixture is given by

$$v_m = xv_v + (1 - x)v_l \tag{6.22}$$

and the two-phase pressure gradient is

$$\left(\frac{\mathrm{d}p}{\mathrm{d}z}\right)_{\text{frict}} = -\left(\frac{m}{A}\right)^2 \frac{2f}{d_e} [xv_v + (1 - x)v_l] \tag{6.23}$$

(the same result could have been obtained, less directly, by substituting the density of the mixture in equation (6.20)).

Comparing (6.23) with the reference liquid-phase pressure gradient (equation (6.21)) and making the further assumption that the friction factor f is unchanged, we see that the two-phase friction multiplier is

$$M = 1 + x(v_v/v_l - 1). \tag{6.24}$$

Since v_v is normally much greater than v_l the two-phase pressure drop is much greater than the liquid-phase pressure drop for the same mass flow rate, even for quite low vapour qualities. This greater frictional resistance is due to the much higher velocities in the two-phase flow.

Equations (6.23) and (6.24) refer to conditions at a point in the channel where the vapour quality is x. For a known variation of x along the channel they can be integrated to give the total frictional pressure drop. With uniform heating and x increasing linearly from 0 at the inlet to x_e at the outlet, the overall friction multiplier is given by

$$\overline{M} = 1 + x_e(v_v/v_l - 1)/2. \tag{6.25}$$

The predictions of the homogeneous model are in reasonable agreement with experimental results, normally being well within a factor of 2.

The most widely used method of calculating two-phase frictional pressure drop is that of Martinelli and Nelson [4]. This was based originally on data for low-pressure air–liquid flows, and extrapolated to high pressures using the fact that $M = 1$ at the critical point (there is no distinction between vapour and liquid at the critical point).

The Martinelli–Nelson correlation can be applied to any liquid, but for the specific case of boiling water at high pressures it is more logical to use a correlation based on data obtained with high-pressure boiling water. Such a correlation is that of Thom [5]. The results did not fit any simple analytical model, and so Thom presented them in the form of tables and graphs of the two-phase friction multiplier as a function of pressure and steam quality.

In fact Thom's predictions for the friction multiplier are given to within about 8% by equation (6.25) (for uniform heating) or equation (6.24) (for constant x). This is an unsatisfactory situation since these equations are based on the homogeneous model, and neither of the assumptions of the homogeneous model is true in this case. It is clear from Thom's measurements of the void fraction that there was appreciable slip between the phases, and, based on a reasonable value of the mean specific volume for a flow with slip, the friction factor could not be considered constant. However, regarding equations (6.24) and (6.25) as purely empirical, they can be used to obtain estimates of the friction multiplier for most purposes.

The range on which the Thom correlation is based is:

pressure	17 to 207 bar	heating	uniform and unheated
quality	0.01 to 0.5	geometry	tube
mixture	water–steam		

The mass velocities were not specified, but can be estimated from the information in reference 12 of Chapter 5 to be in the range 640 to 1500 kg m^{-2} s^{-1}.

For accurate prediction of two-phase frictional pressure drop it is necessary to find a correlation that fits the problem under consideration in respect of all of the parameters listed. Note that none of the correlations mentioned include the mass velocity as a variable. Friction multipliers at low pressures ($<$ 3.5 bar) and low mass velocities (around 135 kg m^{-2} s^{-1}) can be more than twice the values predicted by the Martinelli–Nelson correlation or the homogeneous theory [6].

The total pressure drop

This is simply the sum of the three contributions. The justification for this is that it is the reverse of the procedure used when the correlations are constructed. Experimentally it is not normally possible to isolate the friction pressure drop. Instead the total pressure drop is measured and the contributions due to gravity and acceleration subtracted using equations such as (6.18) and (6.19).

Example 6.1. Water at 277°C and 70 bar enters the bottom of a vertical tube, 12.7 mm i.d. and 1.55 m long. The tube is uniformly heated, with a total power of 39 kW. The flow rate is 0.0882 kg s^{-1}. The friction factor of the tube is known to be 0.0059.

Calculate the total pressure drop.

First we must find the point in the tube where boiling starts. Up to that point there is single-phase flow, after it we have a uniformly heated section with $x = 0$ at the inlet, to which the various equations in the text can be applied directly.

The enthalpy of saturated water at 70 bar is 1267 kJ kg^{-1} and that of the subcooled water at 277°C is 1221 kJ kg^{-1} (i.e. the value for saturated water at 277°C), so the heat supplied over the length l must equal that needed to bring the water up to saturation, i.e.

$$39 \frac{l}{1.55} = 0.0882\,(1267 - 1221)\ \text{kW}$$

or

$$l = 0.161\ \text{m}.$$

The value of the mass velocity G is worth working out since it comes into many of the equations, and many influence the choice of correlation.

$$G = \frac{m}{A} = \frac{0.0882}{\pi/4 \times 0.0127^2} = 696\ \text{kg m}^{-2}\ \text{s}^{-1}.$$

The pressure drop over the non-boiling section is given by equation (6.3)

$$\rho g l + \frac{G^2}{\rho}\frac{2fl}{d_e} = \frac{9.81 \times 0.161}{0.001\,351} + 0.001\,351 \times 696^2 \times \frac{2 \times 0.0059 \times 0.161}{0.0127}$$

$$= 1169 + 98 = 1267\ \text{N m}^{-2}.$$

The equations for the boiling section require the steam quality at exit, given by

$$39\,\frac{(1.55 - 0.161)}{1.55} = 0.0882 \times 1505x\ \text{kW},$$

i.e. $x = 0.263$.

The slip ratio S comes from equation (5.9), and is 1.673.

The last quantity needed is the void fraction at the exit. Equation (5.8) gives $\alpha = 0.812$.

Substituting the various quantities in equation (6.18), for a boiling length of 1.389 m, gives the gravitational pressure drop as 4522 N m^{-2}.

The acceleration pressure drop comes from equation (6.19) and is 2366 N m^{-2}.

The two-phase friction multiplier (equation (6.25)) is 3.533, so the frictional pressure drop along the boiling length is

$$3.533 \times 0.001\,351 \times 696^2 \times \frac{2 \times 0.0059 \times 1.389}{0.0127} = 2984\ \text{N m}^{-2}.$$

The total pressure drop over the full 1.55-m length is

$$1267 + 4522 + 2366 + 2984 = 11{,}100\ \text{N m}^{-2}.$$

The individual components of the pressure drop in this calculation are all within a couple of per cent of the values that would result from following the procedure described in Thom's paper [5].

CRITICAL FLOW THROUGH BURST PIPES

The maximum rate at which the coolant can escape through a burst duct is important in safety analysis, since it determines how quickly the pressure in the primary circuit falls to that of the containment.

If this happened in a gas-cooled reactor the flow out of the break would reach the velocity of sound, and this can be used to calculate the mass flow rate. A similar phenomenon would occur with the two-phase mixture escaping through a hole in a PWR or BWR, when again a critical flow rate is reached, but there is no general agreement as to whether the critical flow velocity equals the velocity of sound in the two-phase mixture.

The fact that the limiting velocity of gas escaping through the break is the velocity of sound may be understood as follows. Consider what happens to the flow rate if the broken pipe, attached to the primary pressure vessel containing gas at a pressure p_0, is subjected to lower and lower back pressures p_b, as shown in Fig. 6.3. If $p_b = p_0$ then there is no flow. As p_b is decreased the flow increases until a critical exit pressure p is reached. Up to this point $p = p_b$, but now the flow velocity at the exit is the velocity of sound in the gas. If p_b is lowered further the negative pressure pulse will travel up-stream at the velocity of sound, but it will never reach the exit of the pipe because the gas there is itself moving at the same velocity in the opposite direction. Consequently the mass flow rate will stay fixed at the critical or choked value.

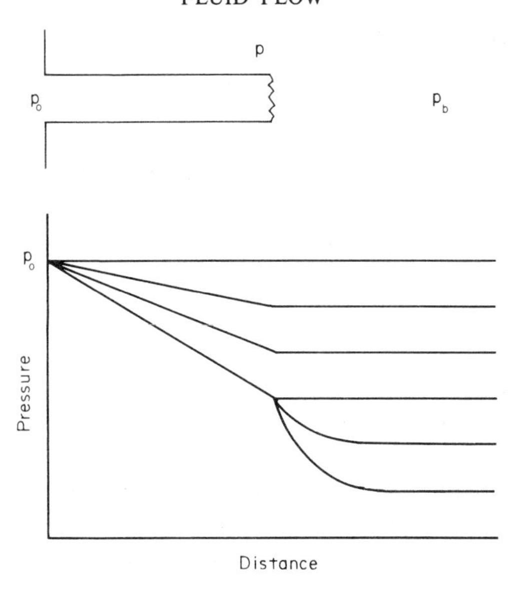

Fig. 6.3. Effect of progressively lowering the back pressure on the flow of gas out of a broken duct.

If the problem is approached from the opposite point of view, that is with p_b fixed and p_0 steadily increasing, the flow still chokes at the limiting speed of sound, though in this case the mass flow rate continues to increase after the choked condition has been reached because the density of the coolant at the exit continues to increase with p_0. The reactor situation is not the same as either of these, since in the reactor p_0 and p_b are fixed and the problem is to find p, the pressure at the point of the break. To show that the critical flow rate is the same regardless of how the flow pattern arises, and that once the flow is choked the exit pressure is about half the reservoir pressure, requires more rigorous analysis.

Critical flow rate for a perfect gas

To estimate the maximum possible rate at which gas could escape from the burst duct we ignore any frictional resistance to the flow along the duct and assume that the gas expands isentropically, obeying pv^γ = constant. Also the flow is assumed to be one dimensional.

The increase in kinetic energy of the gas as it flows along the duct equals the decrease in enthalpy. If the gas starts off in the reservoir with essentially zero kinetic energy then the velocity u at the break is related to the enthalpy h by

$$\tfrac{1}{2}u^2 = h_0 - h$$

where the subscript 0 refers to conditions in the reservoir (this equation is the steady-flow energy equation (6.10), with Q, W, and the potential energy terms zero).

The enthalpy of a perfect gas is $h = c_pT$, where c_p is the specific heat at constant pressure, so

$$u = \sqrt{\{2c_p(T_0 - T)\}}$$

and using the relationship $T^{\gamma}p^{1-\gamma}$ = constant, we can express the velocity in terms of the pressure at the break, p.

$$u = \sqrt{\{2c_p T_0 [1 - (p/p_0)^{(\gamma-1)/\gamma}]\}}. \quad (6.26)$$

The mass flow rate at the break is given by $m = \rho A u$, and since the densities are related by $\rho/\rho_0 = v_0/v = (p/p_0)^{1/\gamma}$ we have

$$m = A\rho_0(p/p_0)^{1/\gamma} \sqrt{\{2c_p T_0 [1 - (p/p_0)^{(\gamma-1)/\gamma}]\}}$$

$$= A\rho_0 \sqrt{\{2c_p T_0 [(p/p_0)^{2/\gamma} - (p/p_0)^{(\gamma+1)/\gamma}]\}}. \quad (6.27)$$

In this expression A, ρ_0 and T_0 are fixed, and we wish to maximise the mass flow rate by varying p. Differentiating $(p/p_0)^{2/\gamma} - (p/p_0)^{(\gamma+1)/\gamma}$ with respect to p/p_0 and putting the result equal to zero gives

$$\frac{2}{\gamma}\left(\frac{p}{p_0}\right)^{(2/\gamma-1)} - \frac{\gamma+1}{\gamma}\left(\frac{p}{p_0}\right)^{[(\gamma+1)/\gamma-1]} = 0$$

or

$$\frac{p}{p_0} = \left(\frac{2}{\gamma+1}\right)^{\gamma/(\gamma-1)}. \quad (6.28)$$

The critical velocity corresponding to this maximum flow rate is found by substituting back into equation (6.26),

$$u = \sqrt{\{2c_p T_0 (1 - 2/(\gamma + 1))\}}$$

and replacing T_0 by the properties of the gas at the break using first $T_0 = T(p_0/p)^{(\gamma-1)/\gamma}$ and then $T = pv/R$ gives

$$u = \sqrt{\{c_p(\gamma - 1)pv/R\}}.$$

Using the basic relationships $c_p = c_v + R$ and $\gamma = c_p/c_v$, we obtain

$$u = \sqrt{\{\gamma pv\}} = \sqrt{\{\gamma RT\}} \quad (6.29)$$

which is the velocity of sound in a perfect gas.

Returning to equation (6.28) for the critical pressure ratio, and substituting the values of γ corresponding to ideal monatomic, diatomic and polyatomic gases, i.e. 1.67, 1.4 and 1.33, gives values of p/p_0 of 0.49, 0.53 and 0.54 respectively. So the critical pressure ratio is about half.

Note that the pressure p at the break cannot be less than p_b, so if $p_0 < 2p_b$ the flow is no longer choked, and the flow rate is given by equation (6.27) with $p = p_b$.

Example 6.2. The maximum credible accident for a certain Magnox reactor is considered to be a sudden double-ended guillotine break in one of the CO_2 coolant ducts. These ducts take the coolant from the core to the boiler, and on the outside are directly exposed to the atmosphere.

If the CO_2 pressure is 14 bar, its average temperature 260°C, and the internal diameter of the duct is 1.2 m, estimate the maximum possible flow rate of coolant out of the break. The ratio of the specific heats of CO_2 under these conditions is 1.24, giving a critical pressure ratio of 0.56.

Given that the total amount of CO_2 in the primary circuit is 40 tonnes, and the thermal capacity of the system is such that the CO_2 temperature stays at 260°C, estimate the time required for the core pressure to fall to 2 bar.

The mass flow rate is $2A\rho u$, where A is the cross-sectional area of the duct, and the factor of 2 is due to the assumption of unimpeded flow from each of the broken ends. The speed of sound at the break is $\sqrt{\{\gamma RT\}}$.

To obtain the gas constant for one kg of CO_2 we divide the universal gas constant by the molecular weight, i.e. $R = 8314/44 = 189.0 \text{ J kg}^{-1} \text{ K}^{-1}$.

For an isentropic expansion the temperature of the gas at the break is given in terms of the properties in the core by

$$T = (273 + 260) \times 0.56^{(1.24-1)/1.24} = 476 \text{ K}$$

and so the speed of sound is

$$(1.24 \times 189 \times 476)^{1/2} = 334.0 \text{ m s}^{-1}.$$

The density of the escaping gas is

$$\rho = \frac{p}{RT} = \frac{0.56 \times 14 \times 10^5}{189 \times 476} = 8.71 \text{ kg m}^{-3}.$$

So the initial mass flow rate is

$$2 \times \pi/4 \times 1.2^2 \times 8.71 \times 334 = 6580 \text{ kg s}^{-1}.$$

If this initial mass flow rate persisted the primary circuit would empty in around $40/6.58 = 6$ s.

However, as the pressure in the primary circuit falls the density of the escaping gas falls in direct proportion, and so does the mass flow rate (since the temperature and speed of sound stay constant). If the total mass of CO_2 in the primary circuit is M we can write

$$\frac{dM}{dt} = -6580 \frac{p}{p_{\text{initial}}} = -6580 \frac{M}{M_{\text{initial}}} = -\frac{M}{6}$$

or

$$M = M_{\text{initial}} \, e^{-t/6}.$$

So the pressure and quantity of gas fall exponentially with a $1/e$ time constant of 6 s.
The time required for the pressure to fall to 2 bar is

$$-6 \ln (2/14) = 11.7 \text{ s}.$$

The analysis of the above example would not be valid for pressures less than about 2 bar since the flow would no longer be choked. The total time to depressurise, that is the time during which the flow pattern in the primary circuit is dominated by the flow of coolant towards the break, is considered to be around 40 s.

Critical flow rate for a two-phase liquid

In the hypothetical case of a broken coolant duct in a water-cooled reactor, such as a PWR or BWR, the flow through the break will consist of a two-phase mixture of liquid and vapour. Although in the PWR the coolant is initially just water, as it flows to the break the fall in pressure will cause it to boil and some of it will turn to steam.

The analysis of the critical flow rate is similar in principle to that adopted for the single-phase flow: isentropic expansion from the main pressure vessel or reservoir to the point of the break is assumed, and the pressure p at the break is varied to obtain the maximum flow rate. With two-phase flow there are the additional problems of the mass transfer between the phases, which may not be sufficient to maintain equilibrium, and of slip, with the liquid and vapour travelling at different velocities.

One theoretical model is that of Moody [7]. This model assumes thermodynamic equilibrium between the phases, but, given that assumption, subsequently aims to establish a maximum possible flow rate. Both pressure at the break and slip ratio are regarded as variables that may be used to maximise the flow rate. The assumption of thermodynamic equilibrium between the phases is probably reasonable if the break occurs some distance from the main vessel, so that there is time for equilibrium to be established as the mixture flows along the pipe.

The properties of the mixture in the reservoir and of the liquid and vapour at the exit from the broken pipe are as shown in Fig. 6.4. Note that h_0 is the enthalpy of unit mass of whatever is in the reservoir; it could refer to a mixture of liquid and vapour.

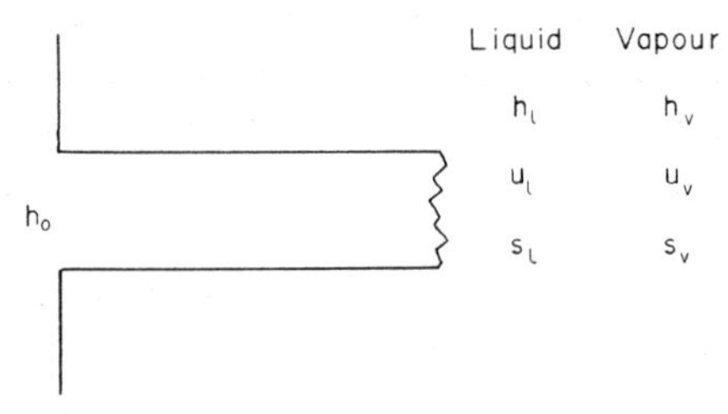

Fig. 6.4. Flow of a two-phase mixture out of a broken duct. Properties in the reservoir and at the point of the break.

Applying the steady-flow energy equation between the reservoir and the break gives

$$h_0 = x(h_v + \tfrac{1}{2}u_v^2) + (1-x)(h_l + \tfrac{1}{2}u_l^2)$$

and since it is convenient to work with just one velocity we substitute for u_l using the slip ratio $S = u_v/u_l$, giving

$$\tfrac{1}{2}u_v^2\,[x + (1 - x)/S^2] = h_0 - xh_v - (1 - x)h_l. \qquad (6.30)$$

The total mass flow rate, of vapour and liquid, is

$$m = \rho_v A_v u_v + \rho_l A_l u_l$$

and the mass velocity is

$$G = \frac{m}{A} = \rho_v u_v \frac{A_v}{A} + \rho_l \frac{u_v}{S}\frac{A_l}{A}.$$

In terms of specific volumes, and the void fraction $\alpha = A_v/A$,

$$G = \frac{u_v}{v_v}\,[\alpha + (1 - \alpha)\, v_v/v_l S]$$

and using equation (5.8) for α gives

$$G = \frac{u_v/v_v}{x + (1 - x)Sv_l/v_v}$$

and substituting from equation (6.30) for u_v gives

$$G^2 = \frac{2}{[xv_v + (1 - x)Sv_l]^2}\;\frac{[h_0 - xh_v - (1 - x)h_l]}{[x + (1 - x)/S^2]}. \qquad (6.31)$$

This is only an intermediate equation so far as the Moody analysis is concerned, but it is the final result of the homogeneous equilibrium theory for the critical flow rate [8]. In the homogeneous equilibrium theory the additional assumption of a homogeneous flow with $S = 1$ is made, and the maximum flow rate is found by choosing lower and lower pressures at the break and calculating G using equation (6.31) with $S = 1$, until the maximum value of G is reached.

Returning to the analysis of the Moody theory, S in equation (6.31) is regarded as a variable that may be used to maximise G, that is we require a minimum value of

$$[xv_v + (1 - x)Sv_l]^2\,[x + (1 - x)/S^2].$$

Differentiating this expression with respect to S and setting the result equal to zero gives

$$2[xv_v + (1 - x)Sv_l]\,(1 - x)v_l\,[x + (1 - x)/S^2] + [xv_v + (1 - x)Sv_l]^2\,(1 - x)\,(-\,2/S^3) = 0.$$

This equation can be considerably simplified. First the common factors cancel, and then, after multiplying out, the terms in $1/S^2$ drop out, leaving

$$S^3 = v_v/v_l. \tag{6.32}$$

Substituting this result back into equation (6.31) gives

$$G^2 = \frac{2\,[h_0 - xh_v - (1-x)h_l]}{v_v^2\,[x + (1-x)\,(v_l/v_v)^{2/3}]^3}\,. \tag{6.33}$$

We still have to maximise the mass flow rate with respect to the pressure at the break, but it is not possible to do this analytically because the enthalpies, specific volumes and pressures cannot be related to one another by convenient analytical expressions. In the original paper the results of computer calculations for the critical pressure ratio p/p_0 are presented, for a range of values of p_0 and h_0. The p/p_0 values show little variation, and for the most part are very close to the average value of about 0.61, which itself is not very different to the critical pressure ratios for gases. If we accept this value for the pressure ratio then equation (6.33) can be used to calculate critical flow rates without any further information (apart from tables of liquid and vapour properties).

For a given reservoir pressure p_0 and enthalpy h_0, and assuming that the pressure at the break $p = 0.61\,p_0$ is greater than the back pressure, it is not immediately obvious how the exit quality x is calculated. This is where the assumption of isentropic expansion is used. The entropy at the break s equals that in the reservoir s_0 and

$$\begin{aligned} s &= xs_v + (1-x)s_l, \\ s_0 &= x_0 s_{v0} + (1-x_0)s_{l0}, \\ h_0 &= x_0 h_{v0} + (1-x_0)h_{l0}. \end{aligned}$$

The Moody theory is successful in predicting an upper limit to the flow rates from long pipes. Experimental results lie below, but not far below, the theoretical predictions [9]. Also the homogeneous equilibrium model (i.e. equation (6.31) with $S = 1$) provides a reasonably close lower limit. However, the Moody theory is not entirely correct: experimental results for very long pipes (length to diameter ratio of 40 or more) lie very close to the predictions of the homogeneous equilibrium theory, and measurements of slip ratio give values much closer to unity than those predicted by equation (6.32). This suggests that in practice the slip ratio is lower than that assumed in the Moody theory, which would tend to give a lower flow rate, and that except in very long pipes thermal equilibrium is not quite reached, which would tend to give higher flow rates (because less vapour is generated).

A model that allows for the two phases not being in equilibrium, and proposes empirical expressions to calculate the exchanges of mass, heat and momentum, is that of Henry and Fauske [10]. This is probably the best model to use for an accurate prediction of the critical flow rate.

For safety analysis it is important to be reasonably sure that the prediction is an upper limit, and for this reason the Moody analysis is often preferred. In practice it provides a satisfactory upper limit for short pipes, provided there is some vapour present initially in the reservoir ($x_0 > 0.01$). With short pipes and saturated or subcooled water in the reservoir, the flow rates are higher than predicted by either Moody or Henry and Fauske theories because there is insufficient time for much vapour to be generated.

Example 6.3. A circular duct 0.7 m i.d., connected to a vessel containing saturated water at 70 bar pressure, suddenly bursts. Assuming unimpeded flow from both sides of the break, and thermodynamic equilibrium between the water and steam, calculate the maximum possible flow rate out of the broken duct.

The assumptions are those of the Moody analysis so we can use equation (6.33). First the values of the properties at the break, and hence the steam quality, have to be found.

The pressure at the break is $0.61 \times 70 = 42.7$ bar. By interpolation in the tables the following values are obtained for 42.7 bar pressure:

$$s_v = 6042.0 \text{ J kg}^{-1} \text{ K}^{-1}, \quad h_v = 2799.3 \times 10^3 \text{ J kg}^{-1}, \quad v_v = 0.046\,54 \text{ m}^3 \text{ kg}^{-1},$$
$$s_l = 2832.1 \text{ J kg}^{-1} \text{ K}^{-1}, \quad h_l = 1106.6 \times 10^3 \text{ J kg}^{-1}, \quad v_l = 0.001\,261\,2 \text{ m}^3 \text{ kg}^{-1}.$$

Since the expansion is isentropic we have

$$s_0 = xs_v + (1 - x)s_l$$

where s_0 is the entropy of saturated liquid at 70 bar, 3122 J kg^{-1} K^{-1}. Substituting the values gives $x = 0.090\,31$.

h_0 is the enthalpy of saturated liquid at 70 bar, 1267×10^3 J kg^{-1}, which completes the list of quantities needed. When the values are inserted into equation (6.33) the mass velocity G is found to be 36,800 kg m^{-2} s^{-1}.

The mass flow rate out of the two 0.7-m diameter ends is

$$2 \times \pi/4 \times 0.7^2 \times 36.800 = 28{,}300 \text{ kg s}^{-1}.$$

The condition of the water in the vessel in the above example, saturated at 70 bar, is somewhere between PWR and BWR conditions.

For the example involving a gas-cooled reactor we were able to make a rough estimate of the pressure in the primary circuit as a function of time, because the pressure is proportional to the mass of gas present. When the reactor is full of liquid the problem is more difficult. To take an extreme case a vessel full of cold water at high pressure need lose hardly any water at all following a break in the pipework, and the only factor limiting the rate of fall of pressure would be the speed of sound in the liquid, which would determine the progress of the rarefaction wave. Less than a second would be required for the entire contents to fall to essentially atmospheric pressure.

The first stage of a loss of coolant accident in a PWR would be similar in that the pressure would fall immediately to the saturation pressure of the water leaving the core. At this point the water at core exit temperature would start to flash into steam, and further fall of pressure would be controlled by the rate at which the two-phase mixture could leave the break. The mass flow rate calculated in the above example would be quite representative of that from a PWR after the first second, and coupled with a total water content in the primary circuit of, say, 180 tons suggests a quite fast depressurisation. Detailed calculations suggest that the containment pressure would be reached in about 20 seconds. BWRs tend to have smaller ducts in relation to the inventory of water, leading to a slightly slower depressurisation.

In the next chapter estimates are made of the temperatures reached by the fuel rods during the loss of coolant accident.

References

1. MOODY, L. F. Friction factors for pipe flows. *Trans ASME* **66,** 671 (1944).
2. ROGERS, G. F. C. and MAYHEW, Y. R. *Engineering thermodynamics, work and heat transfer*, Longman, 1967 (2nd edition, S.I. units).
3. OWENS, W. L. Two-phase pressure gradient, pp. 363–368 of *International developments in heat transfer*, Part II, ASME, 1961.
4. MARTINELLI, R. C. and NELSON, D. B. Prediction of pressure drops during forced circulation boiling of water. *Trans. ASME*, **70,** 695–702 (1948).
5. THOM, J. R. S. Prediction of pressure drop during forced circulation boiling of water. *Int. J. Heat Mass Transfer* **7,** 709–724 (1964).
6. HUANG, M. and EL-WAKIL, M. M. A visual and frictional pressure drop study of natural circulation single component two-phase flow at low pressures. *Nucl. Sci. Engng* **28,** 12–19 (1967).
7. MOODY, F. J. Maximum flow rate of a single component, two-phase mixture. *Trans. ASME Series C, J. Heat Transfer* **87,** 134–141 (1965).
8. STARKMAN, E. S., SHROCK, V. E., NEUSEN, K. F. and MANEELY, D. J. Expansion of a very low quality two-phase fluid through a convergent-divergent nozzle. *Trans. ASME Series D, J. Basic Engineering* **86,** 247–256 (1964).
9. ARDRON, K. H. and FURNESS, R. A. A study of the critical flow models used in reactor blowdown analysis. *Nucl. Engng Design* **39,** 257–266 (1976).
10. HENRY, R. E. and FAUSKE, H. K. The two-phase critical flow of one-component mixtures in nozzles, orifices, and short tubes. *Trans. ASME Series C, J. Heat Transfer* **93,** 179–187 (1971).

Problems

1. The flow of coolant in a PWR is vertically upwards, parallel to the 10.7-mm o.d. fuel rods, which are on a square lattice with a pitch of 14.3 mm. The average temperature and velocity are 300°C and 4.5 m s^{-1} respectively. The fuel rods are 3.15 m long. Calculate the frictional pressure drop due to the surface of the rods. Assume the rods are smooth and ignore any effects of local boiling.
2. Find the other pressure drops in the channel of question 1, i.e.:
   (a) Gravitation pressure drop.
   (b) Effect of support grids (six grids, each with a loss coefficient of 1.2).
   (c) Entrance and exit effects (assuming sudden change from fuel-rod geometry to space free of solid obstructions above and below fuel assembly).
3. Because of corrosion problems in a CO_2-cooled reactor it is proposed to change to He. The reactor loses 2 tonnes of CO_2 a day through leakage to the atmosphere. If no changes are made to seals, etc., estimate what the leakage rate would be with He.

   Assume that leakage occurs by turbulent flow through narrow channels between the faces of seals, etc., with a constant value of the friction factor, and negligible acceleration pressure drop. Treat the gases as perfect. Variations of temperature along the channel will be unimportant compared with variations of pressure.
4. A rig for the study of flow instabilities consists of a number of parallel channels. Water at 60 bar flows through the channels via inlet and outlet headers and is boiled by heaters. Each channel receives 1 MW uniformly distributed along its length. If saturated water enters each channel at 3.2 kg s^{-1} compare the frictional pressure drop with the value for the same mass flow rate under single-phase conditions.
5. If the channels in question 4 are in fact smooth 50 mm i.d. circular tubes, 3 m long, estimate all three components of pressure drop. The tubes are vertical, and the flow is upwards.
6. A proposed design of HTR is to be cooled by helium at 50 bar. The primary circuit and the boilers are contained within the prestressed concrete pressure vessel, but a 120-mm i.d. pipe takes coolant out of the pressure vessel to a treatment plant. If this pipe suddenly breaks derive an expression for the pressure within the reactor as a function of time, assuming a maximum possible flow rate out of the break. What is the pressure 2 minutes from the start of the incident?

Because of the large thermal capacity of the graphite in the core the average temperature of the helium in the pressure vessel stays close to 500°C throughout. Initial helium content is 30 tonnes.

7. A vessel contains saturated water at 70 bar. A 0.6-m i.d. duct connected to the vessel suddenly bursts. Assuming unimpeded flow from both sides of the break, negligible frictional resistance along the duct, and thermodynamic equilibrium between the phases, calculate the initial flow rate for
   (a) homogeneous flow with $S = 1$,
   (b) S chosen to maximise the flow rate.

   In each case you may assume a critical pressure ratio of 0.61.
8. A reactor contains water at 70 bar, with an average steam quality of 10%. Assuming a sudden break in one of the ducts outside the main pressure vessel, calculate the initial mass velocity of the coolant out of the break. The flow may be assumed homogeneous, expansion within the duct isentropic, and the critical pressure ratio is 0.61.

CHAPTER 7

Safety Analysis

INTRODUCTION

After a year or so's operation a 1000-MW(e) nuclear reactor will contain around 4×10^{10} curies of radioactivity. Since the maximum amount of most radioactive isotopes that is permitted in the human body is around 10^{-5} curies there is clearly an immense potential danger should some of the activity escape outside the power plant. However, similar statements could be made about many industrial processes, and in the case of nuclear power the dangers are at present purely hypothetical. No one has been killed by radiation arising from the commercial operation of nuclear power, though there have been accidents in experimental reactors and reprocessing plants [1]. The main function of safety analysis is to ensure that even in an accident the activity is contained, preferably within the fuel cans.

The danger arises from the possibility of radioactivity being released, and not from the possibility of a nuclear explosion. All nuclear excursions are self-limiting in the sense that as the assembly of nuclear material heats up it expands, becomes subcritical, and the neutron chain reaction stops. In an atomic bomb the nuclear materials are held together as long as possible by surrounding them with conventional explosive which is detonated first. It is difficult to see how a comparable situation could arise in a reactor.

Nearly all of the activity in the reactor is due to the fission products in the fuel cans, and before any of this activity can get out of the power station the cans must fail, the primary coolant circuit must fail, and even then most reactors are provided with a containment. If all three layers of protection are broken it does not follow that most of the fission products will escape. At normal reactor temperatures only a few per cent of the activity is present in gaseous or volatile compounds that could leave the UO_2 pellets.

Maximum credible accident

The safety case for most nuclear power stations has been presented in terms of the "maximum credible accident", or, equivalently, the "design basis accident". This is the worst accident that it is believed can happen, and the safety analysis must show that no harm will come to any member of the public as a result of the accident.

The analysis of accidents involves all branches of nuclear engineering, and an individual safety report will be required for each power station. For example, one question that will require a detailed answer is: Can the reactor always be shut down? However, in spite of the differences between reactor types and between individual reactors of the same type, the maximum credible accident for most power reactors is substantially the same. It is the depressurisation or loss-of-coolant accident, and it so happens that the main problems involved in predicting the response of the reactor to this accident concern the flow of coolant through the core and out of the broken pipe and the transient increase in temperature of the fuel cans.

Loss of coolant accident

In nearly all pressurised reactors the maximum credible accident is a sudden loss of pressure and loss of coolant following a break in one of the main coolant ducts outside the pressure vessel. Sudden failure of the main pressure vessel itself would be an example of an "incredible accident". In many cases the layout of the primary coolant circuit is as shown in Fig. 7.1. In fact, Fig. 7.1 corresponds closely to a PWR, but the flow direction and sequence of components is the same in several reactor types. Starting with the primary coolant flowing upwards through the core, it then leaves the primary pressure vessel, flows down through the boilers, into the pumps, and back via the inlet ducts to the main pressure vessel and the core again. Normally there are several such loops of outlet duct, boiler, pump and inlet duct, and in the worst case it is assumed that just one of these loops is fractured in one position, but the pipe is taken to be broken clean through and the two broken ends move far enough apart for the coolant to discharge unimpeded through both open ends. Bearing in mind the large

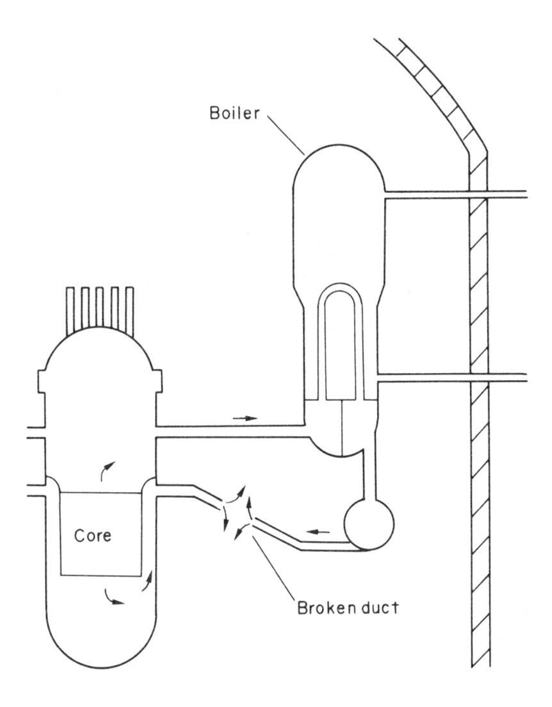

Fig. 7.1. Flow patterns in the primary circuit immediately after a break in an inlet duct. In the bottom of the core the normal flow direction is reversed, and in parts of the core the flow may stagnate.

diameter piping used for these ducts (around 1 m), it is not surprising that the flow patterns throughout the primary circuit are dominated by the flow of coolant towards the breach. With a break in one of the coolant outlet ducts the flow through the core will continue to be upwards, and cooling of the fuel rods will continue. With a break in an inlet duct the coolant in the core can reach the break by following two different paths. Coolant at the top of the core will tend to go through the outlet duct and the boiler, while coolant at the bottom of the core will tend to go straight to the inlet duct, reversing the normal flow direction. At some point within the core the two tendencies will cancel out and the coolant will not flow in either direction. This possibility of flow stagnation is very serious, because that part of the core will receive very little cooling during the loss of pressure.

Note that even after the reactor has been shut down, and a trip based on a rate of pressure drop signal should occur within seconds of the break, there is still a need for cooling because there are still a number of heat sources in the fuel. Fairly short-lived heating arises from the dying away of the fission reaction and the stored heat in the fuel, while throughout the accident and for a long time afterwards there is heat from the decaying fission products. Since in this accident one of the layers of protection between the fission products and the outside world, the primary coolant circuit, has already been breached it is essential that the fuel cans remain intact. Whether or not the cans fail depends largely on the temperature that they reach during the accident, also on the time spent at temperature and the internal fission gas pressure. The accident can be divided roughly into two phases: the first phase is during the fall in pressure to the pressure of the containment or of the atmosphere, and is characterised by fluctuating flows and heat-transfer coefficients that are difficult to predict; in the second phase a steady if greatly reduced flow of coolant can be established through the core.

TIMESCALES OF THE TRANSIENT FLOW AND HEAT-TRANSFER PROCESSES

Estimate of depressurisation timescale

The phenomenon of critical flow out of a broken pipe was discussed in Chapter 6. For the two examples considered there the initial loss of coolant was very rapid, with most of the coolant leaving in the first 10 seconds or so. The containment pressure is reached in about half a minute. In the next section we will show that the timescales associated with the transient heat-conduction processes in the fuel rod are rather shorter than this, so at the end of the blowdown it is reasonable to assume thermal equilibrium in the fuel rod. Since we will not be making any further use of the detailed results obtained part of the argument is relegated to Appendix 1.

Temperature distribution in fuel pellet following sudden total loss of cooling

A simplification of the real situation in a reactor following a break in a main coolant duct is to assume no cooling at all of the fuel rods, and an approximate idea of the transient behaviour can be obtained by assuming that it is the fuel pellet that is suddenly thermally isolated, neglecting the residual fission heating and the decay heating. This simplified problem, for constant thermal conductivity, has a fairly straightforward analytical solution.

The complete differential heat conduction equation, for radial flow of heat in a cylinder is (Appendix 1a)

$$\rho c \frac{\partial T}{\partial t} = \frac{k}{r} \frac{\partial}{\partial r} r \frac{\partial T}{\partial r} + H. \tag{7.1}$$

For the period after the reactor has shut down, and ignoring the decay heat, $H = 0$. Introducing the thermal diffusivity $K = k/\rho c$, the equation becomes

$$\frac{1}{K} \frac{\partial T}{\partial t} = \frac{1}{r} \frac{\partial}{\partial r} r \frac{\partial T}{\partial r}.$$

A solution containing exponentially decaying functions of time seems reasonable, such as $T = F(r)\mathrm{e}^{-mt}$, and substituting this into the above equation gives

$$\frac{\mathrm{d}^2 F}{\mathrm{d}r^2} + \frac{1}{r} \frac{\mathrm{d}F}{\mathrm{d}r} + \frac{m}{K} F = 0$$

which is Bessel's equation of zero order, and the solution is

$$T = B\, J_0 \left\{ \sqrt{\left(\frac{m}{K} \right)}\, r \right\} \mathrm{e}^{-mt} \tag{7.2}$$

where T is the temperature above the initial surface temperature and J_0 is the Bessel function of zero order of the first kind. The value of m comes from the boundary condition that there is no heat flow at the surface of the pellet, that is, $\mathrm{d}T/\mathrm{d}r = 0$ at $r = a$, or $J_0' (\sqrt{(m/K)}\, r) = 0$ at $r = a$. In fact there are an infinite number of roots of this equation, and a complete solution for the temperature therefore will involve an infinite number of terms of the form of equation (7.2). Considering just one root α given by $J_0' (\alpha) = 0$ gives

$$m = \frac{\alpha^2 K}{a^2}$$

and

$$T = B\, J_0 \left(\frac{\alpha r}{a} \right) \mathrm{e}^{-(\alpha^2 Kt/a^2)}. \tag{7.3}$$

In other words, the time-dependent transient behaviour depends only on the parameter Kt/a^2 and the radius dependence on r/a. So results expressed in terms of these two dimensionless parameters are valid regardless of the size or composition of the cylinders. This conclusion is quite general provided the boundary condition is a specified state of affairs at $r = a$ which does not change with time after $t = 0$.

The values of B come from the temperature distribution at $t = 0$, and if this distribution is $f(r)$ then the complete solution is [2]

$$T = \frac{2}{a^2}\left\{\int_0^a rf(r)\mathrm{d}r + \sum_{n=1}^{\infty} \mathrm{e}^{-\alpha_n^2 Kt/a^2} \frac{J_0(\alpha_n r/a)}{J_0^2(\alpha_n)} \int_0^a rf(r)J_0\left(\frac{\alpha_n r}{a}\right)\mathrm{d}r\right\}. \tag{7.4}$$

For a solid-fuel pellet the initial temperature distribution following steady operation at full power is

$$f(r) = \frac{R}{4\pi k}\left\{1 - \frac{r^2}{a^2}\right\}, \tag{7.5}$$

i.e. equation (3.4) with $T_{of} = 0$.

The first term in equation (7.4) is just the final average temperature of the fuel. With the aid of various properties of Bessel functions the second integral in equation (7.4) can be performed (see appendix 1b) and the result simplified.

The final result for the temperature in the fuel pellet as function of time is

$$\frac{T}{R/4\pi k} = \frac{1}{2} - 4\sum_{n=1}^{\infty} \mathrm{e}^{-\alpha_n^2 Kt/a^2} \frac{J_0(\alpha_n r/a)}{J_0(\alpha_n)} \frac{1}{\alpha_n^2} \tag{7.6}$$

where T is the temperature above the initial fuel surface temperature, and the α_n are the positive roots of $J_0'(\alpha) = 0$ (equivalently of $J_1(\alpha) = 0$).

Curves for the temperature distribution following the complete loss of cooling, for various values of the dimensionless time Kt/a^2, are drawn in Fig. 7.2. For the times shown the infinite series in equation (7.6) converges very rapidly, and in fact only the first three terms are needed. At shorter times the convergence is worse, and at $t = 0$ even the first five terms give a very poor match to the initial temperature distribution.

For values of Kt/a^2 greater than about 0.1 the first term in the series dominates the behaviour with a time constant of $a^2/K\alpha_1^2$. The time for the surface temperature to rise within 3% of its final value is given by $Kt/a^2 = 0.2$. For a 10-mm diameter UO_2 fuel pellet this corresponds to $t = 7$ s. In Appendix 1c we show that this timescale is not significantly extended when heat transfer to the cladding is included.

Incidentally the conclusion that the time for heat to diffuse a distance a is of the order of a^2/K is quite general. We shall use this result in Chapter 10.

THE SOURCES OF HEAT

During the loss-of-coolant accident there are four sources of heat that will cause the cladding temperature to rise. These are: delay in shutting the reactor down after loss of cooling; residual fission heating as the neutron chain reaction dies away; the heat produced by the decaying fission products; and the internal energy initially stored in the fuel. In UO_2-fuelled reactors, with their very high fuel temperatures, the stored energy is the main heat source immediately after the postulated break in the coolant duct, but after half a minute or so

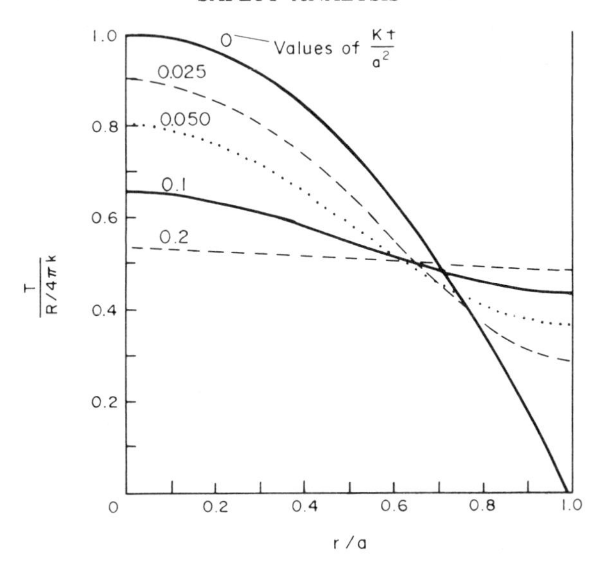

Fig. 7.2. Progressive equalisation of temperatures within a fuel pellet following sudden total loss of cooling. The results are given in terms of dimensionless time Kt/a^2 and dimensionless radius r/a.

the only source of heat is that due to decay of the fission products, and since some of these are very long lived some long-term method of heat removal will be required, possibly for years.

Any delay in making the reactor subcritical following loss of cooling simply gives rise to a certain number of seconds of full power heating. The other sources need more detailed examination.

Residual fission heating

This topic is included here for completeness. A full understanding of it requires rather more knowledge of radioactive decay and reactor kinetics than it was possible to include in the brief introduction of Chapter 1.

It is necessary to distinguish between *prompt* neutrons that are emitted virtually instantaneously in fission, and *delayed* neutrons that are emitted later during the decay of certain fission products. There are six delayed neutron emitters among the fission products, with half-lives ranging from a few seconds to about a minute. Although less than 1% of the neutrons are delayed the neutron chain reaction cannot proceed without them, if the reactor is at or very close to criticality. So any change in power level following a change in the reactivity of the core is delayed because of the time required for the delayed neutrons to catch up. The important result of this is that the response time of the reactor during normal operation is several seconds or longer, making control fairly straightforward.

So it is not possible to instantaneously stop the fission process. Quite apart from the fact that the shutdown rods will take about 1 s to reach the bottom of the core after they are released, the neutron chain reaction does not stop just because the reactor is subcritical and the neutron multiplication constant below unity; it continues at a much lower and diminishing level. This is because of the delayed neutrons.

Since the prompt neutrons do respond very fast once the reactor is subcritical, and die away in a fraction of a second, there is a point a short while afterwards when the prompt neutrons have fallen to a new low level and the concentrations of the delayed neutron emitters are scarcely changed from the levels at full power operation. This makes it quite easy to calculate the new power level since a pseudo-equilibrium exists about 1 s after the reactor goes subcritical.

During normal operation the neutron concentration n is given by

$$\frac{dn}{dt} = -\Sigma_a \phi_0 + k_p \Sigma_a \phi_0 + \sum_{i=1}^{6} \lambda_i N_i = 0, \tag{7.7}$$

i.e. equation (1.5), the neutron diffusion equation mentioned in Chapter 1, but simplified by omitting the contribution due to neutrons diffusing into the volume of interest, that is the equation strictly applies to an infinite reactor. Also the delayed neutron contribution is made clear. λ_i and N_i are the decay constants and concentrations of the various delayed neutron emitters, k_p the multiplication constant for the prompt neutrons by themselves. So if β is the delayed neutron fraction, and k the normal multiplication constant, then

$$k = 1 = k_p + \beta. \tag{7.8}$$

Shortly after the reactor goes subcritical a temporary equilibrium exists where

$$\frac{dn}{dt} = -\Sigma_a \phi + k_p' \Sigma_a \phi + \sum_{i=1}^{6} \lambda_i N_i = 0. \tag{7.9}$$

k_p' is the new prompt neutron multiplication factor and ϕ the new neutron flux. With slight rearrangement equation (7.9) can be divided by equation (7.7) to give the ratio of the new to old flux levels which is also the ratio of the power levels:

$$\frac{\phi}{\phi_0} = \frac{1}{1 + \dfrac{k_p - k_p'}{\beta}}. \tag{7.10}$$

This equation is valid incidentally for finite reactors; the inclusion of the neutron diffusion term complicates the analysis, but it does not change the final result.

The new power level depends then on the reduction in reactivity. For the loss-of-coolant accident a quick and large reduction can be assumed. Whatever other problems the sudden break in one of the coolant ducts may pose, difficulty of detection is not one of them. Also in a water reactor the loss of moderator will add to the effect of the shutdown rods. Taking $k_p - k_p' = 5\%$ as an example, and since $\beta = 0.0064$ for U^{235}, there is a "prompt jump" in power level to about 11% of its previous value.

After this the fission power continues to fall but the behaviour is complicated by the fact that the six delayed neutron emitters decay with different decay constants. If the delayed neutrons are regarded simply as one group with a suitably weighted average decay constant λ then the fission power at time t after the step decrease in reactivity, as a fraction of full power, is [3]

$$\frac{1}{1+\dfrac{k_p-k_p'}{\beta}}\,e^{-\lambda t/\{1+\beta/(k_p-k_p')\}} \tag{7.11}$$

where λ for U^{235} is 0.08 s^{-1}.

Returning to the example where the multiplication constant fell by 5%, equation (7.11) shows that the fission heating falls below the fission product decay heating at $t = 11$ s and continues to decrease rapidly after that. If the normal full power output from the fuel rod is R W m^{-1}, then integrating equation (7.11) from $t = 0$ to $t = \infty$ gives the total energy contributed by the fission process as $1.6R$ J m^{-1}, and the great bulk of this is in the first 20 s.

So the total effect of the residual fission heating is only equivalent to 1 or 2 seconds of full power operation.

Fission product decay heat

The most widely used compilation of fission product decay-heat data is that of Shure [4], and his results for the total energy-production rate as a fraction of full power are shown in Fig. 7.3. At short times the results are based on experimental measurements of power output as a function of time, at longer times where the individual isotopes contributing to the decay heat are known the results are based on the fission yields of the different isotopes and their decay constants and decay energies. The American Nuclear Society Standard on decay

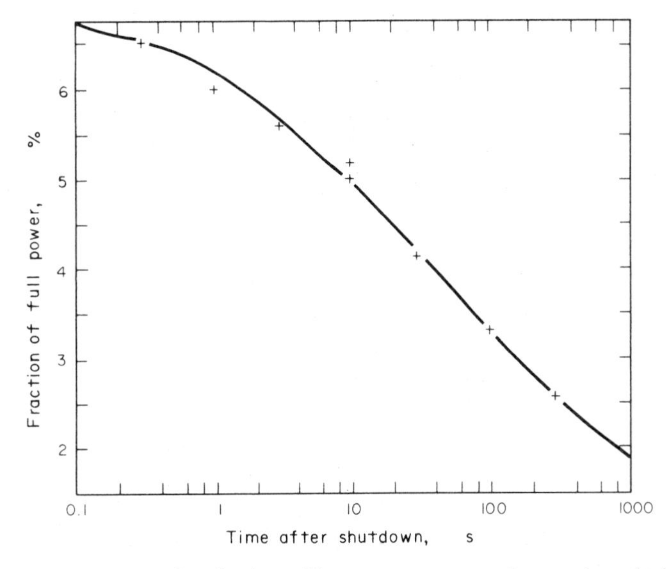

Fig. 7.3. Fission product decay heat after shutdown. The crosses are approximate values obtained from equation (7.12).

heating is based on these results [5]. Recently minor changes for the decay heating at long times after shutdown have been suggested in an updating of the earlier work [6], but the power level for short times after shutdown was left unchanged.

It is convenient to have analytical expressions for the decay heat, and Shure suggests an expression consisting of the sum of eleven exponentially decaying terms, which is physically reasonable since the decay heat is due to the summed effect of the individual isotopes, each of which is decaying according to a law of this type, although there are many more than eleven of them. A more convenient expression (quoted in [7]) for shutdown power as a fraction of full power is

$$Ct^{-y} \tag{7.12}$$

where different values of C and y are used for different times after shutdown, as follows:

t s	C	y
0.1 to 10	0.060 25	0.0639
10 to 150	0.076 55	0.1807
150 to 10^6	0.1301	0.2834

The values resulting from equation (7.12) are compared with the original compilation in Fig. 7.3. The agreement is within about 4%.

All the results that have been mentioned so far are for an infinitely long period of reactor operation prior to shutdown, which in practice, so far as the immediate consequences of an accident are concerned, means that the reactor must have been operating for over a year. If in fact the reactor has only been working for a time t_o before shutdown at time $t = 0$, then the decay heat can easily be corrected. There will be no contribution from fission products that built up before time $t = -t_o$, that is, the residual effect of fission products that were present at $t = -t_o$ must be subtracted off, and the fractional decay power is now given by:

$$Ct^{-y} - C'(t_o + t)^{-y'} \tag{7.13}$$

where the dash covers the possibility that t and $t_o + t$ might be in different time intervals giving different values of C and y.

The total effect of the decay heat in the first 20 s after the reactor goes subcritical is found by integrating equation (7.12) between $t = 0$ and $t = 20$ and is $1.026R$ J m^{-1}. (An equation of the form of (7.12) obviously cannot be used at $t = 0$, to cover the missing 0.1 s it is reasonable to assume a constant decay power equal to that at $t = 0.1$ s.)

Stored internal energy

During normal operation the temperature distribution in the fuel is parabolic. Following a loss of cooling the temperatures throughout the fuel and cladding will tend to equalise, since a temperature gradient can only be supported by a continuing heat flow. The centre fuel temperature will fall, the cladding temperature will rise. Since clad integrity is what matters it is the rise in the cladding temperature that is of concern.

The stored energy in the fuel, above the fuel surface temperature, in a cylindrical element, radius r, thickness dr, is

$$2\pi r \mathrm{d} r \rho c\,(T_r - T_{of})$$

and using equation (3.4) this becomes

$$2\pi r \mathrm{d} r \rho c \frac{R}{4\pi k_f}(1 - r^2/a^2)$$

and the total energy stored in the fuel above the fuel surface temperature is

$$\int_0^a 2\pi r \mathrm{d} r \rho c \frac{R}{4\pi k_f}\left(1 - \frac{r^2}{a^2}\right) = \frac{\rho c R}{2k_f}\left[\frac{r^2}{2} - \frac{1}{a^2}\frac{r^4}{4}\right]_0^a = \frac{a^2 \rho c R}{8k_f} = C_f \frac{R}{8\pi k_f} \qquad (7.14)$$

since the thermal capacity of the fuel m^{-1} is $C_f = \pi a^2 \rho c$. The fuel mean temperature is $R/8\pi k_f$.

If the can is treated as a plane wall then the average heat flux through it is $R/2\pi r_{av}$ where $r_{av} = (b + a)/2$, and the average temperature in the can wall, which is equal to the temperature half-way through, is

$$\frac{R}{k_c 2\pi r_{av}} \frac{(b - a)}{2}$$

above the can surface temperature.

So the total energy stored in the fuel rod, above the can surface temperature, is

$$C_c \frac{R}{2\pi k_c} \frac{(b - a)}{(b + a)} + \left(T_{of} - T_s + \frac{R}{8\pi k_f}\right) C_f \qquad (7.15)$$

and if this energy were to be uniformly distributed throughout fuel and can then the can temperature rise would be

$$\frac{C_c}{C_f + C_c} \frac{R}{2\pi k_c} \frac{(b - a)}{(b + a)} + \frac{C_f}{C_f + C_c}\left(T_{of} - T_s + \frac{R}{8\pi k_f}\right) \qquad (7.16)$$

where C_c, the clad thermal capacity, is $2\pi r_{av}\,(b - a)\,\rho_c c_c$.

To the extent that $R/8\pi k_f$ is far the largest temperature difference and $C_f \gg C_c$, expression (7.16) approximates to $R/8\pi k_f$, i.e. for negligible clad and gap resistance to heat transfer and negligible can thermal capacity, the can temperature rise would be $R/8\pi k_f$.

Putting representative values for a UO_2-fuelled, Zircaloy clad, rod into equation (7.15) shows that the stored energy amounts to about $6R$ J m^{-1}, easily the most important single contribution to the rise in can temperature.

SIMPLE MODEL FOR CLAD TEMPERATURE DURING TRANSIENT

The main point of interest in a loss of coolant accident is the highest temperature reached by the cladding. If there is little or no loss of heat during the depressurisation then the maximum clad temperature will increase steadily with time, and the value when the coolant pressure has fallen to containment pressure will be the highest temperature the clad has experienced up to that point. Also, if this is 20 s or more since the start of the accident, there has been time for the energy present in the fuel at the start to redistribute itself, and the clad temperature can be calculated assuming equilibrium has been reached. In other words, the model does not attempt to predict detailed temperature distributions during the early part of the transient and the only use that is made of the calculations on the timescales of the various processes is to justify the assumption that equilibrium has been reached.

The sources of heat are dealt with as follows: the stored energy and any extra energy arising from delay in making the reactor subcritical are treated as in the previous section; the fission product decay heat is integrated up to the time at which the clad temperature is being calculated; the residual fission heat, which cannot be calculated accurately without considerable information both about the reactor and the accident, is assumed to be equivalent to 1.5 s of full power heating, and to arise in the first 10 s of the accident.

The stored energy term can be corrected to allow for the fact that there will be some heat transfer from the surface of the fuel rod, either to the coolant or to the moderator. If at the time that the cladding temperature is being calculated the decay power and rate of heat loss from the surface balance, then there will be something like the normal parabolic distribution of temperature within the fuel, reduced in amplitude in proportion to the power, and this represents stored energy which is not available to increase the clad temperature.

No attempt is made to analyse the flow through the core during the loss of coolant, so it is not possible to calculate heat-transfer coefficients from the flow conditions. Instead a constant average value of heat-transfer coefficient has to be assumed. Since the model does not provide clad temperatures as a function of time during the loss of pressure, the loss of heat from the fuel rod is based on an average can temperature equal to the mean of the initial and final temperatures. In other words, an iterative procedure is required, first an estimate of clad temperature at the end of the first stage of the transient is made assuming no heat transfer from the rod, then this temperature is used to calculate the heat lost to the coolant or moderator and a better estimate of final temperature is made. The model is pessimistic because it underestimates the heat lost in the early stages of the accident. Figure 7.2 shows that the initial clad temperature rise is very rapid. The true heat loss is higher than that calculated from an average temperature equal to the mean of the initial and final temperatures.

After the first stage of the accident, which normally will coincide with the coolant pressure reaching essentially containment pressure, the only source of heat is the fission product decay heat, and even with no cooling at all the can temperatures will only rise slowly. However, some definite cooling mechanism must come into use quite quickly. Compared with full power operation the heat-transfer coefficients are very low, and the main barrier to heat transfer is to the outside of the fuel rod, so a single value of temperature is sufficient to characterise the behaviour of the fuel rod.

The use of the model is probably best made clear by a couple of examples.

Example 7.1. The maximum credible accident in a Magnox reactor with a steel pressure vessel is a sudden break in a bottom coolant duct, followed by 40 s of core flow stagnation. Estimate the maximum temperature of the Magnox cladding at the end of the 40 s given the following information.

The fuel rods are of natural uranium metal in finned Magnox cans. The maximum rating is 40 kW m^{-1}, and the thermal capacities of fuel and can are 2000 and 1300 J m^{-1} K^{-1}, respectively. The temperature drops across the cladding and the fuel to clad gap may be neglected. There is a 5-s delay before the reactor is made subcritical. The fuel radius is 14 mm and the initial can temperature is 500°C.

Because of the core flow stagnation it is assumed that no heat is lost to the coolant, but a small amount of heat is lost by radiation to the graphite moderator. The emissivity of Magnox, based on a smooth 50-mm diameter cylinder circumscribing the fins, is 0.6 and that of the 100-mm diameter graphite cooling channel, in which the fuel element is centrally placed, is 0.85. The large thermal capacity of the graphite ensures that its temperature stays constant at 350° throughout.

First it is necessary to check that 40 s is sufficient for the temperatures to equalise. Taking values for the properties from Table 3.1 the value of t for $Kt/a^2 = 0.2$ is found to be 4.0 s, so there is ample time.

The stored energy is given by equation (7.15), which in this case simplifies to

$$\frac{RC_f}{8\pi k_f} = 2.41R.$$

Thirty-five seconds from the time when the reactor goes subcritical the decay power is 0.040 of the full power output, so a fraction 0.040 of the stored energy is not available to increase the can temperature, and the corrected value is $2.41R\,(1 - 0.040) = 2.31R$. The energy due to the 5 s delay in shutting down is just $5R$, and that from the residual fission heating is $1.5R$.

Integrating the fission product decay heat up to $40 - 5 = 35$ s gives

$$R\left\{0.07 \times 0.1 + \frac{0.0602}{0.9361}\left[10^{0.9361} - 0.1^{0.9361}\right] + \frac{0.0765}{0.8193}\left[35^{0.8193} - 10^{0.8193}\right]\right\} = 1.70R.$$

Adding all the energy terms together and dividing by the total thermal capacity gives the first estimate of the temperature rise as 127.4°C, i.e. the temperature rise for no cooling.

The average temperature of the can during the 40 s is taken to be $(500 + 627.4)/2 = 563.7$°C, and the rate of heat loss by radiation during this time is given by the following equation [8]:

$$\frac{\sigma A_1 (T_1^4 - T_2^4)}{\dfrac{1}{\varepsilon_1} + \dfrac{A_1}{A_2}\left(\dfrac{1}{\varepsilon_2} - 1\right)} \qquad (7.17)$$

where subscript 1 refers to the fuel element surface temperature and 2 to the wall of the graphite channel. In this case A_1 is the area of a cylinder circumscribing the fins. $\sigma = 5.67 \times 10^{-8}$ W m^{-2} K^{-4} is Stefan's constant.

Evaluating equation (7.17) gives a rate of heat loss of 1730 W m^{-1}, which incidentally balances the rate of decay heating at 40 s, so even after that there is no immediate need to restart the circulators in the undamaged primary coolant loops. The total heat loss in the 40 s is 6.92×10^4 J m^{-1}, equivalent to a fall in temperature of 20.7°C. A further iteration is not justified in this case, so the final estimate of the can temperature at the end of depressurisation is 607°C.

A couple of comments on the above example are worth making. Firstly, the accepted value of the can temperature rise is about 10°C less, due partly to an allowance for axial conduction to regions of the fuel element where the rating is lower than the maximum value of 40 kW m^{-1}. Secondly, given a rating of 40 kW m^{-1}, the accident limits the temperature in normal operation to 500°C, since Magnox melts and catches fire at 650°C. This shows the profound influence an unlikely hypothetical accident can have on normal operation of the reactor.

Example 7.2. Following a burst coolant duct in a PWR the water leaves the core in 20 s. The reactor goes subcritical at 2 s and the critical heat flux is exceeded at 3 s from the break, after which the heat-transfer coefficient is only 150 W m^{-2} K^{-1}. The fuel rods consist of 9.4-mm diameter UO_2 pellets inside a 10.7-mm diameter Zircaloy can, and the maximum linear rating is 45 kW m^{-1}. In normal operation the coolant is at 300°C and the can-coolant and fuel-clad heat-transfer coefficients are 40,000 and 5000 W m^{-2} K^{-1} respectively. Estimate the can temperature at the end of the 20 s.

After the reactor pressure has fallen to that of the containment the emergency core-cooling system provides a heat-transfer coefficient of 40 W m^{-2} K^{-1} during the refill stage. Show that the fuel rod continues to heat up, initially at a rate of 1.4°C s^{-1}, and that the maximum temperature is not reached until about 60 s from the break.

Not all the information needed to attempt a solution to this problem is given, but reasonable estimates can be made. For a start it is reasonable to assume that the 2 s of normal heat output before the reactor goes subcritical is cancelled out by the good cooling during this time. If anything there will be a net heat loss during this time since the high water velocities and increased turbulence due to boiling will give higher than normal heat-transfer coefficients. In the remaining 1 s before the critical heat flux is exceeded normal cooling is assumed.

The dimensions of the fuel rod are not very different to those of the example considered in the sections on transient timescales, so the temperatures should equalise in under 10 s.

With low conductivity UO_2 the stored energy term is far the most important, and to evaluate equation (7.15) average values of the properties are needed. For the temperatures involved in this problem the UO_2 thermal conductivity, specific heat and density are 2.5 W m^{-1} K^{-1}, 350 J kg^{-1} K^{-1} and 10,000 kg m^{-3} respectively. The corresponding values for Zircaloy, from Table 3.1, are 13, 350 and 6500. Expression (7.15) involves the difference between the fuel surface temperature, T_{of}, and the can surface temperature T_s.

The average heat flux in the cladding is $R/\pi(a + b)$, so the temperature drop through the cladding is

$$\frac{R}{\pi k_c} \frac{(b-a)}{(b+a)} = 71.3 \text{ K}.$$

The fuel to clad temperature difference is

$$\frac{R}{2\pi a} \frac{1}{h_g} = 304.8 \text{ K}.$$

The fuel thermal capacity, per metre length, is $\pi a^2 \rho_f c_f = 242.9$ J m^{-1} K^{-1}, and that of the cladding is $\pi(a + b)(b - a)\rho_c c_c = 46.7$ J m^{-1} K^{-1}.

Substituting these values in equation (7.15) the energy stored in the fuel rod above the can surface temperature is 267 kJ. However, at the end of the 20 s the decay heat will be at 0.0454 of the full power level, and approximately this fraction of the stored energy is therefore not available. The stored energy contribution to the temperature rise is reduced to $(1 - 0.0454) \times 267 = 254.9$ kJ.

The decay heat is worked out for 18 s and comes to $0.936R$ or 42.1 kJ.

The residual fission heat is $1.5R$ or 67.5 kJ.

The heat removed between 2 and 3 s after the break contributes $-$ 45 kJ.

Adding all the energy contributions together and dividing by the total thermal capacity gives the first estimate of the can surface temperature at the end of the loss of coolant as 1103°C above the initial can surface temperature. The initial can surface temperature is the coolant temperature plus the can to coolant temperature difference, i.e.

$$300 + \frac{45{,}000}{\pi \times 0.0107 \times 40{,}000} = 333.5°\text{C}.$$

So with no cooling the clad temperature at the end of blowdown would be 1436°C, and the average clad temperature during blowdown, that is the mean of the initial and final temperatures, would be 885°C.

The coolant temperature will not remain at 300°C throughout the blowdown, evaporation of the water will ensure that the water temperature will tend to follow the falling saturation temperature. Taking 200°C as the average coolant temperature, the heat lost in 17 s will be

$$\pi \times 0.0107 \times 150 \times (885 - 200) \times 17 = 58.7 \text{ kJ}$$

and the fall in temperature corresponding to this is 203°C, so the second estimate of can surface temperature at the end of blowdown is 1233°C. Further estimates lead to a final value for the clad temperature at the end of blowdown of about 1260°C.

For the second part of the problem the timescales are longer and the temperature within the fuel rod fairly uniform.

At the end of blowdown the decay heating is at a rate of $0.0454R$ or 2043 W m^{-1} and the heat removed by the emergency core cooling system is

$$\pi \times 0.0107 \times 40 \times (1260 - 50) = 1627 \text{ W m}^{-1}$$

where a temperature of 50°C has been assumed for the emergency core cooling water (the temperature must be less than 100°C or the water will immediately flash into steam).

So the fuel rod continues to heat up, at an initial rate of

$$\frac{2043 - 1627}{242.9 + 46.7} = 1.4\text{°C s}^{-1}.$$

This heating will continue until the decay heat falls to about 1627/45,000 = 0.036 of the full power output, which Fig. 7.3 shows will occur at about 65 s after shutdown. In fact this is a slight overestimate since as the can temperature rises it will lose more heat. A maximum clad temperature at 60 s from the break appears reasonable.

The above example is quite involved, also it has important practical implications, so a number of comments are in order. The maximum clad temperature that is allowed in this accident is in fact 1200°C at the present time [9], and given the approximate nature of the simple model used in the example this maximum clad temperature is consistent with a rating of 45 kW m^{-1}. A proper solution of this problem would, of course, require a transient analysis performed on a computer, with heat-transfer coefficients based on a calculation of the flow conditions. Even these calculations require checking against model tests, because the problem is in fact too difficult to be solved from first principles. Transient three-dimensional flow problems are difficult to solve at the best of times, and when there are also the difficulties of two phases, water and steam, with heat and mass transfer between them, and a complicated geometry, then little confidence can be placed in such a calculation unless it has successfully predicted the result of a model test similar to the real problem.

These model tests extend up to what is essentially a very small PWR. The LOFT (Loss of Fluid Test) facility has a 55-MW (thermal) core, one intact loop representing three loops of a four-loop PWR, and a blowdown loop [10]. The blowdown loop has orifices and quick-acting valves to simulate breaks in the pipe. The nuclear tests are not complete, but they indicate reasonable agreement between measured and predicted maximum cladding temperatures.

The heat-transfer coefficients used in Example 7.2 are both on the low side, the more crucial of the two, the value during the blowdown, is rather lower than the value to be expected in stable film boiling, but is a value quoted as giving good agreement with a PWR model test [11].

The times at which the reactor becomes subcritical and at which the critical heat flux is exceeded are obviously very important. The two events are linked in that they both depend on the generation of steam and the increased void fraction and quality. With the rapid fall in pressure and increase in the quantity of steam in the core the two events are likely to happen close together and soon after the break. Also the shutdown rods should enter the core at about 2 s after the break. An uncertainty of 1 s in the difference between the timing of the two events gives an uncertainty of about 150°C in the value of the maximum clad temperature.

Throughout the refill phase of the accident water is being supplied to the core. Eventually the core floods with water. The quenching of the fuel rods is accompanied by a sudden fall in temperature and rise in heat-transfer coefficient.

DISCUSSION OF LOSS-OF-COOLANT ACCIDENTS

The difficulty with the loss-of-coolant accident is the suddenness with which core-flow stagnation and a two orders of magnitude drop in heat-transfer coefficient can occur. If normal cooling could be maintained for just a few seconds longer much of the stored energy could be removed, and the maximum temperature reached by the can would be much lower. The rate of fall of pressure could be reduced by having smaller diameter ducts (and more of them), or by fitting flow restrictors so that in the event of a break the critical flow occurs at the smaller cross-section of the restriction rather than at the broken end of the duct. The more recently constructed gas-cooled reactors have the entire primary circuit inside a prestressed concrete pressure vessel, there are no main coolant ducts outside, and a sudden depressurisation with core-flow stagnation is considered incredible.

Another method of reducing the severity of the clad temperature rise is to reduce the rating of the fuel rods. This can be done without reducing the power produced per kg of uranium if the fuel rods are made smaller.

While removal of decay heat in liquid-cooled reactors is assured once the rods are in contact with the liquid, in gas-cooled reactors there is, in principle, a problem if the operating pressure is too high. For a given temperature rise gas flowing through a passage of cross-sectional area A is able to remove heat in proportion to $A\rho uc$. Comparing normal and post-accident conditions, A is unchanged, c virtually so, u will depend on the speed of the circulators and will be similar. So the heat-removal capability falls in proportion to the density or pressure. The same is true of the heat-transfer coefficient, $h = St\rho uc$, since the Stanton number will not be very different if the post-accident flow is still turbulent. Even an hour after the reactor is shut down the decay heat is running at 1.3% of full power, so on the basis of this simple argument the operating pressure of the reactor should not be more than $100/1.3 = 77$ atmospheres. In the case of a gas-cooled fast reactor with no graphite moderator to act as a heat sink the decay-heat-removal problem would become serious in much less than an hour.

THE PROBABILITY APPROACH TO REACTOR SAFETY

The maximum credible accident approach to reactor safety is not entirely satisfactory, there may be more serious accidents which would harm members of the public, and which ought to be considered. The suggestion was made by Farmer [12] that all conceivable accidents should be considered, and estimates made of their seriousness and of the likelihood of them occurring. Accidents that were more dangerous than the "maximum credible accident" could be accepted provided the probability of them occurring was sufficiently low. The seriousness of the accident is measured by the amount of radioactivity released, and the question as to whether the accident is acceptable or not would be resolved by reference to a graph such as that in Fig. 7.4. A release of 10^4 curies would be acceptable provided it happened less frequently than one in 10,000 years for a given reactor, that is with a probability of less than 10^{-4} per reactor year. A release of 10^6 curies would only be acceptable at the 10^{-6} probability level, and so on. The reason for the curved portion of the graph giving lower probabilities for small activity releases is that a relatively large number of small releases, while of little concern to the public, would not be acceptable to the operators of the plant.

The probability approach requires more accidents to be analysed, though of course once it is clear that an accident lies well on the acceptable side of the dividing line there is no reason to analyse it in great detail. The difficulty arises in determining some of the probabilities. A probability of 10^{-6} or once in a million reactor years certainly cannot be decided on the basis of direct experience. There have only been about 2000 reactor years of experience in total. One approach that can be adopted is to divide the accident into a number of separate

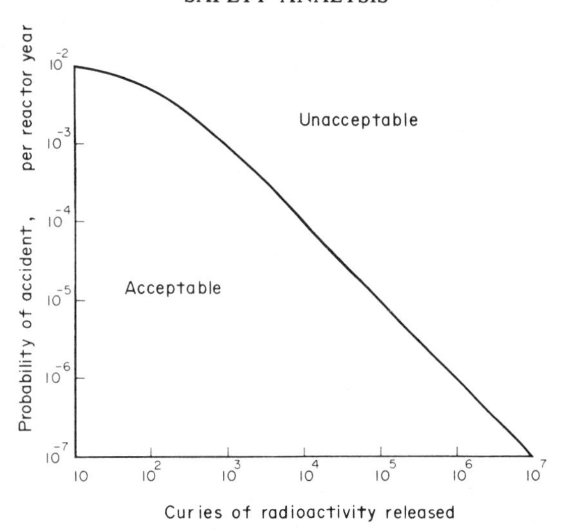

Fig. 7.4. Dividing line between acceptable and unacceptable accidents on the basis of probability of occurrence and seriousness of consequences.

independent failures, all of which are required before the accident can occur. For example, a basic fault is failure to shut the reactor down when required. Suppose there are three separate systems of shutdown rods, and any one of these systems is sufficient to shut the reactor down by itself. Since the rods are not called upon to operate very often a failure probability for a given system of less than 10^{-2} per reactor year can be established by actual testing, and such testing is done at regular intervals. If now the three sets of rods are quite independent of one another, then the likelihood of all three failing at the same time is only $(10^{-2})^3 = 10^{-6}$ per reactor year. The key point in this argument is the assumption of independence of the three systems. It is quite possible for one event to put a number of systems out of action, a "common mode" failure; for example, a fire at the Browns Ferry plant in the U.S.A. destroyed many control and instrumentation systems, including all automatic and remote control of the emergency core-cooling system and all nuclear instrumentation [13]. However, the plant was brought safely under control. Incidentally, failure of the electricity supply would not put the shutdown systems out of action. The rods are only held out of the core by the maintenance of the supply. If the supply failed the rods would drop in automatically.

Another potentially very serious event is a sudden failure of the main pressure vessel. It is not possible to use the same kind of argument to establish a low failure probability in this case, but there is extensive experience of non-nuclear pressure vessels. Based on this experience, but arguing a greater reliability for nuclear vessels on the grounds of greater care in manufacture and inspection, failure probabilities of around 10^{-7} per reactor year have been suggested [14]. In the case of prestressed concrete pressure vessels there is no useful non-nuclear experience but it is possible to argue that failure would not be sudden; there would be warning in the form of cracks and leaks in the concrete. Since the prestressing cables are physically separate a failure in one cannot directly spread to others, and tests on model vessels show a progressive form of failure, with cracks appearing before the internal gas pressure falls significantly.

The Three Mile Island accident

A difficulty with the probability approach is that one cannot quantify the probability that an important factor has been overlooked. Perhaps the most serious accident at a commercial nuclear plant, considering the number of things that went wrong and some of their implications, was that at Three Mile Island in the U.S.A. in 1979 [15]. Some of the phenomena that were revealed in this accident appear to have received little attention in previous safety analyses.

The reactor was a PWR and the accident was of the depressurization type, but the coolant escaped comparatively slowly through a pressure relief valve that had stuck open rather than through a broken pipe. The initial cause was a simultaneous failure of both the normal and emergency systems for feeding water to the boilers. This led to a rapid dryout of the boilers and rise in temperature and pressure of the primary circuit. The pressure relief valve (in the pressurizer) opened on the rise in pressure and the reactor tripped. All of this happened in the first few seconds. During the course of the next hour a variety of automatic and manual attempts were made to establish a flow of water through the core, using the high-pressure water-injection system, hampered by steam in the main primary pumps causing excessive cavitation and vibration, and by the fact that the operators did not know that the relief valve was open. Later still the pressure was deliberately lowered to allow the automatic low-pressure water injection system to operate.

Two unexpected features of this accident were that a large bubble of steam and gas formed over the core, at times preventing cooling water reaching the upper part of the core, and that there was some evidence of a hydrogen explosion in the containment building. It was known that water reacts with Zircaloy cladding at high temperatures to produce hydrogen, but the implications of large quantities of gas being produced appear to have received little attention. During the course of the accident the cladding split on most of the fuel rods and about half of the fission product gases escaped from the core. However, the radiation doses received by the public were low, and even on the site the doses were within the recommended annual limit.

The reactor safety study

It is important to have some idea of what the risks to the public are and how they compare with other risks to which the public are exposed. The only recent study to do this in any detail is the reactor safety study commissioned by the U.S. Atomic Energy Commission under the independent direction of Professor Rasmussen [14]. The study was based on an operating PWR and an operating BWR of fairly recent design, with a population distribution around the reactor equivalent to the average of nuclear sites in the U.S. The risks for the two types of reactor were found to be similar, and so were averaged and then multiplied by 100 to give the risks for 100 reactors, a number that will be reached in about 1981.

These risks are compared with risks from other man-caused and natural disasters in Figs. 7.5 and 7.6. While the curve for 100 nuclear reactors is entirely hypothetical considerable parts of some of the other curves are based on experience. The serious reactor accidents are all associated with core melting. In the PWR the largest cause is a loss-of-coolant accident following a small break in a pipe, coupled with failure of the emergency core-cooling systems (small breaks are more serious than large ones because they are much more likely to happen). In the BWR failure of the decay heat-removal systems after transient caused shutdowns is

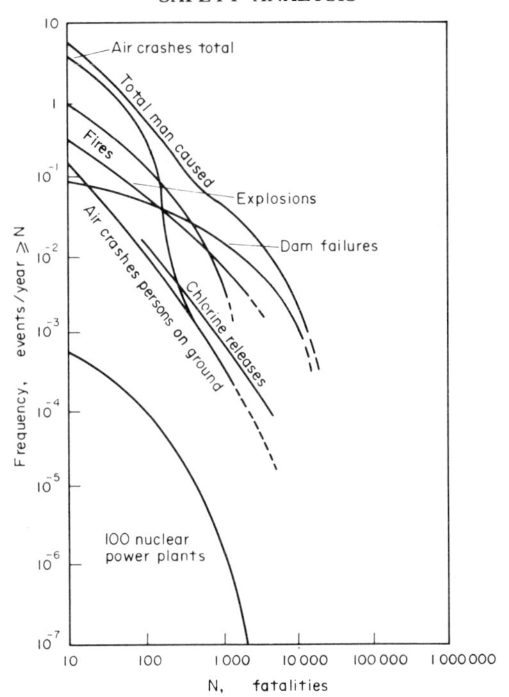

Fig. 7.5. Estimated frequency of various man-caused accidents versus number of fatalities (reproduced from [14], with permission).

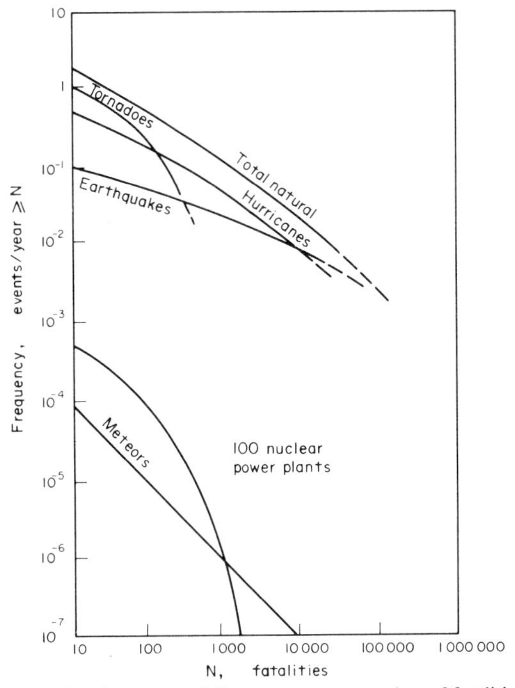

Fig. 7.6. Estimated frequency of various natural disasters versus number of fatalities (reproduced from [14], with permission).

more important. However, a variety of accidents contribute to the risks including some accidents that are only possible because of the presence of safety systems needed to cope with other accidents.

The study shows that the risks associated with accidents at nuclear power stations are much smaller than those associated with a number of other activities. Also the reactor accident is not unique in its potentially very serious consequences. Of course, all these accidents pale into insignificance compared with the annual total of death and injury on the roads. There are about 50,000 deaths a year in road accidents in the U.S. Indeed it can be argued that one car is as dangerous as one nuclear power station. The risk of a fatal accident is about 5×10^{-4} per power plant per year. With 100 million vehicles the risk per vehicle is similar.

THE SODIUM-COOLED FAST REACTOR

With sodium as the coolant there is no need for high pressures and the depressurization type of accident is irrelevant. The fuel rods must always be in contact with the coolant, even when the reactor is shut down. In the pool type of reactor this is ensured by a leak jacket around the main tank and by having all penetrations of the main tank above core level.

A possible accident sequence that has received much attention is that of local boiling of the sodium, followed by melting and rearrangement of the fuel. Propagation to a more serious incident could result from increased reactivity in the new geometry, or from a vapour explosion. The initiating event could perhaps be a blockage of the inlet of one subassembly. This in fact happened in an experimental fast reactor and extensive fuel melting resulted [16]. The subassembly inlet was flat, so it was possible for a flat metal sheet that had broken loose to rest against the inlet and block the flow; subassembly inlets are now of very complicated shape, making sudden near total blockage on the inlet virtually impossible. Since the coolant in a fast reactor is a long way below its boiling-point the flow has to be reduced to about one-third of the normal value to give bulk boiling at the subassembly outlet. This reduction in flow would require all but a few per cent of the inlet to be blocked.

If it is assumed that a local blockage has somehow occurred, leading to boiling in part of the subassembly, and the fault has not been detected by the rise in temperature at the subassembly outlet or by the noise of boiling, then failure of fuel rods and fuel melting may result. Analysis of this type of complicated fluid-flow and heat-transfer situation becomes very problematical.

The existence of vapour explosions is known from many fields, for example explosions have resulted from the sudden mixing of water and molten iron in steelworks. Preconditions for significant energy release in a reactor accident are that there should be extensive fuel melting and sudden and intimate mixing of the molten UO_2 with the liquid sodium. Even then it is not clear that the temperature at the fuel–sodium interface will be high enough for the nucleation of boiling [17], since the materials are assumed to be finely divided and the likelihood of there being a suitable surface cavity nucleation site on a given fragment is virtually zero.

An alternative to theoretical analysis is of course direct testing in a reactor. Boiling has been deliberately induced in two experimental reactors, by reducing flow or introducing blockages. It is possible for the sodium to boil for several hours with little damage to the fuel rods [18]. Even with fuel and clad melting there is no sign of energetic fuel-coolant interactions [19].

The sodium-cooled fast reactor is not of course unique in having a liquid coolant that conceivably could vaporise and no longer provide adequate cooling. Water reactors operate with a liquid coolant which is already either at or very close to its boiling-point. It is interesting to note that localised subassembly faults have not proved troublesome in practice in water reactors, and it has not been considered necessary to install instrumentation for the rapid detection of local faults. Water reactors differ from the sodium-cooled fast reactor in two important respects however. Firstly, the power density is lower in the water reactor, and the volume of vapour produced for a given amount of heat is less. However, these effects are largely offset by the much greater temperature rise required to reach boiling-point in the sodium reactor. Secondly, in the water-cooled reactor, as in all thermal reactors, the fuel rods and moderator are carefully positioned to give close to the maximum possible reactivity. It is unlikely therefore that any random rearrangement in the later stages of a severe accident would lead to an increase in reactivity. The fast reactor has no moderator, and it is conceivable that an accident that involved melting and slumping of the fuel could lead to an increase in reactivity.

References

1. THOMPSON, T. J. and BECKERLEY, J. G. (eds.), *The technology of nuclear reactor safety*, Vol. 1, M.I.T. Press, 1964.
2. CARSLAW, H. S. and JAEGER, J. C. *Conduction of heat in solids*, Oxford University Press, 1959, p. 204.
3. GLASSTONE, S. and SESONSKE, A. *Nuclear reactor engineering*, Van Nostrand Reinhold, 1967, p. 239.
4. SHURE, K. *Fission product decay energy*, WAPD-BT-24, 1961, pp. 1–17.
5. AMERICAN NUCLEAR SOCIETY, Standard ANS 5.1, Decay energy release following shutdown of uranium fueled thermal reactor, 1971.
6. SHURE, K. Fission Product Decay Energy, 1972, Re-evaluation, WAPD-TM-1119 (U.S. Atomic Energy Commission Research and Development Report).
7. WALTERS, C. T., GENCO, J. M. and RAINER, G. E. Heat transfer analysis in a loss of coolant accident. *Nucl. Engng Design* **7,** 123 (1968).
8. HOLMAN, J. P. *Heat transfer*, 4th edn., McGraw-Hill, 1976, p. 299.
9. Report to the American Physical Society by the Study Group on Light Water Reactor Safety. *Rev. Mod. Phys.* **47,** Supplement 1 (1975).
10. *Nuclear Engineering International*, 1979, Jan., p. 3 and p. 34, also July, p. 5.
11. JOHNSEN, G. W. and LARSON, T. K. Predictions and analysis of Semiscale blowdown heat transfer tests with RELAP4. *Trans. Am. Nucl. Soc.* **23,** 299–300 (1976).
12. FARMER, F. R. Siting criteria – a new approach, pp. 303–318 of *Containment and siting of nuclear power plants*, IAEA, Vienna, 1967.
13. *Nuclear Engineering International* **20,** 461 (1975).
14. U.S. ATOMIC ENERGY COMMISSION, Reactor safety study – an assessment of accident risks in U.S. commercial nuclear power plants, WASH-1400, 1974.
15. *Nuclear Engineering International*, May 1979, pp. 10–11.
16. MCCARTHY, W. J. and JENS, W. H. A review of the Fermi reactor fuel damage incident, Paper Va–1. *Proc. Int. Conf. Safety of Fast Reactors*, Aix-en-Provence, 1967.
17. FAUSKE, H. K. On the mechanism of uranium dioxide–sodium explosive interactions. *Nucl. Sci. Engng* **51,** 95–101 (1973).
18. SMITH, D. C. G., BAGLEY, K. Q., GREGORY, C. V., LEET, G. O. and TAIT, D. DFR special experiments, *Int. Symp. Design, construction and operating experience of demonstration LMFBRS*, IAEA-SM-225/49, 1978.
19. DICKERMAN, C. E., BARTS, E. W., DE VOLPI, A., HOLTZ, R. E., MURPHY, W. F. and ROTHMAN, A. B. Recent results from TREAT tests on fuel, cladding and coolant motion. *Ann. Nucl. Energy* **3,** 315–322 (1976).

Problems

1. A solid cylindrical fuel pellet, of constant thermal conductivity, is producing heat at a rate R W/m in a reactor. The rate of heat generation is uniform throughout the fuel and the flow of heat is radial. Supposing that it were possible to suddenly remove the fuel pellet from the reactor and prevent both further heat generation and further cooling from the surface, show that the temperature of the surface would rise by $R/8\pi k$.

2. A reactor is operating continuously at a power level of 3000 MW (th) for several months and is then shut down. What is the power due to the decay of fission products
   (a) one minute,
   (b) one hour, after shut down?
3. It is desired to inspect a fuel rod very quickly after irradiation in a reactor. The rod is placed in the reactor for a week and experiences a linear rating of 40 kW/m. The proposal is to inspect it 24 hours after it is taken out. The rod is 10 mm o.d. and to be mounted in ambient air at 20°C, which should provide a heat-transfer coefficient due to natural convection of around 15 W m^{-2} K^{-1}. How hot will the cladding surface get?
4. It is believed that the sequence of events after a break in a coolant duct in a certain water-cooled reactor would be as follows.

   The reactor goes subcritical at 2 s, and the critical heat flux is exceeded at 3 s, after the break. The combined effect of delay in inserting the shutdown rods and residual fission heating is equivalent to 3.5 s of full power operation. The water takes 25 s to leave the core.

   The fuel consists of 12 mm o.d. UO_2 pellets inside a 13.6-mm o.d. Zircaloy can. In normal operation the rating and cladding surface temperature are 40 kW m^{-1} and 300°C respectively, and the fuel to clad heat-transfer coefficient is 6000 W m^{-2} K^{-1}. Estimate the clad temperature at the end of the 25 s, assuming no heat transfer from the surface after the critical heat flux is exceeded.
5. (a) If in question 4 there had been a heat-transfer coefficient of 100 W m^{-2} K^{-1} (to water at an average temperature of 200°C), after the critical heat flux, what would the cladding temperature have been?
   (b) If the blowdown is followed by an adiabatic "heat up" lasting 30 s, what is the new cladding temperature? (following part (a)).

CHAPTER 8

Core Thermohydraulic Design

INTRODUCTION

In the previous chapters the various factors that influence the thermohydraulic design of the reactor have been explained. However, they have, for the most part, been applied to single points inside the reactor where it was assumed that local conditions were known. There is considerable variation in local power generation within the core, both radially and axially, and it is often not obvious where the most severe conditions will occur.

The highest power production will be encountered roughly in the centre of the core. Consequently, with UO_2 fuel, the maximum fuel temperature will be found near this position, and also the maximum can temperature following a sudden loss of coolant (if applicable), and the maximum internal fission gas pressure. However, neither the maximum can temperature in normal operation nor the minimum critical heat flux ratio occur at this position, and more detailed analysis is required.

The overall variations of heat output and temperature rise are often expressed by hot channel factors. The most detailed information comes from a subchannel analysis performed by computer, in which it is accepted that the thermal conditions vary radially even within a given fuel assembly.

In view of the high capital cost of a nuclear reactor, some insight into the overall design is provided by assuming that the objective is to obtain as much heat out of the core as possible. The implications of this for a gas-cooled reactor and a boiling water reactor are examined.

MAXIMUM CAN TEMPERATURE IN A COOLANT CHANNEL

The following analysis to find the position and value of the maximum can temperature in a coolant channel assumes a constant heat-transfer coefficient. It would not apply therefore to a BWR.

The temperature on the outer surface of the fuel can is the local coolant temperature plus the can to coolant temperature difference. The temperature of the coolant increases continuously as it flows along the channel; the can to coolant temperature difference reaches a maximum half-way along the channel where the heat flux is greatest. As a result the can temperature reaches a maximum some way beyond the mid-point. It is important to know the value of this maximum temperature and the position where it occurs. In some reactor systems the maximum permitted can temperature is a limiting feature of the design, and this factor as much as any other determines the amount of heat that can be generated in the core.

In many cases the axial variation of power along the channel may be approximated by a cosine function, based on the extrapolated core length L'. If the core proper, that is the region containing the fuel rods, is surrounded by a reflector, then the neutron flux within the core behaves as though the core were extended in all directions by an amount called the reflector savings, which for a light water reactor is about 30 mm and for a graphite-moderated reactor up to 500 mm. So if the heat flux is q_0 in the centre of the channel, and the total perimeter of all the fuel rods in the channel is s, then at a position z beyond the centre of the channel, as shown in Fig. 8.1, the rate of heat input per unit length is

$$qs = q_0 s \cos(\pi z/L') \tag{8.1}$$

and the total heat input from the inlet to the channel up to z is

$$\int_{-L/2}^{z} q_0 s \cos(\pi z/L')\, \mathrm{d}z = \frac{q_0 s L'}{\pi}\left\{\sin(\pi z/L') + \sin(\pi L/2L')\right\} \tag{8.2}$$

so the temperature of the coolant at z is

$$T_z = T_1 + \frac{1}{mc}\frac{q_0 s L'}{\pi}\left\{\sin(\pi z/L') + \sin(\pi L/2L')\right\} \tag{8.3}$$

where T_1 is the temperature of the coolant at inlet to the channel, m the mass flow rate and c the specific heat at constant pressure.

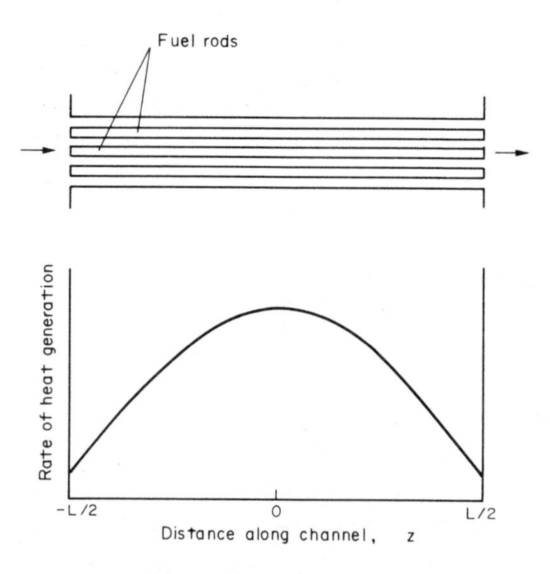

Fig. 8.1. Cosine distribution of heat generation along a fuel channel.

Assuming a constant heat-transfer coefficient h, the can to coolant temperature difference is q/h, so the can surface temperature T_s is given by

$$T_s - T_z = \frac{q_0}{h}\cos(\pi z/L'). \tag{8.4}$$

Superimposing equation (8.4) on (8.3), as shown in Fig. 8.2, we see that the maximum can temperature occurs somewhat beyond the centre of the channel. To find the maximum temperature we substitute for T_z from (8.3) into (8.4) giving

$$T_s = T_1 + \frac{1}{mc}\frac{q_0 sL'}{\pi}\left\{\sin(\pi z/L') + \sin(\pi L/2L')\right\} + \frac{q_0}{h}\cos(\pi z/L') \tag{8.5}$$

setting $\mathrm{d}T_s/\mathrm{d}z = 0$ to find the maximum gives

$$\frac{1}{mc}\frac{q_0 sL'}{\pi}\frac{\pi}{L'}\cos(\pi z/L') - \frac{q_0}{h}\frac{\pi}{L'}\sin(\pi z/L') = 0$$

or

$$\tan(\pi z/L') = \frac{L'sh}{mc\pi} = y. \tag{8.6}$$

Consideration of the right-angled triangle in Fig. 8.3 shows that for this value of z $\sin(\pi z/L') = y/(1 + y^2)^{1/2}$ and $\cos(\pi z/L') = 1/(1 + y^2)^{1/2}$. Substituting these values back into equation (8.5) gives the maximum can surface temperature

$$T_{\max} = T_1 + \frac{q_0 sL'}{mc\pi}\left\{\frac{y}{\sqrt{(1+y^2)}} + \sin\frac{\pi L}{2L'} + \frac{1}{y}\frac{1}{\sqrt{(1+y^2)}}\right\}$$

or

$$T_{\max} = T_1 + \frac{q_0 sL'}{mc\pi}\left\{\sqrt{\left[\left(\frac{mc\pi}{L'sh}\right)^2 + 1\right]} + \sin\frac{\pi L}{2L'}\right\}. \tag{8.7}$$

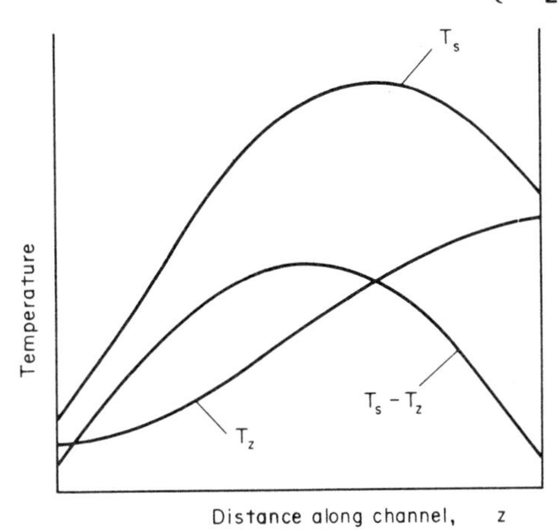

Fig. 8.2. Coolant temperature T_z and cladding temperature T_s as a function of distance along the channel.

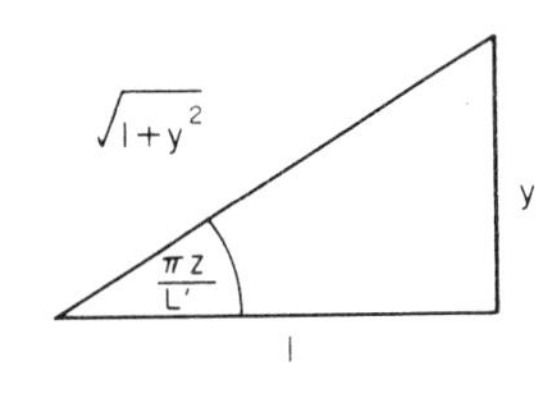

Fig. 8.3.

Frequently this result is expressed as a ratio of temperature rises, $T_{max} - T_1$, to the total coolant temperature rise $T_2 - T_1$ where T_2 is the coolant outlet temperature. From equation (8.3)

$$T_2 - T_1 = \frac{2q_0 sL'}{mc\pi} \sin(\pi L/2L') \tag{8.8}$$

and dividing this into (8.7) gives

$$\frac{T_{max} - T_1}{T_2 - T_1} = \frac{1}{2} + \frac{1}{2}\left\{\left(\frac{mc\pi}{L'sh}\right)^2 + 1\right\}^{1/2} \operatorname{cosec}(\pi L/2L') \tag{8.9}$$

and since the definition of the Stanton number is $St = h/\rho uc = hA/mc$, we have

$$\frac{T_{max} - T_1}{T_2 - T_1} = \frac{1}{2} + \frac{1}{2}\left\{\left(\frac{A\pi}{StsL'}\right)^2 + 1\right\}^{1/2} \operatorname{cosec}(\pi L/2L'). \tag{8.10}$$

Frequently T_{max} is fixed by material properties of the can, such as oxidation by the carbon dioxide in AGRs or the danger of melting in Magnox reactors. For a given T_1 it is important to have a high value of T_2, both to increase $T_2 - T_1$ to reduce the mass flow rate and hence pumping power required for a given heat output, and to raise the temperature at which heat is supplied to the boiler, which will increase the thermodynamic efficiency of the steam cycle. Not all of the parameters in the right-hand side of the equation (8.10) can be varied in order to increase T_2. For power reactors L/L' is always close to unity, and L' itself is influenced by reactivity considerations (the height and diameter of the core should be similar for maximum reactivity), so effectively a high value of T_2 requires a high value of Sts/A.

The assumption of a cosine distribution of power generation is particularly good for PWRs where the reactivity is partly controlled by a boron salt dissolved in the water, and the influence of control rods with their local distortions of the neutron flux is less. Also a single fuel rod runs the full length of the core. When several rods or clusters of rods are stacked on top of one another in the same channel then the flux is distorted due to the gaps in the fuel, and higher fluxes and higher can temperatures result at the ends of the individual rods.

In light water moderated reactors the distinction between L and L' is hardly worth making. $L'-L$ is about 0.06 m in a channel length of at least 3 m.

The maximum fuel temperature

The maximum fuel temperature may be found in exactly the same way. From Chapter 3 we have equation (3.19) for the fuel centre to can surface temperature difference:

$$T_f - T_s = \frac{R}{4\pi k}\left[1 - \frac{2r_h^2}{(a^2 - r_h^2)} \ln(a/r_h)\right] + \frac{R}{2\pi a h_g} + \frac{R}{2\pi k_c} \ln(b/a).$$

Relating the linear rating R to the heat flux q by $R = q2\pi b$, and using equation (8.4) to replace T_s by T_z gives

$$T_f - T_z = \frac{qb}{2k}\left[1 - \frac{2r_h^2}{(a^2 - r_h^2)}\ln(a/r_h)\right] + \frac{qb}{h_g a} + \frac{qb}{k_c}\ln(b/a) + \frac{q}{h}$$

or

$$T_f - T_z = Bq = Bq_0 \cos(\pi z/L') \tag{8.11}$$

where

$$B = \frac{b}{2k}\left[1 - \frac{2r_h^2}{(a^2 - r_h^2)}\ln(a/r_h)\right] + \frac{b}{ah_g} + \frac{b}{k_c}\ln(b/a) + \frac{1}{h}.$$

Equation (8.11) has exactly the same mathematical form as equation (8.4), so when the maximum fuel temperature is found the steps in the analysis are the same except that $1/h$ must be replaced by B. Making this substitution in equation (8.9) the maximum fuel temperature is given by

$$\frac{T_{f,\max} - T_1}{T_2 - T_1} = \frac{1}{2} + \frac{1}{2}\left\{\left(\frac{mc\pi B}{L's}\right)^2 + 1\right\}^{1/2} \operatorname{cosec}(\pi L/2L'). \tag{8.12}$$

With uranium dioxide fuel by far the largest temperature difference occurs within the fuel itself, with the consequence that the maximum fuel temperature is found close to the centre of the core where the energy generation rate is highest. Similarly the highest can temperature reached in a loss-of-cooling accident is likely to be found near the centre of the core.

MINIMUM CRITICAL HEAT-FLUX RATIO

In water-cooled reactors the possibility of exceeding the critical heat flux is more important than any limitation on can temperature. Again the most severe conditions will be encountered in one of the central channels of the core, and within this channel the worst conditions will be found somewhat beyond the mid-point. As the water enters the channel and flows towards the mid-point the critical heat flux decreases, and the actual heat flux increases. So the critical heat flux ratio, i.e. critical heat flux divided by actual heat flux, steadily deteriorates. Beyond the mid-point the critical heat flux continues to fall (because the coolant enthalpy is still rising), but for a while the actual heat flux stays nearly constant. In consequence the minimum value of the critical heat flux ratio occurs somewhat beyond the centre of the channel (see Fig. 8.4).

Even with simplifying assumptions a general analysis of this problem is not possible, because there is no generally accepted correlation for critical heat flux. In what follows then we assume that a BWR is being designed to a specified minimum critical heat-flux ratio, that

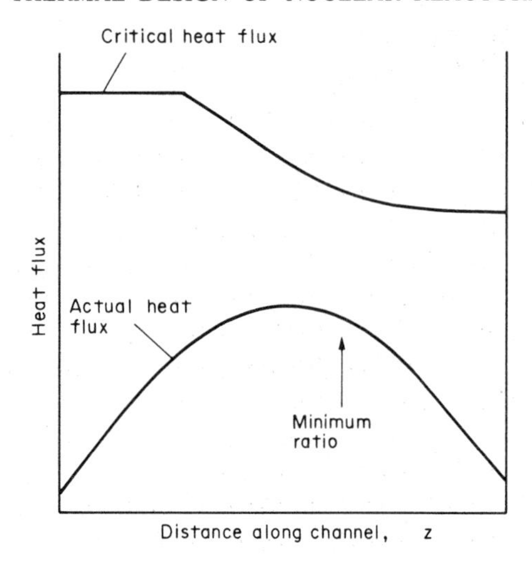

Fig. 8.4. Position of minimum critical heat-flux ratio.

the axial variation of power production follows a cosine function, and that the critical heat-flux correlation takes the form

$$q_{crit} = C - Dx \tag{8.13}$$

where C and D are constants and x is the steam quality (the Hench–Levy correlation, equations (5.26) and (5.27), takes this form at high mass velocities).

The local rate of heat input to the channel, and the total heat input from the channel inlet to a position z, are given by equations (8.1) and (8.2). The heat flux in the centre of the channel, q_0, that appears in these equations, may be replaced by the total channel power Q using

$$Q = \frac{2q_0 sL}{\pi} \sin(\pi L/2L')$$

(i.e. equation (8.2) with $z = L/2$).

For a water reactor it is reasonable to ignore the reflector savings and put $L = L'$, so

$$Q = \frac{2q_0 sL}{\pi}$$

and the total heat input up to z becomes

$$\frac{Q}{2}\{\sin(\pi z/L) + 1\}. \tag{8.14}$$

This energy is used partly in bringing the water up to its saturation temperature and partly in producing steam, so if the inlet subcooling is Δh we have

$$\frac{Q}{2}\{\sin(\pi z/L)+1\} = m\Delta h + xmh_{lv}$$

or

$$x = \frac{Q}{2mh_{lv}}\{\sin(\pi z/L)+1\} - \frac{\Delta h}{h_{lv}}. \tag{8.15}$$

Substituting this in equation (8.13) gives the critical heat flux as a function of distance along the channel:

$$q_{\text{crit}} = C - D\left[-\frac{\Delta h}{h_{lv}} + \frac{Q}{2mh_{lv}}\{\sin(\pi z/L)+1\}\right]. \tag{8.16}$$

Since the actual heat flux is $q_0 \cos(\pi z/L) = Q\pi/2sL \cos(\pi z/L)$ the critical heat flux ratio becomes

$$\frac{1}{\cos(\pi z/L)}\left[\frac{2sL}{Q\pi}\{C + D\Delta h/h_{lv}\} - \frac{sLD}{\pi m h_{lv}}\{\sin(\pi z/L)+1\}\right]. \tag{8.17}$$

To simplify subsequent working we will write this expression

$$\frac{\dfrac{E}{Q} - \dfrac{F}{m}\{\sin(\pi z/L)+1\}}{\cos(\pi z/L)} \tag{8.18}$$

where

$$E = \frac{2sL}{\pi}\{C + D\Delta h/h_{lv}\} \tag{8.19}$$

and

$$F = \frac{sLD}{\pi h_{lv}}. \tag{8.20}$$

To find the position where the minimum value of the critical heat flux ratio occurs expression (8.18) is differentiated with respect to z and the result set equal to zero. After some simplification the condition turns out to be

$$\sin(\pi z/L) = \frac{1}{(Em/FQ) - 1} \tag{8.21}$$

or

$$\sin(\pi z/L) = \frac{1}{2m\,(h_{lv}\,C/D + \Delta h)/Q - 1}\,. \tag{8.22}$$

To find the minimum value of the critical heat flux ratio equation (8.21) is substituted back into equation (8.18), using the standard relation $\cos(\pi z/L) = (1 - \sin^2(\pi z/L))^{1/2}$. Again some simplification of the resulting expression is needed, following which the minimum critical heat-flux ratio is found to be

$$\frac{E}{Q}\left\{1 - \frac{2FQ}{Em}\right\}^{1/2} \tag{8.23}$$

or

$$\frac{2sL}{\pi Q}\left\{C + D\Delta h/h_{lv}\right\}\left\{1 - \frac{Q}{(h_{lv}\,C/D + \Delta h)m}\right\}^{1/2}. \tag{8.24}$$

So, if the mass flow rate and total channel power are known, this expression gives the minimum critical heat-flux ratio. It is important to check that the values of x (given by equation (8.15)) and of G, the mass velocity, are consistent with the critical heat flux correlation used.

HOT-CHANNEL FACTORS

The rate at which heat is generated in different parts of the core depends on the local fuel enrichment and neutron flux, that is upon a reactor physics calculation. So far as the thermal design is concerned the most severe conditions will be encountered in one or more "hot" channels, where perhaps the heat flux will approach the maximum permissible value. The results of the reactor physics calculation are frequently presented in terms of hot-channel factors, which relate conditions in the "hot" channel to the average conditions for the whole core.

There is no general agreement on the definitions of these hot-channel factors, partly because the same information can be presented in more than one way, partly because a definition that is convenient for one reactor type may not be convenient for another. In water reactors where the heat output may be limited by the critical heat flux it is the maximum value of the heat flux that is of interest, and the following definitions are often used in connection with PWRs:

$$F_q^N = \text{nuclear heat flux factor} = \frac{\text{maximum heat flux in core}}{\text{mean heat flux in core}}, \tag{8.25}$$

$$F_z^N = \text{axial nuclear factor} = \frac{\text{maximum heat flux in hot channel}}{\text{mean heat flux in hot channel}}, \tag{8.26}$$

$$F_r^N = \text{radial nuclear factor} = \frac{\text{mean heat flux in hot channel}}{\text{mean heat flux in core}}. \tag{8.27}$$

It follows from the above definitions that

$$F_q^N = F_z^N F_r^N. \tag{8.28}$$

These nuclear factors are calculated on the assumption that everything is as specified in the design, but there are various reasons why the actual maximum core heat flux might be higher than the design value. For example, the fuel pellets might be denser than the nominal value, or larger, or more highly enriched. It is important to distinguish between random effects that are equally likely to increase or decrease the heat flux, and systematic effects that only work one way. In this case the variations in density, diameter and enrichment are all random within their respective tolerances, so there is no reason to suppose that the maximum values of all three quantities will occur simultaneously. This is now a statistical problem, and an engineering hot-channel factor F_q^E is defined to take all these effects into account.

So the total heat flux hot-channel factor (or hot-spot factor) is given by

$$F_q = F_q^N F_q^E = \frac{\text{actual maximum heat flux at core hot spot}}{\text{mean heat flux in core}}. \tag{8.29}$$

Values of F_q^E are typically around 1.06 [1].

In connection with BWRs a different terminology is often used. The radial factor is called the relative assembly power or the radial peaking factor. The axial factor is split into two parts: the axial peaking factor which is concerned with axial variation of heat flux in a given fuel rod; and the local peaking factor which is concerned with variation between rods in a given assembly at a given axial position. The total peaking factor is just the product of the other three factors.

Example 8.1. Find the axial nuclear factor for a reactor where the hot channel has a cosine distribution of heat generation with zero extrapolation distance.

The heat flux as a function of position is

$$q = q_0 \cos(\pi z/L)$$

where z is the distance beyond the centre point of the channel and L is the channel length.

The maximum heat flux occurs in the centre of the channel and is q_0. The average heat flux is

$$\frac{1}{L}\int_{-L/2}^{L/2} q_0 \cos(\pi z/L)\,\mathrm{d}z = \frac{q_0}{\pi}\Big[\sin(\pi z/L)\Big]_{-L/2}^{L/2} = \frac{2q_0}{\pi}$$

and the axial nuclear factor is given by

$$F_z^N = \frac{\text{maximum heat flux in hot channel}}{\text{mean heat flux in hot channel}} = \frac{\pi}{2} = 1.57.$$

If there is a significant extrapolation distance then the axial distribution will be flatter and the value of F_z^N slightly below 1.57. If the axial distribution is even less uniform than the simple cosine, such as might be caused in practice by the presence of a nearby control rod, then the value could be higher than 1.57.

A similar calculation could be done for the radial nuclear factor, using the heat flux distribution of a bare homogeneous cylindrical core with zero extrapolation distance which is

$$q = q_{\max} \cos(\pi z/L)\, J_0\, (2.404r/r_0)$$

where r is the radial distance from the centre line of the core, r_0 the outer radius and J_0 is the Besel function of the first kind of zero order. The result of this calculation would be a radial nuclear factor of 2.316 and hence an overall nuclear heat-flux factor of 3.638. However, in practice steps are taken to flatten the radial distribution in order to bring the power level of the outer assemblies closer to that of the hot channel, and so raise the total power output of the core. In enriched reactors this is done by using more highly enriched fuel in the outer channels, and even in natural uranium reactors some flattening is possible by putting the new fuel in the outer channels and using neutron absorber rods in the centre of the core. With radial flux flattening the fuel in a given channel, which is normally held in a single assembly for loading and unloading, is uniform in its properties. Axial flattening would require axial variations in enrichment or absorber material, and is not normally used.

In addition to the heat-flux hot-channel factors there are also enthalpy rise hot-channel factors, that relate the peak to the average enthalpy rise.

If all the channels in the reactor are of the same design and not fitted with gags or orifices (e.g. PWR), then there will be substantially the same mass flow through each. Consequently the variations in specific enthalpy rise will be in proportion to the variations in radial heat generation, i.e. F_r^N. More accurately, the overall enthalpy rise hot-channel factor is given by

$$F_{\Delta h} = \frac{\text{enthalpy rise in hottest channel}}{\text{core average enthalpy rise}} = F_r^N F_{\Delta h}^E \tag{8.30}$$

where $F_{\Delta h}^E$ is the engineering hot-channel factor for enthalpy rise. $F_{\Delta h}^E$ covers not only random variations in heat generation and mass flow, but also systematic effects due to some of the flow through the core by-passing the fuel channels and due to mixing of coolant between channels (the last effect is beneficial as far as the hot-channel is concerned since mixing must reduce the hot-channel temperatures).

While the various hot-spot factors are useful in preliminary design and in giving a quick idea of how successfully the neutron flux profiles have been flattened, the information they provide is too crude for many purposes. For example, if the minimum value of the critical heat-flux ratio is required, the total heat-flux hot-channel factor gives the maximum value of the actual heat flux in the core, which will be found close to the centre of the core, but the minimum critical heat-flux ratio does not occur at this position.

In gas-cooled reactors it is frequently the cladding temperature that is the limiting factor. The nominal maximum cladding temperature in the hottest channel is calculated on the basis that everything is as designed and for a smoothed heat-flux distribution along the channel. The various systematic effects that might cause the actual temperature to be higher than this are then considered. For example, if the individual fuel rods are quite short, and several clusters of rods are required to fill a channel, then the ends of the individual rods will receive a higher thermal neutron flux. This effect is called end peaking. Another systematic effect will arise if the channel is next to a control-rod position. The sum of the systematic effects is added to the nominal maximum temperature. Next the random effects due to the various manufacturing tolerances are combined statistically at a certain probability level and added on. This gives the actual maximum cladding temperature.

GAGS

In reactors that have physically distinct coolant channels it is usual to control the flow through individual channels by means of gags (orifices). Since it is convenient to make all the coolant channels and fuel assemblies the same then, in the absence of any special provision to restrict the flow, the mass flow rate through each channel would be the same. Consequently, the specific enthalpy of the coolant emerging from the channels near the edge of the core would be much lower than that coming from the hotter channels in the centre of the core. This is undesirable for two reasons: the mass flow rate through the edge channels is higher than that needed for adequate cooling and so the total mass flow through the core and the pumping power are unnecessarily high; also when the coolant from the various channels mixes together before arriving at the boilers its mean enthalpy is unnecessarily low. Consequently gags are fitted to match the mass flow rate in each channel to the heat input. In some circumstances it may be possible to restrict the flow in the peripheral channels even further, thus raising the coolant outlet temperature above that of the centre channels. This could apply in a gas-cooled reactor limited by a maximum permitted can temperature. The lower energy generation rates at the edge of the core mean that there is a low can to coolant temperature difference, and so higher coolant temperatures are acceptable.

In PWRs the bundles of fuel rods are not surrounded by a wrapper that would prevent cross flow, so it is not possible to control the flow past individual fuel bundles. This has the disadvantages mentioned above, but they are less serious than they might be in some other reactor types. With a liquid coolant the pumping power is relatively low, and the variation in enthalpy at the outlets of the different parts of the core is small simply because the enthalpy rise across the core is itself small.

SUBCHANNEL ANALYSIS

Earlier in this chapter the problem of the axial variation in heat transfer along a coolant channel was considered in some detail. The mass flow rate through the channel was assumed to have a known, constant, value (controlled by the gag setting). Also it was assumed that at any given axial position the coolant could be adequately described by a single value of the enthalpy and the fuel-rod surfaces by one temperature and one heat flux. For many reactor types these are reasonable assumptions, and many reactors have been designed and built using essentially this type of analysis, though with an accurately predicted axial variation of energy generation rather than a simple cosine.

If a more detailed analysis is required then the usual method of sub-dividing one of the main coolant channels is to define subchannels bounded by neighbouring fuel rods. This is done by drawing imaginary lines linking the centres of neighbouring rods, as in Fig. 8.5(a), where the subchannel in a fuel element with a square lattice is seen to be bounded by four fuel rods and four rod to rod gaps. Each subchannel can be assigned a different enthalpy value and, if required, each of the four cladding surfaces can have a different temperature. Calculation of the cladding temperatures will require some model to determine the fraction of the heat generated in each rod that flows through each section of the surface. Frequently it will be sufficient to assume a uniform radial flow of heat out of the fuel rods. The new feature that is introduced by subchannel analysis is that coolant may flow through the imaginary boundaries of the subchannel, taking heat and momentum with it.

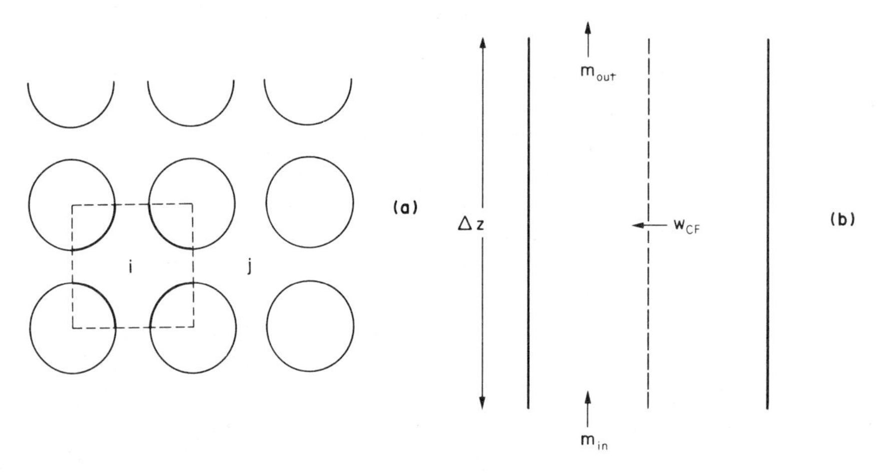

Fig. 8.5. Subchannel analysis: (a) construction of the subchannel, (b) mass flow rates in a simplification of the real situation: subchannel i is assumed to be only connected to subchannel j.

Subchannel analyses of one sort or another are now used as an aid to the design of all main reactor types. They are particularly important in PWRs where there are no separate main cooling channels, so an analysis is required in which an individual rod bundle is regarded as a subchannel. Also they are useful in reactors where the distribution of moderator around the fuel rods is not uniform, such as reactors moderated by graphite or heavy water where all or most of the moderator lies outside the fuel rod assembly. Thermal neutrons enter the cluster from outside. Some are absorbed in the outer rods of the cluster, so there is a lower neutron flux and a lower energy generation rate in the rods near the centre.

To perform the analysis it is first necessary to apply the conservation of mass, energy and momentum to each subchannel. The equations that follow are substantially the same as those used in a number of computer codes (e.g. [2], [3]). The subchannel i shown in Fig. 8.5(b) is, in fact, connected to four other subchannels, but to simplify the equations we will assume that it is only connected to subchannel j. It is a straightforward matter to include the extra terms for the other three channels. We assume that the inlet conditions are known (from the previous step in the calculation) and that the problem is to calculate the outlet conditions a distance Δz further up the channel.

If m is the mass flow rate in subchannel i then conservation of mass requires

$$m_{\text{out}} = m_{\text{in}} + w_{CF} \tag{8.31}$$

where w_{CF} is the cross-flow mass flow rate into subchannel i.

If h is the specific enthalpy of the coolant then conservation of energy requires

$$m_{out}h_{out} = m_{in}h_{in} + Q + w_{CF}h_{CF} + w_{mix}h_j - w_{mix}h_i \qquad (8.32)$$

where Q is the rate at which heat is supplied to the subchannel from the fuel rods, plus any direct γ-ray heating in the coolant. h_{CF} is the enthalpy associated with the cross flow and is h_j if w_{CF} is positive, i.e. flow into subchannel i, and it is h_i if w_{CF} is negative. w_{mix} is the flow associated with turbulent diffusion and is always positive. Note that there is an equal flow in each direction, so w_{mix} does not appear in equation (8.31). The enthalpies h_j and h_i are average values for the step, i.e. $h_i = (h_{in} + h_{out})/2$.

Conservation of momentum is applied in the form net force equals rate of change of momentum. With velocities denoted by u this gives

$$A\left[p_{in} - p_{out} - g\rho\Delta z - \frac{k}{2\rho}\left(\frac{m}{A}\right)^2 - \frac{1}{\rho}\left(\frac{m}{A}\right)^2\frac{2f\Delta z}{d_e}\right] = m_{out}u_{out} - m_{in}u_{in} \ldots$$

$$\ldots - w_{CF}u_{CF} - w_{mix}u_j + w_{mix}u_i. \qquad (8.33)$$

On the left-hand side of the equation there are terms for the pressure loss due to gravity, due to the support grid (if there is a grid in this step), and due to friction on the fuel-rod surfaces. k the grid loss coefficient and f the friction factor are functions of Reynolds number, but can be worked out from the known inlet conditions. The right-hand side of the equation can be interpreted as total momentum flowing out of the subchannel per second minus total momentum flowing in. As before, the properties of the cross flow depend on the direction of the cross flow. If $w_{CF} > 0$ then $u_{CF} = u_j$ and if $w_{CF} < 0$ then $u_{CF} = u_i$. Once again u_j and u_i are average values for the step.

Extension of the above equations to the case where subchannel i is connected to several other subchannels is simply a matter of adding cross-flow terms for each of the subchannels.

The difficulty with using the equations for the subchannel analysis lies of course in the cross flow and mixing terms, since the other terms are reasonably well understood. In a fully developed flow the transverse turbulent velocities are approximately a fixed fraction of the main forward velocity, so it is reasonable to suppose that w_{mix} is proportional both to the main subchannel velocity u and to the area available for transverse flow, i.e.

$$w_{mix} = \text{constant} \times \rho u \delta \Delta z \qquad (8.34)$$

where δ is the gap between neighbouring fuel rods. Some models of turbulent mixing agree with this equation, others have a weaker dependence on δ and an effect of subchannel geometry. The effect of grids is generally considered to be an increased level of turbulence and is allowed for simply by multiplying equation (8.34) by a constant factor (up to 2).

Cross flow is usually calculated from the difference in pressure between subchannels and a radial-loss coefficient. A complication in applying this principle is that there is an inertial effect, whereby the high axial velocity of the coolant makes it difficult for the coolant to move sideways and the cross flow is less than would be expected from the lateral pressure gradient [2,4]. These lateral pressure gradients are very small compared with the axial ones, and can lead to instabilities in the calculation since a very small pressure difference gives rise to a very large cross flow.

A considerable simplification results if it is assumed that there are no lateral pressure differences. The cross flow can now be calculated from the three conservations equations (as in the THINC-II computer code [2]). Applying the same reasoning to our simplified problem with only two interconnected subchannels, the unknown quantities are u_{out}, w_{CF}, h_{out} and p_{out} for each channel, eight unknowns in all (ρ is determined by h). The eight equations required are the three conservation equations for each channel plus $p_{out,j} = p_{out,i}$ and $w_{CF,j} = - w_{CF,i}$. The equations are non-linear, so an iterative method of solution is used. The equations are rearranged in such a way that it is possible to assume that various quantities in non-sensitive positions are unchanged from the previous step. The resulting equations are linear, and give first estimates of the unknown quantities.

For boiling coolants equation (8.33) needs to be modified; both the grid-loss coefficient and the friction factor should be multiplied by two phase friction multipliers. In Chapter 6 it was shown that the homogeneous theory provides a close approximation to the friction multiplier (equation (6.24)), and the same multiplier is often used for the grid term. However, an analysis based on these equations completely fails to predict the pronounced tendency for the voids in a two-phase flow to prefer to flow in the more open subchannels. To get reasonable agreement with experiment extra "void drift" terms must be added to each of the conservation equations [5]. The reason for this "void drift" phenomenon is not entirely clear.

INCREASING HEAT OUTPUT IN GAS-COOLED REACTORS

In this section we examine the ways in which the heat output of a gas-cooled reactor may be increased, given that the maximum can temperature is fixed by materials considerations, and that only a limited fraction of the gross power output may be consumed in the pumps.

The heat output per second from the core is the heat flux from the surface of the fuel cans times the total heat transfer surface area, or

$$Q = h\Delta TsL$$

where h is the heat-transfer coefficient, ΔT the average can to coolant temperature difference, s the total perimeter of the fuel cans and L their length. Using the definition of Stanton number, St, the equation becomes

$$Q = St\rho uc\Delta TsL. \tag{8.35}$$

The heat output can be increased by increasing any of the parameters in equation (8.35), though ΔT is limited by the maximum permitted can temperature, and L is equal to the height of the core and for maximum reactivity should be similar to the core diameter. The coolant velocity is limited by the pumping power needed to circulate the coolant.

Assuming that all the pressure drop is associated with the frictional resistance of the fuel can surfaces then the pumping power (equations (6.11) and (6.16)) is

$$P = \frac{1}{\rho_1} m\Delta p = \frac{1}{\rho_1} \frac{m}{\rho} \left(\frac{m}{A}\right)^2 \frac{2fL}{d_e}$$

where the density ρ_1 at the pump has been distinguished from the average density ρ in the core. Using the definition of equivalent diameter $d_e = 4A/s$, and the fact that mass flow rate $m = \rho A u$, the pumping power becomes

$$P = \rho u^3 \frac{fLs}{2} \frac{\rho}{\rho_1}. \tag{8.36}$$

Equations similar to these for Q and P have been used in a number of analyses [6], often with further restrictive assumptions such as that Reynolds analogy may be used to relate St and f [7], or that the channel mass flow rate is fixed [8]. In the analysis that follows no further restrictions are imposed.

Ideally an optimisation of the design would aim at a minimum cost for the electricity produced by the power station per kWhr, starting with known figures for the capital cost of the various components as a function of size and for the fuel costs. Without this information all we can say is that for a given reactor type the result of the optimisation is likely to show that a fixed fraction of the gross power output should be taken by the pumps. The problem then is to obtain the maximum possible heat out of the core with a given fraction of that output consumed in circulating the coolant.

Dividing equation (8.36) by equation (8.35) to find the P/Q ratio, and rearranging, we find that the coolant velocity is given by

$$u = \left[\frac{\rho_1}{\rho} \frac{P}{Q} \frac{2Stc\Delta T}{f}\right]^{1/2}. \tag{8.37}$$

So for a given reactor type (fixed c and ΔT) and given P/Q the velocity is almost constant. Substituting this expression back into equation (8.35) we finally obtain

$$Q = sL\left[2\rho\rho_1 c^3 \Delta T^3 \frac{St^3}{f} \frac{P}{Q}\right]^{1/2}. \tag{8.38}$$

Remembering that ΔT and P/Q are fixed, and ignoring the trivial possibility of increasing the heat output simply by increasing the size of the core, there are still a number of distinct methods of increasing Q:

(a) s can be increased for a given core size and fuel inventory by either using smaller fuel rods or by putting fins on the cans.

(b) Raising the pressure will increase ρ and hence Q in direct proportion.

(c) Roughening the fuel can surfaces will be worthwhile provided St^3 increases faster than f. In fact, this underestimates the benefit of surface roughening since not all of the pressure drop in the primary circuit is associated with the fuel can surfaces [9].

(d) Assuming that the analysis remains valid if we contemplate the more drastic step of changing the coolant, then the coolant properties come into the equation via the $\rho^2 c^3$ term (ignoring the weak dependence of St and f on Reynolds number; a more sophisticated analysis is available that includes this effect [10]). For a given temperature and pressure ρ is proportional to the molecular weight M and c is related to the molar specific heat c_m by $c_m = Mc$. So the property term becomes c_m^3/M. c_m is roughly constant for a gas with a given number of atoms in the molecule, and increases as the number of atoms in the molecule increases.

So from this point of view the best gas to use would be hydrogen (H_2) with a reasonable value of c_m and the lowest possible value of M. However, hydrogen is ruled out by its chemical activity and explosion hazard. The gases that actually are used, carbon dioxide and helium, have similar values of c_m^3/M at reactor temperatures.

While equation (8.38) gives the quantity of heat produced, it is important to bear in mind also the quality of the heat. Its usefulness in producing power depends on the temperature at which it is delivered to the boiler, that is on T_2.

Equation (4.16) gives

$$T_2 - T_1 = \Delta T St \frac{sL}{A}$$

so if the thermal performance is fixed, i.e. T_2, T_1 and ΔT are fixed, then increases in St or s will have to be offset by increases in the total flow area A (the same conclusion follows from equation (8.10)).

MAXIMISING STEAM PRODUCTION SUBJECT TO FIXED CRITICAL HEAT FLUX RATIO

The following example of maximising reactor heat output subject to constraints concerns a BWR. Assuming that the "hot" channel is limited by a minimum critical heat-flux ratio, and that the critical heat-flux correlation is of the form of equation (8.13), then the analysis earlier in this chapter is valid and we can use equation (8.23) as our starting-point:

$$N = \frac{E}{Q}\left\{1 - \frac{2FQ}{Em}\right\}^{1/2}$$

where N is the minimum critical heat flux ratio and E and F are given by equations (8.19) and (8.20).

Rearranging the equation gives

$$Q^2 + \frac{2FEQ}{mN^2} - \frac{E^2}{N^2} = 0.$$

Using the standard quadratic equation solution gives the total channel power output Q as

$$Q = -\frac{FE}{mN^2} \pm \left\{\left(\frac{FE}{mN^2}\right)^2 + \frac{E^2}{N^2}\right\}^{1/2}$$

and since we are only interested in the positive values of Q we can write

$$Q = \frac{FE}{mN^2}\left\{\left(1 + \frac{m^2N^2}{F^2}\right)^{1/2} - 1\right\}. \tag{8.39}$$

Q increases steadily with m, also if F and E are replaced using their defining equations, it can be shown that Q increases with s, the total perimeter of the fuel cans.

However, it is not Q as such that should be maximised, but rather the heat that is usefully applied in steam production. This is $Q - m\Delta h$ or

$$\frac{FE}{mN^2}\left\{\left(1 + \frac{m^2N^2}{F^2}\right)^{1/2} - 1\right\} - m\Delta h \tag{8.40}$$

where Δh is the inlet subcooling.

To find the mass flow rate that will give the maximum steam production expression (8.40) is differentiated with respect to m, giving

$$-\frac{FE}{m^2N^2}\left\{\left(1 + \frac{m^2N^2}{F^2}\right)^{1/2} - 1\right\} + \frac{FE}{mN^2}\,\frac{1}{2}\left(1 + \frac{m^2N^2}{F^2}\right)^{-1/2}\frac{2mN^2}{F^2} - \Delta h = 0,$$

i.e.

$$\frac{m^2N^2}{F^2}\left(1 + \frac{m^2N^2}{F^2}\right)^{-1/2} - \left(1 + \frac{m^2N^2}{F^2}\right)^{1/2} + 1 = \frac{\Delta h m^2N^2}{FE},$$

or

$$\left(1 + \frac{m^2N^2}{F^2}\right)^{-1/2}\left\{\frac{m^2N^2}{F^2} - 1 - \frac{m^2N^2}{F^2}\right\} + 1 = \frac{\Delta h m^2N^2}{FE}$$

so

$$m^2 = \frac{FE}{\Delta h N^2}\left\{1 - \left(1 + \frac{m^2N^2}{F^2}\right)^{-1/2}\right\}. \tag{8.41}$$

The easiest way to solve this equation is to note that in the region of interest the right-hand side of the equation varies comparatively slowly with m. For a first attempt at the solution m on the right-hand side can be replaced by a roughly guessed value of, say, 30 kg s^{-1}. The value of m obtained from this first attempt can now be used for a second, more accurate, attempt, and so on. In practice, only a couple of iterations are required. The value of N used with the Hench–Levy correlation is 1.9 (reference [5], p. 118).

The total channel power is now found from equation (8.39). The values of the mass velocity G and steam quality x must, of course, be checked against the limits of validity of the critical heat flux correlation used.

Although equation (8.41) gives the mass flow rate required to produce the maximum amount of steam, it does not follow that this value of m would be used in practice. This is a case where the maximum value of a quantity is a little misleading. When equation (8.40) is plotted as a function of m the maximum is seen to be rather flat. For example, at half the mass flow rate corresponding to maximum steam production, for typical BWR conditions, the rate of steam production is only reduced by about 20%. Since this is accompanied by a very much lower pressure drop and pumping power it might in practice be preferred.

References

1. TONG, L. S. and WEISMAN, J. Thermal analysis of pressurised water reactors. *Am. Nucl. Soc.* 1970, p. 240.
2. CHELEMER, H., WEISMAN, J. and TONG, L. S. Subchannel thermal analysis of rod bundle cores. *Nucl. Engng Design* **21,** 35–45 (1972).
3. WEISMAN, J. and BOWRING, R. W. Methods for detailed thermal and hydraulic analysis of water cooled reactors. *Nucl. Sci. Engng* **57,** 255–276 (1975).
4. TAPUCU, A. Studies on diversion cross-flow between two parallel channels communicating by a lateral slot. *Nucl. Engng Design* **42,** 297–306 (1977).
5. LAHEY, R. T. and MOODY, F. J. The thermal hydraulics of a boiling water nuclear reactor. *Am. Nucl. Soc.* 1977, p. 125.
6. MELESE-D'HOSPITAL, G. Merit index for gas-cooled reactor heat transfer. *Nucl. Sci. Engng* **50,** 83–85 (1973).
7. DIAMOND, J. and HALL, W. B. Heat removal from nuclear power reactors. *J. Brit. Nucl. Energy Conf.* **1,** 227–240 (1956).
8. WALKER, V. and WILKIE, D. The wider application of roughened heat transfer surfaces as developed for advanced gas-cooled reactors. *Symp. on High Pressure Gas as Heat Transport Medium*, Inst. Mech. Eng., London, Paper 26.
9. WILKIE, D. Criteria for choice of surface form for gas-cooled reactors. *Nucl. Engng Int.*, pp. 215–217 (1971).
10. LYALL, H. G. A comparison of helium and CO_2 as reactor coolants. *J. Nucl. Energy* **26,** 49–60 (1972).

Problems

1. A fuel assembly in a PWR contains 208 fuel rods, each 3.66 m long and 10.7 mm o.d., on a square lattice with a pitch of 14.4 mm. The total flow area in the assembly is 2.58×10^{-2} m^2. The water pressure and velocity are 150 bar and 4.8 m s^{-1} respectively.

   In a typical assembly the water enters at 290°C and leaves at 318°C. Find the value and position of the maximum temperature on the outside of the cladding. Assume a cosine distribution of heat generation with zero extrapolation distance, negligible radial variation and negligible cross flow between neighbouring fuel assemblies.
2. In the hottest channel of the PWR of question 1 the fuel assembly design is just the same, and the water pressure and flow rate are unchanged, but the heat output is higher. Water enters at 290°C and leaves at 335°C. At the same axial position where the maximum cladding temperature occurred in question 1 there is now local boiling. Confirm this and find the cladding temperature.
3. An experimental gas-cooled fast breeder reactor is being designed. The fuel channels are vertical, of length L, and the gas flows upwards past the roughened surface of the fuel cans also of length L. Roughening the surface increases the heat-transfer coefficient to a value α times that for a smooth surface. However, the friction factor is also greatly increased, so it is proposed to keep the bottom part of the fuel can smooth, since the can temperature there will be below the maximum permitted level even without the improved heat-transfer coefficient.

Derive an expression for the maximum can temperature in a channel where the mass flow rate is m, the heated perimeter of the fuel cans is s, and the can surface is roughened along the whole length. Assume a cosine distribution of heat generation along the channel with zero extrapolation distance.

Hence show that the transition from smooth to rough surface must occur below a position z given by

$$(1 + x^2)^{1/2} = \sin \frac{\pi z}{L} + \alpha x \cos \frac{\pi z}{L}.$$

z is the distance measured above the mid point of the channel, $x = \pi m\, c/Ls\alpha h$, c is the specific heat of the coolant and h the heat-transfer coefficient for the smooth surface.

4. A limitation on the design of gas-cooled reactors is the fact that an appreciable fraction of the gross electrical output may be required to drive the gas circulators. Assuming that the core inlet and outlet temperatures can be regarded as fixed, and that the work done by the circulators appears in the coolant as heat only after it has traversed the core, show that the net power produced is of the form $AW - BW^3$, where W is the coolant mass flow rate and A and B depend on the thermal efficiency, E, of the steam cycle (take $E = 0.4$ for the calculations). Friction factors may be assumed independent of W.

   What fraction of the gross power produced by the turbine will be required to drive the circulators if
   (a) the net power produced is to be a maximum?
   (b) the overall thermal efficiency (net power produced/heat produced by reactor) is to be a maximum?

5. The fuel assembly in a BWR has 49 fuel rods, 14.3 mm o.d. and 3.66 m long. The pressure is 69 bar and the inlet sub-cooling 12°C. If the channel is being designed to a minimum critical heat-flux ratio of 1.9, what mass flow rate will give the maximum steam production and what is the corresponding channel power?

   Assume that the second equation of the Hench–Levy critical heat-flux correlation applies, and that the mass velocity G is high enough for the correlation to become essentially independent of G. The distribution of heat generation follows a cosine with zero extrapolation distance.

   With half the mass flow rate calculated above, what would the channel power be?

   For each case calculate G (channel is square, 138 mm side), and steam quality at the position of the minimum ratio.

CHAPTER 9

Steam Cycles

INTRODUCTION

Nuclear reactors produce heat, but the desired end product in nearly all commercial reactors is electricity. The process for converting the heat to electricity is essentially the same for nuclear power stations as for coal- or oil-fired power stations. The heat is used to boil water, and the steam then expands through a turbine, driving the generator.

The temperatures in water-cooled reactors are much lower than in the boilers of conventional power stations. Consequently the steam is produced at much lower temperatures and the thermal efficiency is lower. Also, the steam tends to become too wet during its expansion through the turbine, and provision must be made for removing the water drops.

Gas-cooled reactors need a large pumping power to circulate the gas, because of the low coolant density. For a given heat output the mass flow rate and hence pumping power can be reduced if the core inlet temperature is lowered. However, this reduces the thermal efficiency of the steam cycle. An optimisation of the complete plant can only be done by considering the primary coolant circuit and the steam circuit together.

Although the energy conversion process does not follow the Carnot cycle, it is useful to bear the Carnot cycle efficiency in mind. It is $1 - T_c/T_h$, and applies to any reversible heat engine that receives all its heat at a temperature T_h and rejects heat entirely at T_c. For a high efficiency it is important to have T_h as high as possible, and T_c as low as possible. Although it may not be possible to supply all the heat at the highest temperature in the cycle and reject heat only at the lowest temperature, this ideal situation should be approached as closely as possible.

THE TEMPERATURE–ENTHALPY DIAGRAM

The steam generator, other than in the BWR, is a shell and tube heat exchanger, with the higher pressure fluid flowing inside the tubes, and the lower pressure fluid flowing round the outside of the tubes (a small tube can be designed to withstand a high pressure more easily than a large pressure vessel). The simplest arrangement is the counterflow heat exchanger where both fluids flow more or less axially along the length of the boiler, but in opposite directions. Changes of state within the boiler are often plotted as temperature versus change in total enthalpy or temperature versus distance along the boiler, as in Fig. 9.1. As drawn, with all the lines straight and a constant temperature in the water–steam mixture once boiling starts, the graph is for constant specific heats and negligible pressure drop. In the boiler the steady-flow energy equation reduces to the form: heat supplied = increase in enthalpy.

Since heat losses are negligible the gain in total enthalpy of the secondary coolant as it flows through is equal to the decrease in total enthalpy of the primary coolant. Between any two points in the steam generator

$$\Delta H_{\text{prim}} = \Delta H_{\text{sec}} \tag{9.1}$$

so a vertical line on the T versus ΔH graph represents physically adjacent points in the boiler.

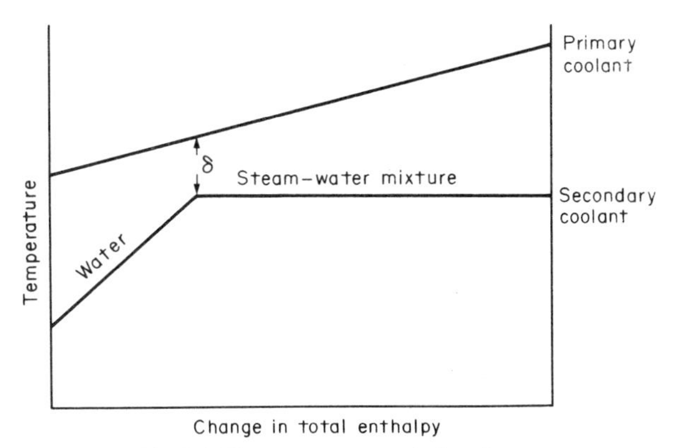

Fig. 9.1. The temperature enthalpy diagram.

A critical feature of the design is the pinch-point temperature difference, i.e. the closest approach of the two lines on Fig. 9.1. Everywhere in the heat exchanger the primary coolant must be hotter than the secondary coolant (or heat transfer would cease). The value of the pinch-point temperature difference is a compromise between having a small cheap boiler (high δ) and having a good steam cycle efficiency (small δ). If the steam is superheated before leaving the steam generator there is a second pinch point at the exit.

If the mass flow rates of the primary and secondary coolants are m_p and m_s then equation (9.1) becomes

$$m_p \Delta h_p = m_s \Delta h_s \tag{9.2}$$

and for rough calculations the changes of temperature can be expressed by $\Delta h = c\Delta T$.

An alternative to the counterflow heat exchanger would be to have the two fluids flowing in the same direction. With the same primary coolant temperatures and the same pinch-point temperature difference this arrangement would inevitably give worse steam conditions (lower temperature and pressure) and is not used in nuclear power stations. The flow arrangement actually used may be more complex than the simple counterflow pattern, and influenced by considerations of mechanical support and plant layout.

So far as the overall design of the plant is concerned the important temperatures are those at inlet and outlet of the boiler for each of the circuits, and the pinch-point temperature difference. It is not possible to specify each of these temperatures independently; equation

(9.2) must be satisfied and any one of the temperatures may be regarded as being determined by the others, as will be illustrated in the following example.

Example 9.1. Primary coolant from a PWR enters a counterflow steam generator at 310°C and leaves at 280°C. Dry saturated steam is produced at 50 bar. If the pinch-point temperature difference is 20°C, find the ratio of the mass flow rates in the primary and secondary circuits, and the temperature of the feed water. Neglect any pressure changes.

First we note that the saturation temperature at 50 bar is 263.9°C, so the bulk temperature of the steam–water mixture has this value all the way from the pinch-point to the steam outlet, as shown in Fig. 9.2. Further, since the pinch-point temperature difference is 20°C, the temperature of the primary fluid at the pinch point is 283.9°C. We can now apply equation (9.2) between the steam exit and the pinch point.

$$m_p\,[h_l\,(310°\text{C}) - h_l\,(283.9°\text{C})] = m_s h_{lv}(50b).$$

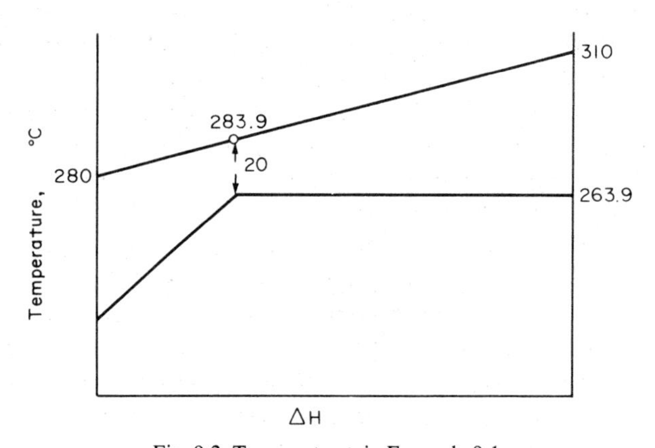

Fig. 9.2. Temperatures in Example 9.1.

The enthalpy change on evaporation, h_{lv}, is readily found in tables, but the water in the primary circuit is subcooled. Fortunately the properties of liquid water are almost independent of pressure, so there is little error in using saturated water properties at the correct temperature. This gives

$$m_p/m_s = 1639/(1402 - 1257) = 11.30$$

(values of h are in kJ kg^{-1}).

To find the feed water temperature we apply equation (9.2) between the feed water inlet and the pinch point.

$$m_p\,[h_l\,(283.9°\text{C}) - h_l\,(280°\text{C})] = m_s\,[h_l\,(50b) - h_l(T_f)]$$

or

$$11.3\,[1257 - 1237] = 1155 - h_l\,(T_f)$$

giving $h_l\ (T_f) = 929$, and the feed water temperature is found by reverse interpolation in the tables to be 216.8°C.

The above example shows that the primary circuit flow rate is much greater than that in the secondary circuit. This is because in the primary circuit the energy flow is accomplished by changes of temperature rather than by changes of phase.

THE BASIC RANKINE CYCLE

The simple ideal cycle on which the actual cycles are based is shown in Fig. 9.3 on the temperature entropy diagram, and in Fig. 9.4 the corresponding points are shown on the layout of the plant. Starting with water from the condenser, its pressure is raised in the pump (1–a). The high pressure water is heated up to boiling point in the first section of the boiler (a–2), and then turned into steam (2–3). The steam now expands through the turbine (3–4) and drives the generator. Lastly, the low-pressure steam is condensed back into water.

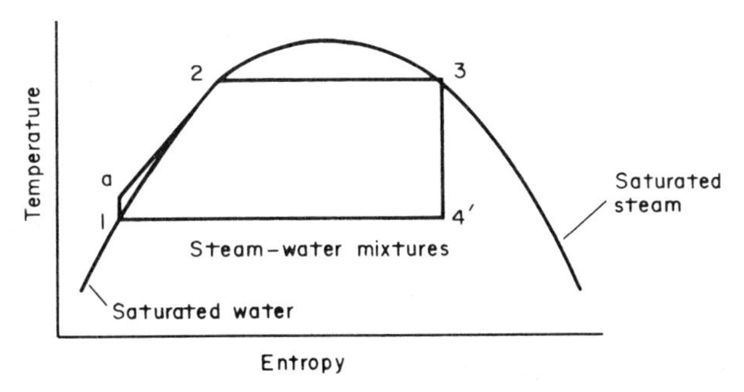

Fig. 9.3. The basic Rankine cycle.

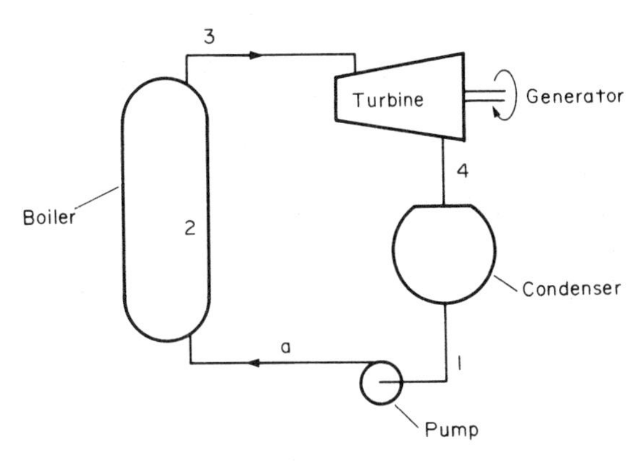

Fig. 9.4. The points of the Rankine cycle superimposed on the layout of the plant.

Since liquids are almost incompressible the increase in temperature on passing through the pump is in fact much smaller than indicated in the figure. Drawn to scale it would not appear at all, and process 1–2 would follow the saturation line. In the ideal cycle the expansion through the turbine is assumed to be isentropic (the prime indicates that 4′ represents the end point of the ideal expansion, not the actual condition of the steam at point 4).

Changes of potential and kinetic energy of the water/steam around the circuit are small and normally neglected, so the steady-flow energy equation reduces to

$$Q = W + \Delta H$$

and since in the turbine no heat is exchanged and in the boiler no work is done we have the simple relations: work out of the turbine equals the decrease in enthalpy of the steam; and, as before, heat supplied in the boiler equals the increase in enthalpy of the water/steam. The ratio of these two quantities is the thermal efficiency of the steam cycle. A high thermal efficiency is important because it means that a given electrical power output can be met with a smaller and cheaper nuclear plant.

In practice, of course, there is some increase in entropy as the steam expands through the turbine, and the simplest way to allow for this is to use an experimentally determined *isentropic efficiency*:

$$\text{isentropic efficiency} = \frac{\text{actual work out of turbine}}{\text{work out for an isentropic expansion}}$$

$$= \frac{\text{actual enthalpy drop in turbine}}{\text{enthalpy drop in an isentropic expansion}}.$$

Values of the isentropic efficiency are typically around 0.85.

In view of the importance of enthalpy values in steam cycle calculations it is useful to have a chart that gives enthalpy values directly. The enthalpy–entropy diagram (or Mollier chart) for unit mass of water/steam is shown in Fig. 9.5. The shape of this chart can be roughly

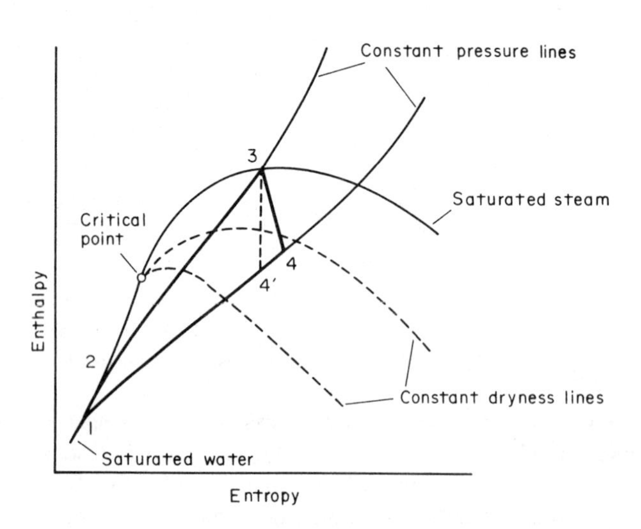

Fig. 9.5. Enthalpy–entropy diagram for unit mass of water/steam.

explained as a distorted version of the temperature–entropy graph. In the region where there is a mixture of water and steam the constant pressure lines rise steeply, since both enthalpy and entropy increase as the mixture changes from saturated water to saturated steam. The enthalpy increase in going from saturated water to a mixture with a dryness fraction x is xh_{lv}, and the entropy increase is xh_{lv}/T_{sat}, since entropy $= \int dQ/T$. Consequently the constant pressure lines in the wet steam region can be divided into equal intervals of dryness fraction x, and lines of constant dryness drawn on the chart. These are important because in practice the turbine will not operate satisfactorily if the steam is too wet.

The ideal Rankine cycle is shown in Fig. 9.5 with the isentropic expansion (dashed line) ending in point 4′, and the real expansion ending at point 4. If the inlet and outlet pressures of the turbine are known the procedure for finding points 4′ and 4 using the chart is as follows. Starting with the known steam condition at inlet to the turbine a vertical (isentropic) line is drawn down to the exhaust pressure to locate point 4′. The enthalpy at point 4 is found using

$$\text{isentropic efficiency} = \frac{h_3 - h_4}{h_3 - h_{4'}}$$

and 4 lies on the exhaust pressure line at the point where the enthalpy is h_4.

There are two reasons why excessive wetness in the steam in the turbine is undesirable. Firstly, the isentropic efficiency falls as the steam wetness increases, roughly at the rate of a 1% drop for each 1% increase in wetness. This is partly because the drops of water hitting the turbine blades tend to slow them down, but mostly because the steam and water are not in thermal equilibrium, resulting in additional losses due to heat transfer between the phases. Secondly, if the steam wetness rises much above 12% (i.e. dryness below 88%) the drops of water hitting the blades will cause unacceptable erosion. Since in practice only that part of the enthalpy–entropy chart lying above a dryness fraction of about 0.8 is used in finding the steam condition at the end of the turbine expansion, i.e. points 4 and 4′, the rest of the chart is normally omitted.

The thermal efficiency of the Rankine cycle is limited, as is that of the Carnot cycle, by the temperature T_h at which heat is added and by the temperature T_c at which heat is rejected. In most reactor designs T_h cannot be increased because of temperature limitations in the core. Water in particular is not a high-temperature reactor coolant. Since the critical temperature and pressure of water are 374°C and 221 bar respectively, there is little scope for increasing core outlet temperatures much above the present levels of 310° to 320° (PWR). If the water at the core outlet were brought up to the critical conditions the quite modest improvement in the temperature would be accompanied by one-fifth the density and nearly double the pressure. To achieve the same moderating effect with the reduced density the flow area between the fuel rods would have to be increased by a factor of 5. The increased capital cost of the larger, higher pressure, core would outweigh any improvement in thermal efficiency. In fact, a single pressure vessel to contain the core would be difficult to construct with present techniques.

The low temperature in the cycle is limited by the availability of cooling water. If cooling water at 15°C is available from the sea or a river and is allowed to rise in temperature to 25°C before discharge, and the pinch-point temperature difference in the condenser is 5°C, then the steam will condense at 30°C (saturation pressure 0.042 bar). Clearly it will not be possible to do much better than this, so T_c is largely fixed by the location of the power station and the time of year.

FEED WATER HEATING (REGENERATION)

Heat rejection in the Rankine cycle occurs entirely at the lowest temperature in the cycle, but not all of the heat in the boiler is supplied at the highest temperature; some heat is required to bring the feed water up to the boiling-point.

If the heat required between points 1 and 2 (Figs. 9.3 and 9.4) could be supplied internally within the cycle then all the heat supplied by the reactor would be at the highest temperature, the boiling-point, and for an ideal reversible cycle the efficiency would equal that of the Carnot cycle.

The way in which this is done is to extract some of the steam at intervals in the turbine, and use this steam to warm the feed water in a number of feed heaters, as shown in Fig. 9.6. The two feed heaters shown are of the closed type, that is, they are shell and tube heat exchangers with the steam and water flows kept separate. The condensed steam from the higher temperature heater is throttled to the pressure of the steam in the next, lower temperature, feed heater, and mixed with it. The other type of feed heater is the open or direct contact feed heater where the steam bled off from the turbine and the feed water are simply mixed together.

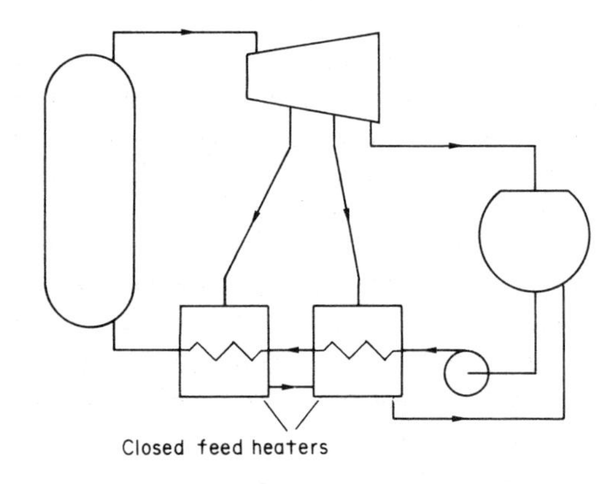

Fig. 9.6. Improvement of Rankine cycle using feed heating.

From the thermodynamic point of view it is wasteful to supply heat at an unnecessarily high temperature, so in practice as many as six or seven feed heaters will be used, so that the temperature of the steam in each one is only slightly above that of the feed water. Most of the feed water heaters are normally of the closed type, since in the closed heater there is no need to have the steam and the feed water at the same pressure, and one feed water pump can supply a series of closed feed water heaters. A train of open feed water heaters on the other hand would require an extra pump after each heater.

To simplify calculations involving feed water heaters it is often assumed that they are perfect heat exchangers, i.e. that there is no pinch-point temperature difference between the primary and secondary sides. So the temperature of the feed water leaving equals that of the condensed steam (i.e. equals the saturation temperature of the bled steam).

In a conventional power station the feed water is in fact brought very close to the boiling-point before entering the boiler. In a nuclear power station, as we shall see later, the feed water temperature is somewhat lower.

PRACTICAL CYCLES FOR WATER REACTORS

The properties of water and steam cannot be accurately expressed by simple equations, so it is difficult to use analytical methods to derive, for example, an equation for the thermal efficiency of a steam cycle. Instead the calculation proceeds from first principles using tabulated values of properties where necessary. In order to derive the maximum benefit from comparing the results of different calculations all the examples will assume that the steam enters the turbine dry saturated at a pressure of 50 bar, and that the condenser pressure is 0.05 bar. The 50-bar value is fairly typical of PWRs, with some older reactors having a slightly lower pressure. A pressure of 65 bar would be more typical of BWRs, but the difference between 50 and 65 is insufficient to affect any of the general conclusions that follow. The condenser pressure is of course independent of reactor type.

The simplest steam cycle would use a straight expansion from the saturated steam at 50 bar to the condenser pressure. If this is attempted on the enthalpy–entropy chart it immediately becomes clear that this would give excessively wet steam at the end of the expansion. In fact, with an isentropic efficiency of 0.85, the wetness would reach 27% (off the bottom end of the normal h–s chart). It is therefore necessary to expand the steam in at least two stages, perhaps with a high-pressure turbine giving steam of about 12% wetness at the outlet, followed by a moisture separator and then a low-pressure turbine. This arrangement of the plant still gives steam that is slightly too wet at the exhaust of one or other or both of the turbines, so a small amount of either extra moisture separation or of reheat is required. There are three main possibilities:

(a) Use three turbines and two moisture separators.

(b) Keep the two turbines and one moisture separator, but use internal moisture separation to remove additional water within the turbines.

(c) Keep the two turbines and one moisture separator, but use a reheater to superheat the steam after the moisture separator. The superheated steam can expand some way through the low-pressure turbine before it starts to condense, and the exhaust steam is drier.

All three solutions have been used, but (b) and (c) are preferred, (b) because of its simplicity and (c) because the drier steam gives a slightly higher thermal efficiency [1,2]. For the examples we will use method (c), assuming in addition reheat using live steam straight from the boiler to 240°C (since the steam from the boiler at 50 bar condenses at 263.9°C, the temperature of the main steam flow leaving the reheater must be less than this, and a pinch-point temperature difference of around 20°C is normal). The following example is of a cycle without regeneration.

Example 9.2. The boiler of a nuclear power station produces dry saturated steam at 50 bar. The steam expands in the high-pressure turbine to 7 bar. Moisture in then removed in a moisture separator and the dry steam reheated to 240°C before expansion in the low-pressure turbine to the condenser pressure of 0.05 bar. The reheater is of the live steam type, that is, heat is supplied by a proportion of the high-pressure steam taken straight from the boiler, in a shell and tube heat exchanger. The condensed water from the reheater, and the water from the moisture separator, are combined with the water from the condenser and returned to the boiler. See Fig. 9.7 for the layout of the plant.

If the isentropic efficiency of the turbines is 0.85, what is the steam dryness at the exhaust of each of the turbines?

Calculate the thermal efficiency of the cycle. Neglect any pressure drop through the moisture separator or reheater, and any work required in the pumps.

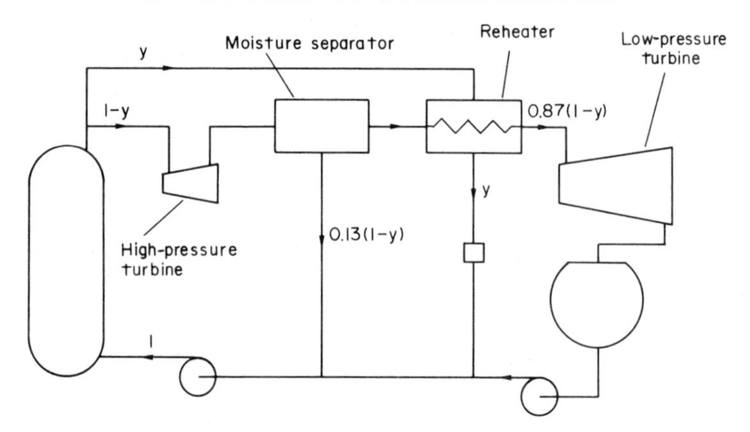

Fig. 9.7. Layout of plant for Example 9.2.

The path followed by the steam in the expansion is sketched on the enthalpy–entropy chart in Fig. 9.8. Starting with saturated steam at 50 bar, an isentropic expansion to 7 bar intersects the constant-pressure line at an enthalpy value of 2442 kJ kg^{-1}. This value can either be read off the chart, or it can be calculated as follows.

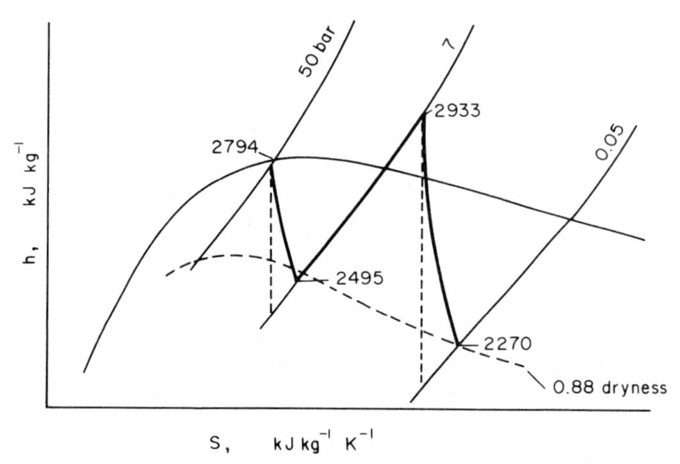

Fig. 9.8. Path followed by steam in the expansion of Example 9.2.

If the dryness fraction of the mixture is x then unit mass of the mixture contains a mass x of steam and $(1 - x)$ of water, and any specific property of the steam–water mixture can be expressed in terms of the specific properties of pure saturated water and of pure saturated steam by:

$$\text{mixture value} = x\,(\text{steam value}) + (1 - x)\,(\text{water value}).$$

First we assume an isentropic expansion and find the dryness fraction x_i that would result.

$$s_v(50\text{ bar}) = s_{\text{mixture}}(7\text{ bar}) = x_i s_v(7\text{ bar}) + (1 - x_i)s_l(7\text{ bar}),$$

$$5.973 = 6.709x_i + 1.992(1 - x_i),$$

$$x_i = 0.8440.$$

The enthalpy at the end of the expansion is given by

$$\begin{aligned} h_i &= x_i h_v(7 \text{ bar}) + (1 - x_i)h_l(7 \text{ bar}) \\ &= 2764x_i + 697(1 - x_i) \\ &= 2442 \text{ kJ kg}^{-1}. \end{aligned}$$

The actual enthalpy drop is only 0.85 of the isentropic drop, so if the enthalpy at the end of the real expansion is h_a

$$\frac{h_v(50 \text{ bar}) - h_a}{h_v(50 \text{ bar}) - h_i} = \frac{2794 - h_a}{2794 - 2442} = 0.85$$

giving $h_a = 2495$ kJ kg^{-1}.

The intersection of this value with the 7-bar pressure line on the chart shows that the steam dryness at this point is about 0.87, or a wetness of 13%.

Alternatively, using tables rather than the chart, the actual dryness at the end of the expansion x_a is given by

$$\begin{aligned} h_a &= x_a h_v(7 \text{ bar}) + (1 - x_a)h_l(7 \text{ bar}) \\ &= 2764x_a + 697(1 - x_a), \end{aligned}$$

so $x_a = 0.870$.

The drops of water are now removed in the moisture separator, and the dry steam (only 0.870 of the flow through the high-pressure turbine), still at 7-bar pressure, is heated up to 240°C in the reheater. Its enthalpy at this point, either read directly off the chart or found by interpolation in the tables is 2933 kJ kg^{-1}.

The expansion through the low-pressure turbine is treated in exactly the same way as the expansion through the high-pressure turbine. The enthalpy values are shown in Fig. 9.8 and the steam dryness at the end of the expansion is 88.0%.

The next problem is to find the mass flow rates in the various parts of the circuit. Consider what happens to 1 kg of steam leaving the boiler. Suppose a fraction y is taken off straight to the reheater. Then the other flows will be as shown in Fig. 9.7.

The value of y is found from an energy balance on the reheater. In the reheater steam at 50 bar condenses, with an enthalpy decrease of 1639 kJ kg^{-1}, and in the process warming up saturated steam at 7 bar (enthalpy 2764 kJ kg^{-1}) to 240°C. Equating heat transferred from one side to the other,

$$1639y = 0.87(1 - y)(2933 - 2764)$$

and $y = 0.0823$.

We now have the steam enthalpies at inlet and outlet of each turbine, and the mass flow rates, so the work output of the two turbines per kg of steam leaving the boiler is

$$(1 - y)(2794 - 2495) + 0.87(1 - y)(2933 - 2270) = 803.7 \text{ kJ kg}^{-1}.$$

To find the heat added in the boiler we need to know the enthalpy of the feed water entering the boiler, h_f. This is given by

$$\begin{aligned} h_f &= 0.87(1-y)h_l(0.05 \text{ bar}) + yh_l(50 \text{ bar}) + 0.13(1-y)h_l(7 \text{ bar}) \\ &= 0.87(1-y)138 + y1155 + 0.13(1-y)697 \\ &= 288 \text{ kJ kg}^{-1}. \end{aligned}$$

In the boiler this water is turned into saturated steam, so the heat added is $2794 - 288 = 2506$ kJ kg^{-1}.

The thermal efficiency is

$$\frac{\text{net work out}}{\text{heat supplied}} = \frac{803.7}{2506} = 0.321.$$

The next example gives some idea of the improvement in thermal efficiency that can be obtained by using feed heating. It can be shown that if only one feed heater is used the best results are obtained by heating the feed water half-way to the saturation temperature. The optimum point to bleed the steam off turns out to be about half-way through the expansion, quite close to the end of the high-pressure turbine.

Example 9.3. The cycle described in Example 9.2 is improved by adding an open feed heater immediately before the boiler. The feed heater is supplied with steam from the exhaust of the high-pressure turbine. Neglecting any work required in the pumps calculate the proportion of the steam from the boiler that must be bled off to the reheater and to the feed heater. What is the new thermal efficiency?

The enthalpy values at the various points in the expansion through the turbines are unchanged from the previous example, so they are still as shown in Fig. 9.8. The flow rates in the various parts of the circuit will be different, however. If for each 1 kg of steam leaving the boiler y kg go to the reheater and z kg to the feed heater, then the flows are as shown in Fig. 9.9.

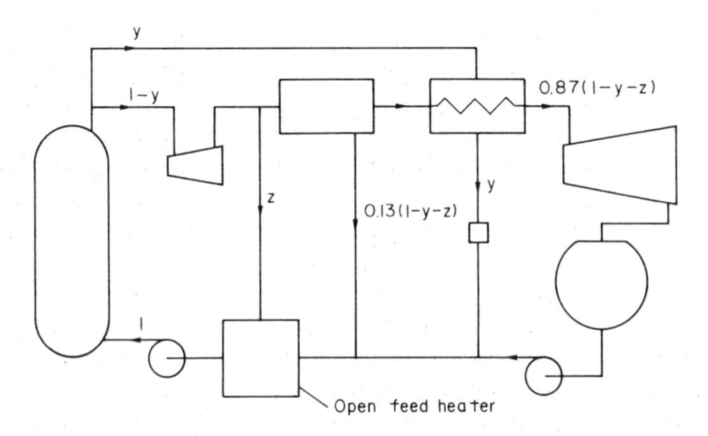

Fig. 9.9. Layout of plant for Example 9.3.

The values of y and z come from energy balances on the reheater and feed heater. Considering first the reheater we havc, much as in the previous example,

$$1639y = 0.87(1 - y - z)(2933 - 2764).$$

In the open feed heater, as in the closed, it is assumed in the ideal case that the condensing steam warms the feed water up to the condensation temperature, i.e. the enthalpy of the feed water leaving is h_l at 7 bar (697 kJ kg^{-1}). This enthalpy is the result of combining four streams:

$$697 = zh\,(\text{h.p. turbine exhaust}) + 0.13(1 - y - z)h_l(7\text{ bar}) + yh_l(50\text{ bar}) + 0.87(1 - y - z)h_l(0.05\text{ bar}),$$

i.e.

$$697 = 2495z + 0.13(1 - y - z)697 + 1155y + 0.87(1 - y - z)138.$$

Solution of the two simultaneous equations for y and z gives

$$\underline{y = 0.0681} \qquad \text{and} \qquad \underline{z = 0.1730.}$$

The work done in the two turbines is

$$(1 - y)(2794 - 2495) + 0.87(1 - y - z)(2933 - 2270) = 716.4\text{ kJ kg}^{-1}.$$

The heat added is $2794 - 697 = 2097$ kJ kg^{-1}.

The *thermal efficiency* is $716.4/2097 = \underline{0.342.}$

A gross thermal efficiency of around 0.34 is in fact typical of water-cooled nuclear reactors, and is close to the best that could be expected for the temperatures involved.

In practice, the cycle is further improved by using several feed heaters. Also the reheating is often done in two stages, first using steam taken from part of the way through the high-pressure turbine, and then using steam direct from the boiler.

PUMPING POWER AND OTHER LOSSES

The pumping power is given in terms of the pressure rise across the pump, Δp, and the overall pump efficiency, η, by $mv\Delta p/\eta$ (equation (6.12)). There are pumps in both primary and secondary circuits, but confining ourselves for the moment to the secondary circuit, we can get an idea of the magnitude of the pumping power by applying the equation to Example 9.2.

In that example there are two pumps, one handling the full flow just before the boiler and raising the pressure from 7 to 50 bar, the other taking $0.87(1 - y)$ of the flow and raising the pressure from 0.05 to 7 bar. The specific volume of water at these two points is 0.001 023 and 0.001 005 m^3 kg^{-1} respectively, so if the efficiency of the pumps is 0.75 the total pumping power per 1 kg of steam leaving the boiler is

$$\frac{1}{0.75}[0.001\,023 \times 43 \times 10^5 + 0.87(1 - y) \times 0.001\,005 \times 6.95 \times 10^5] = 6.61\text{ kJ kg}^{-1}.$$

So from this point of view the useful work out of the steam cycle is reduced to 803.7 − 6.6 = 797.1 kJ kg^{-1}.

Next we must consider what happens to the energy supplied to the pumps. Most of it goes into the water. Assuming that all of it goes into the water the energy that has to be supplied by the boiler is consequently reduced to 2506 − 6.6 = 2499.4 kJ kg^{-1}. The thermal efficiency of the steam cycle is reduced to 797.1/2499.4 = 0.319 (compared to 0.321 when the pumping power was ignored).

The pumping power in the above example amounted to less than 1% of the power output of the turbine, and although we assumed an overall pump efficiency of 0.75 it would make little difference to the Rankine cycle efficiency if we had assumed 0.5 or 1.0. This is the great practical advantage of the Rankine cycle over any cycle that involves compression of a gas or vapour.

For example, a Carnot cycle could be constructed using water/steam as the working fluid, and it would look much as the Rankine cycle in Fig. 9.3, except that the low-temperature heat addition would be avoided by not condensing the steam completely and then compressing the steam/water mixture isentropically to point 2. The thermal efficiency of the ideal isentropic Carnot cycle would be greater than that of the ideal isentropic Rankine cycle. However, the net work out of the Carnot cycle is the work out of the turbine minus the work required in the compressor, and the two terms are of comparable magnitude. In the real cycle the turbine work is reduced, the work required in the compressor increases, and the net work is much less than in the ideal cycle.

It is not possible to calculate the pumping power for the primary circuit without further information. The much smaller pressure rise required in the primary pumps is determined by the frictional resistance to flow round the circuit. However, because of the much higher mass flow rate, the total power required by the primary pumps is comparable with that needed by the secondary pumps (for water cooled reactors).

Another loss arises from the fact that the steam leaves the turbine at a high velocity, carrying a small but significant amount of kinetic energy with it. This is called the leaving loss. The steady-flow energy equation for the turbine, including the kinetic energy terms, is

$$0 = \Delta h + \tfrac{1}{2}\Delta u^2 + W,$$

or

$$W = h_{in} - h_{out} + \tfrac{1}{2}u_{in}^2 - \tfrac{1}{2}u_{out}^2. \tag{9.3}$$

It is difficult to reduce the leaving velocity to the point where $\frac{1}{2}u_{out}^2$ is negligible because of the extremely high volumetric flow rate at the exhaust of the low-pressure turbine. The specific volume of saturated steam at 0.05 bar is 715 times the value at 50 bar, and this ratio is only slightly reduced when account is taken of the water drops in the exhaust steam. The length of the blades in the low-pressure turbine, and hence the flow area available, is limited by centrifugal stresses in the blades. In order to handle the large flow rates without excessive velocities it is common to split the flow between four or even six low-pressure turbine cylinders, compared to just one high-pressure cylinder (pairs of turbine cylinders, with flow in opposite directions in the two members of the pair, are favoured since the end thrusts cancel). It is not economic to have even more low-pressure sections, and in practice there is a small leaving loss. An incidental advantage of feed heating is that the flow rate at the exhaust of the low-pressure turbine is reduced for the same power output.

There are other small losses due to pressure drop through valves, moisture separators and so on. When these pressure drops are known they can be incorporated in the steam-cycle calculation. Considering the station as a whole there are various other pieces of equipment that consume power, and the total extra power required may be comparable with that required by the main primary and secondary pumps (this is not true for gas-cooled reactors where the power required by the primary pumps dominates everything else).

RADIOACTIVE STEAM IN THE BWR

The boiling water reactor is unique in not having a separate secondary circuit. The steam in the turbine contains radioactive nitrogen-16, which emits high-energy β and γ radiation. The N^{16} is formed in an (n,p) reaction in the core from the main oxygen isotope in water, i.e.

$$_8O^{16} + {}_0n^1 \rightarrow {}_7N^{16} + {}_1H^1. \tag{9.4}$$

The level of radiation is high enough to prevent access to the turbine during operation.

The half-life of N^{16} is only 7 s, so the radiation level falls very quickly after shutdown. Also it is feasible to incorporate a storage tank after the condenser, to allow the N^{16} time to decay before it reaches the feed heaters. A 2-minute delay will reduce the N^{16} activity to

$$\left[\frac{1}{2}\right]^{120/7} = 6.9 \times 10^{-6}$$

of its previous level.

Clearly any long-lived activity will come from other isotopes. In practice it is isotopes of heavy elements present in solid particles that may cause trouble, if these particles can circulate through the core and later come to rest in the turbine. It is important to filter out particles and to design the turbine so that there are no pockets or cracks where they might get trapped.

CYCLES FOR HIGH-TEMPERATURE REACTORS

Modern designs of gas- or liquid-metal-cooled reactors are not limited by the temperatures that are available in the core of the reactor, and consequently have almost the same steam conditions as coal- or oil-fired power stations. The limitation now comes from the maximum temperatures that the boiler tubes can withstand. In the U.K. this means that the steam at inlet to the turbine is at around 560°C and 160 bar, regardless of the type of power station. Since 560°C is well over the critical temperature of water there is no question of using saturated steam. The highly superheated steam has the advantage that it does not get so wet in the expansion through the turbine. However, as inspection of the enthalpy–entropy chart will confirm, a straight expansion to the condenser pressure would give excessive wetness at the end of the expansion. It is normal therefore to take the steam back to the boiler after it has been through the high-pressure turbine for one stage of reheat.

NET PLANT EFFICIENCY

The net plant efficiency, defined as electrical power sent out of the power station divided by the rate at which heat is supplied by the reactor, is not very different to the steam-cycle efficiency, but is lower because of power consumed by the primary circuit pumps and a variety of other ancillary equipment. In gas-cooled reactors, because of the low density of the coolant, 5% or more of the gross power output of the turbines is needed to circulate the primary coolant. Since pumping power is proportional to mass flow rate cubed (equation (6.14)) it is not possible to raise the mass flow rate much above the design value. The effect of this is that the optimum feed-water temperature is much lower than it would be in a conventional station.

Figure 9.10 illustrates the disadvantage of using too high a feed-water temperature. Increasing the temperature from T_f to T'_f for fixed steam conditions at outlet from the boiler and fixed pinch-point temperature differences requires a higher temperature at inlet to the reactor (reactor outlet temperature is normally fixed by materials considerations). The rate at which heat is transferred on the primary side of the boiler is given by $mc(T_2 - T_1)$, so if T_1 is increased it will be necessary to increase m to keep the same rate of heat supply. The increased pumping power may outweigh the improved steam cycle efficiency.

In practice a net plant efficiency of around 32% would be typical for a water-cooled reactor, 41% for an advanced or high-temperature gas-cooled reactor. While this gives the gas-cooled reactor a definite advantage it does not completely offset the lower core power densities associated with gas cooling.

A higher thermal efficiency implies a lower cooling-water requirement. A 1000-MW(e) plant with a net efficiency of 32% will reject 1000(68/32) MW(t) of heat, whereas the 41% efficient plant will only reject 1000(59/41) MW(t). The cooling-water flow needed by the more efficient plant is therefore only

$$\frac{59}{41}\frac{32}{68} = 0.68$$

times as much as that of the less efficient plant.

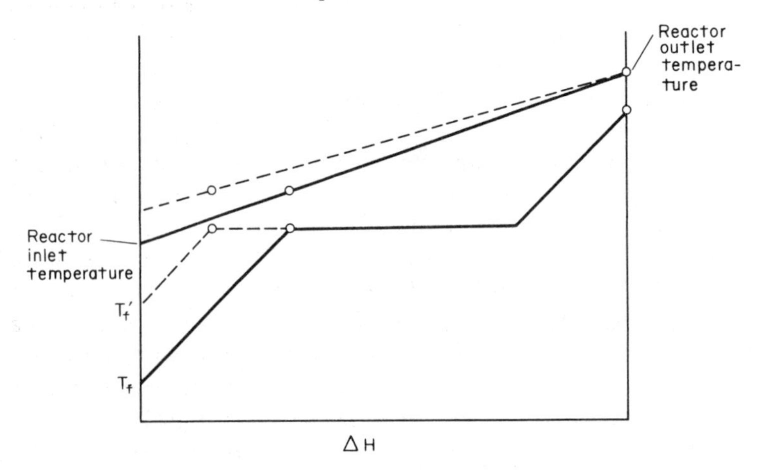

Fig. 9.10. Disadvantage of too high a feed water temperature T_f.

COMBINED HEAT AND POWER GENERATION

Nuclear power stations inevitably produce large quantities of waste heat, and the question naturally arises as to whether this heat could be used for something. For efficient generation of electricity the temperature of the condensing steam must be low and, as we saw earlier, the temperature of the cooling water leaving the condenser is likely to be about 25°C. This temperature is too low to be of much practical use. If the heat is to be used for space heating in homes or commercial premises it will have to leave the power station at approaching 100°C. This will inevitably reduce the efficiency of the station from the point of view of electricity generation, but by how much?

To take a simple example, suppose that the condenser pressure in Example 9.2 was raised to 1.2 bar (saturation temperature 104.8°C), but everything else kept the same. It turns out that the thermal efficiency drops to 0.223, so for each MW of heat supplied by the reactor we get only 0.223 MW of electrical power instead of 0.321 MW. However, we now have (1 − 0.223) = 0.777 MW of heat in addition, as opposed to no usable heat at all when the steam condensed at 0.05 bar.

Expressing this result as heat gained divided by electricity lost, the ratio is 0.777/(0.321 − 0.223) = 7.9. While electricity is certainly more valuable than heat it is not 7.9 times as valuable, so potentially the combined generation of heat and power is more economic than providing the two separately.

A power station producing 1000 MW of heat could supply 200,000 homes with 5 kW each, and although the inclusion of commercial and industrial premises would reduce the size of town implied by these figures, the distribution of such a quantity of heat is clearly an immense undertaking if there are no existing district heating schemes. In countries where there is a tradition of district heating, using large communal boilers, it is easier to connect up the large heating load required. Combined heat and power schemes are extensively used in, for example, West Germany and the U.S.S.R., and in Denmark 10% of homes are supplied by such schemes [3]. Heat from nuclear power stations has not been used in this way in the past because nuclear stations tend to be further away from centres of population. With large insulated pipe lines hot water can be conveyed considerable distances, however, with losses of less than 1% per km, and the economies of scale that are obtained with very large power stations are such that there would be no incentive to use smaller stations closer to the points where the heat is required. In the U.K. it has been thought [4] that the cost of setting up the distribution network would not be justified, though with such a capital intensive scheme the conclusion depends very much on the rate of interest that is assumed.

The modified turbine that we used earlier for the calculation is described as a *back-pressure* turbine, since there is an appreciable back pressure set up opposing the flow of steam through the turbine. This system has the disadvantage that for a given hot-water temperature, i.e. given condenser pressure, the ratio of electricity produced to heat produced is fixed. In practice a combined heat and power station would probably use a *pass-out* turbine, where some of the steam is extracted from the turbine before it reaches the condenser, and is used to heat up the water required for the district heating scheme. This has the advantage of greater flexibility in the ratio of electricity to heat. Although the maximum demands for heat and electricity are likely to occur at roughly the same time, it is possible to increase the electricity production for short periods to its maximum level without significantly affecting the heat received by the consumers, because of the large quantity of heat stored in the pipes of the distribution network.

References

1. BAILY, F. G. and MILLER, E. H. Modern turbine designs for water cooled reactors. *Nucl. Engng*, pp. 29–32 (Jan. 1967).
2. HARRIS, F. R. Nuclear wet-steam turbines (in *Convention on steam plant for the 70s*). *Proc. Inst. Mech. Engrs* **183,** Part 30, 14–23 (1968–9).
3. *The Heating and Air Conditioning Journal*, June 1977, pp. 24 and 42.
4. DEPARTMENT OF ENERGY. District heating combined with electricity generation in the U.K., Energy Paper no. 20, 1977.

Problems

1. Analyse the following cycle to find steam dryness at the end of each of the expansions and thermal efficiency.

   The high-pressure turbine receives dry saturated steam at 60 bar and expands it to 10 bar. Moisture is then removed in a moisture separator and the steam reheated to 260°C (specific enthalpy at this point is 2965 kJ kg^{-1}) before expansion in the low-pressure turbine to the condenser pressure of 0.06 bar. The reheater uses steam straight from the boiler. The condensed water from the reheater, and the moisture from the moisture separator, are combined with the water from the condenser and returned to the boiler.

   The isentropic efficiency of each of the turbines is 0.83. Ignore any other sources of loss.
2. A gas-cooled nuclear power station has the following steam conditions. Temperature and pressure at inlet to turbine 560°C and 160 bar respectively, condenser pressure 0.04 bar.

   Show that reheat is necessary (assume an isentropic efficiency of 0.84).

   If the steam is expanded to 35 bar in the high-pressure turbine, then reheated to 540°C, before final expansion in the intermediate and low-pressure turbines, and there is one contact feedheater which is heated by steam from the h.p. turbine exhaust, calculate:

   (a) steam wetness leaving the low-pressure turbine,

   (b) fraction of the steam mass flow that is bled off to the feedheater,

   (c) the thermal efficiency of the cycle.

   Ignore any pressure drop in the reheater.
3. The primary coolant from a water-cooled nuclear reactor enters a once through, counterflow, steam generator at 325°C and leaves at 295°C. Dry saturated steam at 65 bar is produced. If the feed-water temperature is 235°C, what pinch-point temperature difference was used in the design of this heat exchanger?
4. A BWR produces saturated steam at 65 bar. The steam expands to the condenser pressure of 0.06 bar through a high-pressure turbine to 5 bar, followed by an external moisture separator which produces dry steam again, then the low-pressure turbine. Both turbines have a degree of internal moisture separation. How effective must this internal separation be if the steam dryness at the exhaust of each turbine is to be 0.88 or better, i.e. what proportion of the moisture that would otherwise be expected at the turbine outlet needs to be removed by the internal separation?

   Ignore any pressure drop in the external moisture separator, and take 0.82 for the isentropic efficiency of each turbine.
5. The primary coolant in an AGR is CO_2, at 30-bar pressure. It is limited by materials considerations to a maximum core outlet temperature of 640°C, giving modern steam conditions in the once-through, counterflow, boiler, i.e. 160 bar and 560°C at the outlet.

   If both the pinch temperature differences in the boiler are 80°C, and the feed water temperature is 134°C, what is the temperature of the CO_2 returning to the reactor? What mass flow rate is required in the primary circuit to transfer 1000 MW of heat in the boiler?

   The primary circuit pressure drop is 3.5 bar. What power will be required to drive the pumps if they are 80% efficient? If the net thermal efficiency of the secondary circuit, i.e. (turbine power–power required by secondary pumps)/rate of heat supply in boiler, is 44.0%, what is the overall thermal efficiency, i.e. net power produced by the complete plant/heat supplied by reactor? (Assume that all of the power required to drive the pumps ultimately appears as heat in the coolant.)
6. It is proposed to modify the cycle of question 5 by increasing the feed water temperature to 280°C which will increase the thermal efficiency of the secondary circuit, as defined above, to 46.8%. Will the overall thermal efficiency of the plant improve or not?
7. The cycle of Example 9.2 is modified to produce both heat and power. The saturation temperature in the condenser is raised to 104.8°C. Confirm that the thermal efficiency falls to 0.223.

CHAPTER 10

Fusion Reactors

INTRODUCTION

The controlled production of energy by the fusing together of light nuclei, as opposed to the fissioning of heavy ones, is still at a very early stage of development. Up to the present time the experimental systems have consumed more energy than has been produced by the fusion reaction. Potentially, though, the fusion reactor has a number of advantages. These include an indefinite supply of fuel, little or no long-lived radioactive waste, and very little residual heat when the reactor is shut down. The main effort in this field has naturally been concentrated on demonstrating a reaction where the nuclear energy released equals the energy required to initiate the reaction; until recently comparatively little effort has been put into the engineering problems of building a practical power reactor. Good general reviews of the field are given in references [1] and [2], of conceptual fusion reactor designs in [3], and of heat-transfer aspects in [4] and [5].

In fusion the reacting particles are both electrically charged, and will only come close enough together to allow a reaction if the temperature is high enough for the thermal motion to overcome the electrostatic repulsion. At these very high temperatures the atoms are fully ionised, i.e. the material has become a *plasma*. The main problems lie in heating the plasma up to the required temperature and in confining it long enough for the fusion reactions to occur. The Lawson criterion for a reaction that will generate more energy than is usefully consumed in heating the plasma is

$$n\tau > f(T) \tag{10.1}$$

where n is the number of nuclei per unit volume and τ the confinement time. The function of temperature $f(T)$ is different for each choice of reactants. Equation (10.1) is a minimum condition, and takes no account of the efficiency of the plasma heating process, which may be quite low.

The most promising reaction, i.e. requiring the lowest temperature, is that between the two hydrogen isotopes, D and T:

$${}_1\mathrm{D}^2 + {}_1\mathrm{T}^3 \rightarrow {}_2\mathrm{He}^4 + {}_0\mathrm{n}^1 + 17.6\,\mathrm{MeV}. \tag{10.2}$$

The Lawson criterion for this reaction indicates a minimum value of the $n\tau$ product of about 10^{20} m^{-3} s at a temperature of around 10^8 K (rather hotter than the centre of the sun).

High though this temperature is the initial thermal energy of the deuterium and tritium nuclei is still small compared to the energy released in the reaction. From this point of view then the initial total momentum of the system is small, and since momentum is conserved in nuclear reactions the final total momentum must be small too. Bearing in mind that the mass of the He^4 nucleus (or α particle) is four times the mass of the neutron it follows that the neutron comes off in the opposite direction to the α particle with four times the velocity, and that the energy released in the reaction is divided four to one in favour of the neutron.

Natural hydrogen contains one part in 6500 of deuterium, so this isotope may be obtained in indefinite quantities from water. Tritium, however, does not exist in nature and would have to be bred from lithium as follows:

$$n + {}_3\text{Li}^6 \rightarrow {}_1\text{T}^3 + {}_2\text{He}^4 + 4.8\ \text{MeV} \tag{10.3}$$

and

$$n + {}_3\text{Li}^7 \rightarrow {}_1\text{T}^3 + n + {}_2\text{He}^4 - 2.8\ \text{MeV}. \tag{10.4}$$

Natural lithium is 7.4% Li^6 and 92.6% Li^7. To maintain the supply of tritium a high proportion of the 14.1 MeV neutrons produced in the fusion reaction must react with lithium in a blanket surrounding the plasma.

Although it is generally agreed that the D–T reaction will be the first to be used in power production this reaction does not realise the full potential of the fusion process. Supplies of lithium are large (in the U.K. it has been estimated that there are 10^4 tonnes of lithium in the waste tips from the Cornish china clay mines), but they do not compare with the supplies of water. Also the neutrons produced in the reaction will activate structural materials such as stainless steel or niobium, and the tritium is itself radioactive. With the more difficult D–D reaction there would be for practical purposes no limit to the fuel supply, and the problem of induced activity would be less since fewer neutrons are produced.

MAGNETIC CONFINEMENT

The plasma must not be allowed to come into contact with solid surfaces, since this will damage the surfaces and cool the plasma below its critical temperature. One method of confining the plasma is to use a strong magnetic field. The charged particles are constrained to move in tight helical trajectories along the magnetic field lines. The problem of what happens when the particles reach the end of the field line can be overcome by using a ring or torus-shaped plasma. The main effort at the present time is concentrated on the tokamak design, characterised by a particularly strong toroidal magnetic field parallel to the plasma. This field is produced by the coils of a superconducting magnet. The main components of a reactor system are indicated in Fig. 10.1. In addition to the steady toroidal magnetic field there are other pulsed fields associated with heating the plasma and keeping it in a stable position.

With the magnetic field strengths that can conveniently be generated it is only possible to confine a plasma pressure of about 10 to a 100 atmospheres, leading to the fairly low plasma density of around 10^{20} to 10^{21} ions m^{-3}. Consequently confinement times of around 1 s will be required as a minimum. An indication of the progress that has been made in magnetic confinement is given in Table 10.1.

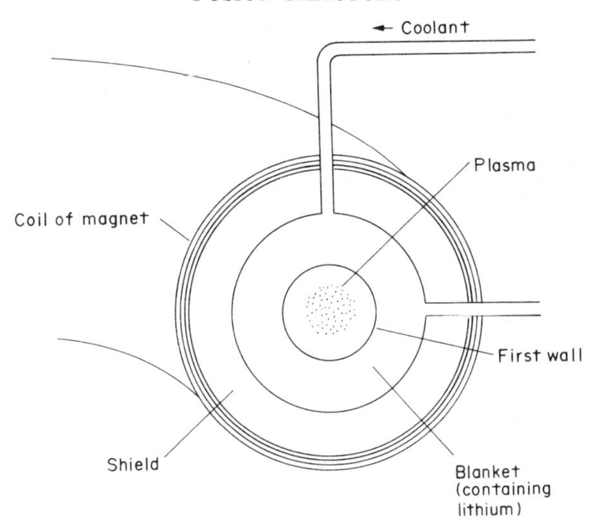

Fig. 10.1. Cross-section through hypothetical magnetically confined fusion reactor.

Table 10.1

Year	τ s	T K	$n\tau$ m^{-3} s
1960	10^{-4}	10^{6}	10^{16}
1970	10^{-2}	5×10^{6}	5×10^{18}
1977	5×10^{-2}	2×10^{7}	2×10^{19}
Needed for reactor	1	10^{8}	10^{20}

To obtain the required high temperature in the plasma it is not sufficient to rely on heating by magnetically induced currents, and it is thought that a beam of very high-energy neutral ions will have to be injected. There are serious problems associated with the development of this device, and with other components of the reactor such as the superconducting magnets and the tritium-processing system. Also materials are needed to withstand the intense neutron irradiation.

THERMAL DESIGN

Since 80% of the fusion energy is associated with the neutrons rather than with charged ions there is limited scope for direct electro-magnetic conversion of the energy. The neutrons are slowed down in a moderating material in a blanket surrounding the plasma, and their kinetic energy is changed into internal energy of the atoms of the blanket. From the point of view of energy conversion then the fusion reactor is just another heat source, and electricity would be produced in the usual way with a steam turbine. Since the coils of the superconducting magnet must be kept at a very low temperature (4.2 K by immersion in boiling liquid helium) they must be shielded from the heating effect of the neutrons and consequently placed outside the blanket, as shown in Fig. 10.1. The distinction between the blanket and shield is that the blanket operates at a high temperature and takes nearly all of the energy while the shield operates at a low temperature and prevents the last few per cent of the energy and radiation reaching the magnets.

The first wall, so called because it is the first wall the radiation from the plasma reaches, is a key part of the design. It must provide a good seal between the plasma region and the blanket, and it is subject to intense radiation damage from the 14.1-MeV neutrons. Another problem is that if ions knocked out of the wall find their way into the plasma they can prevent it reaching the critical temperature, since impurity ions of high atomic number lose energy much more rapidly than the D and T ions. It may be necessary for the first wall to have a liner of low atomic number material, such as graphite.

Because of the irradiation damage it is thought that the thermal loading on the first wall, i.e. the total rate at which energy passes through per unit area, will have to be limited to about 1 MW m^{-2}, and even so the first wall will have to be replaced periodically. An alternative measure of the radiation is the first wall neutron loading, which is the neutron current per unit area times 14.1 MeV. Although both of these quantities are usually expressed in MW m^{-2} neither is a heat flux at the first wall, since the fast neutrons have a considerable range and take most of their energy through the wall, to provide a volumetric heat source in the blanket. This heating decays roughly exponentially with distance from the first wall.

The 20% of the fusion energy associated with the alpha particles is intercepted by the first wall, however, and appears as heat in the first few μm of the wall. If a liner is used then even a thin layer will absorb the alpha particles, and the heat is then transmitted to the first wall by thermal radiation.

So the heat flux that has to be removed by the coolant is only around 200 kW m^{-2}. This is somewhat below the heat fluxes that are encountered in fission reactors, so in principle there is no great difficulty in the heat-transfer design. However, when and if a fusion reactor is built, there will be great pressure to reduce the capital cost for a given power output by increasing the first wall loading.

The choice of coolant for the blanket is discussed after the sections on fluid flow and heat-transfer effects in magnetic fields.

INERTIAL CONFINEMENT

While most fusion research is on magnetic confinement, a quite different approach to the problem should also be mentioned. If a pellet of solid DT is heated up extremely quickly, the critical temperatures can be reached and the fusion reaction can take place before the resulting plasma has time to expand to a low density. This is inertial confinement. Since the timescale is very short it follows from the Lawson criterion that the density must be very high. The pellet of solid DT is heated by an intense pulse of light from a laser, or by an ion beam. The outward momentum of the material ablated from the surface of the pellet compresses the remaining material to many times its normal density. The laser light may not be absorbed very well by a pure DT pellet, so it may be necessary to use a structured pellet with the outer layer chosen for good absorption of the laser energy.

As in the magnetically confined system most of the fusion energy will be carried through the first wall by the 14.1-MeV neutrons. However, because the plasma is now much denser, the alpha particles will lose much of their energy within the plasma itself. Perhaps about 20% of the fusion energy will arrive at the first wall in the form of ions and plasma debris. This energy is absorbed in the first few μm of the wall and gives rise to a serious transient temperature rise, discussed in more detail later.

Again a blanket containing a high proportion of lithium must be provided, but there is no magnetic field.

FLUID FLOW EFFECTS IN STRONG MAGNETIC FIELDS

These effects are limited to electrically conducting coolants and follow from two basic laws of electromagnetism [6,7]. Firstly, if an electrical conductor moves with a velocity u in a magnetic field of magnetic flux strength B, then an electric field is induced in the conductor. Expressed vectorially we have

$$\text{Induced electric field} = \mathbf{u} \times \mathbf{B}. \tag{10.5}$$

Provided there is a return path then the electric field will cause a current i to flow. The force on a conductor carrying a current in a magnetic field is

$$\text{Force} = i(\mathbf{l} \times \mathbf{B}) \tag{10.6}$$

where $\mathbf{l}$ is the length of the conducting path parallel to the direction of current flow. The direction of the force is always such as to oppose the original movement.

So any magnetic field with a component transverse to a liquid metal flow will produce a pressure gradient tending to stop the flow. In the very strong fields of a fusion reactor this pressure gradient is much larger than the frictional pressure gradient. The only requirement is that there should be a return path for the electric current, which there will be if the flow is confined in a metal duct.

Suppose the duct has dimensions $2a$ by $2b$, as shown in Fig. 10.2. If the magnetic field is at right angles to the flow direction we can dispense with the vector notation. The induced voltage across the duct is $2buB$, causing a current to flow as indicated. The electrical resistance of the flow is roughly $b/\sigma aL$ where σ is the electrical conductivity of the liquid

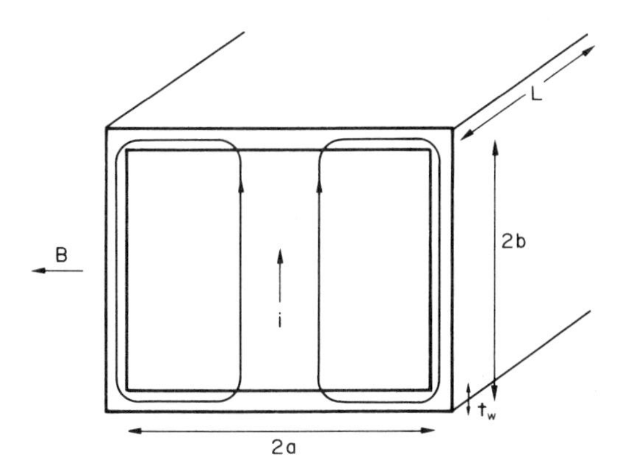

Fig. 10.2. Current induced by transverse magnetic field when a liquid metal flows in a conducting duct (simplified). Direction of flow is into the paper.

metal. The current then returns through the two side walls, where the resistance is $b/\sigma_w t_w L$. So the current is

$$i = \frac{2buB}{(b/\sigma aL + b/\sigma_w t_w L)} = \frac{2uB\sigma_w t_w L}{(1 + C)} \tag{10.7}$$

where $C = \sigma_w t_w/\sigma a$, the wall conductance ratio.

Substituting in equation (10.6) the force is found to be

$$\frac{2uB^2\sigma_w t_w L2b}{(1 + C)}$$

since the current flows a distance $2b$ across the moving liquid metal. This force acts over an area $4ab$, so it is equivalent to a pressure drop of

$$\Delta p = \frac{uB^2\sigma_w t_w L}{a(1 + C)}. \tag{10.8}$$

Note that the duct dimension b has cancelled out of the above derivation; what matters is the half-width of the duct in the direction of the magnetic field. Clearly the derivation is approximate in that we have ignored any variations in velocity across the duct and any variations in the lengths of the paths followed by the electric current. However, the equation works quite well in practice, and can be applied to circular cross-section ducts taking a as the radius.

This magnetohydrodynamic pressure drop can be eliminated either by making the walls of the duct of electrically non-conducting materials ($\sigma_w = 0$), or by routing the ducts parallel to the magnetic field. Unfortunately, there do not seem to be suitable insulating materials that can stand up to conditions in the blanket, and it is not feasible to have the entire coolant flow path parallel to the magnetic field.

In addition to this overall effect of opposing the flow of an electrically conducting coolant the magnetic field has various local effects on the velocity profile and structure of the flow. If the velocity varies from one part of the flow cross-section to another then the induced electric field will vary, and a current can originate in an area of high velocity and flow back through an area of low velocity. This sets up forces that oppose the velocity differences and has the effect of flattening the velocity profile over the bulk of the flow. With a changed velocity profile the friction factor will not be quite the same as in a normal flow. However, for highly conducting liquids, this effect is small compared to the pressure drop given by equation (10.8). More important is the effect of the magnetic field on the turbulence in the flow. By definition the turbulent eddies involve changes in velocity over quite short distances in the flow. The effect of the magnetic field is to damp out the turbulent eddies, and in fact complete suppression of the turbulence is possible.

We can estimate the size of the magnetic pressure stresses acting on a turbulent eddy by following the same chain of reasoning that led to equation (10.8). To short-circuit the process we note that if the eddy has a characteristic dimension δ in all directions, then all linear dimensions in equation (10.8) are replaced by δ. The current returns through more liquid metal in this case, through a region of effective width δ, so $\sigma_w = \sigma$ and $C = 1$. The magnetic stress becomes $uB^2\sigma\delta/2$, where u is now the turbulent velocity, i.e. the difference between the velocity in the eddy and the surrounding liquid. The viscous stress follows from the definition of viscosity and is $\mu u/\delta$. The magnetic stresses will become important in suppressing turbulence when they exceed the viscous stresses, so we are interested in the ratio

$$\frac{\text{magnetic stresses}}{\text{viscous stresses}} = \frac{\delta^2 B^2 \sigma}{2\mu}$$

and since the size of the turbulent eddies is proportional to, and comparable with, the duct half-width a, the ratio is roughly $a^2 B^2 \sigma/\mu$. The square root of this quantity is the *Hartmann number*, $aB(\sigma/\mu)^{1/2}$.

The magnetic and viscous forces both tend to prevent turbulence, so as the Hartmann number increases to values over unity the onset of turbulence is delayed to higher and higher Reynolds numbers. The experimentally determined criterion for complete turbulence suppression is

$$\text{Hartmann number} = aB\left[\frac{\sigma}{\mu}\right]^{1/2} > \frac{Re}{400}. \tag{10.9}$$

There is some uncertainty over the numerical factor. Values between 300 and 500 have been found [4]. We are still assuming here that the magnetic field is transverse to the flow direction, so strictly we are using the transverse Hartmann number. Since the velocities in turbulent eddies are not confined to the main flow direction it is also possible for a parallel magnetic field to affect the turbulence structure, and a corresponding parallel Hartmann number can be defined. Some suppression of the turbulence occurs for parallel Hartmann numbers an order of magnitude greater than those given by equation (10.9).

As an example of the application of equation (10.9) suppose that we have liquid lithium at 1100 K flowing in a 20-mm diameter duct with a transverse magnetic field of 10 tesla. The conductivity and viscosity are 2×10^6 ohm^{-1} m^{-1} and 2.5×10^{-4} Ns m^{-2} respectively, giving a transverse Hartmann number of 9000. So turbulence will be suppressed for Reynolds numbers less than 3.6×10^6. Reynolds numbers greater than this are unlikely to occur in practice since, as equation (10.8) shows, there is an incentive to keep flow velocities down.

HEAT-TRANSFER EFFECTS IN STRONG MAGNETIC FIELDS

The heat-transfer effects follow directly from the magnetic effects and so only apply to electrically conducting coolants. If turbulence is suppressed then there is no mixing of the liquid layers and no convective heat transfer. Heat flow into the coolant is entirely by thermal conduction, and the Nusselt number will be constant, the value of the constant depending on the geometry of the coolant duct and the velocity profile. For circular pipes and uniform velocity (i.e. slug flow) the Nusselt number, as shown in Chapter 4, is 8. For a pessimistic analysis a Nusselt number of 4.36 could be used, corresponding to normal laminar flow (i.e. a parabolic velocity profile). Since in liquid metals, with their high thermal conductivity, much of the heat is transported by molecular conduction even in normal turbulent flows, this reduction in the heat-transfer coefficient is not very serious. In practice it probably does not amount to much more than a factor of 2 on a heat-transfer coefficient that anyway is very high.

A more serious heat-transfer effect might arise in coolants that have a low thermal conductivity but at the same time have an electrical conductivity high enough to give Hartmann numbers above the critical value for turbulence suppression. Such a coolant would normally rely almost entirely on forced convection mixing for its heat transfer, so the change to a magnetically laminarized flow would involve a drastic drop in heat-transfer coefficient. It appears that a molten salt that has been suggested as a reactor coolant, a $LiF-BeF_2$ mixture (called flibe) may come into this category. On the other hand, the electrical conductivity of flibe is not so high as to give a serious magnetic pressure drop.

COMPARISON OF COOLANTS

Since it is necessary to have a large proportion of lithium in the blanket to breed tritium, and lithium, having a low atomic number, is also good at slowing down the neutrons, there are obvious attractions in a design that uses liquid lithium as the coolant. Just the one material could perform all three functions, and nothing else would be required in the blanket apart from structural material to contain the liquid lithium and direct its flow. The disadvantages of liquid lithium are a high chemical activity, which limits the temperature obtainable in contact with the normal structural materials, such as stainless steel, and high pumping losses where the flow passes through the magnetic field. These magnetohydrodynamic losses will of course apply to any liquid metal coolant, and appear to be prohibitive.

The molten salt, flibe, mentioned earlier, has the advantage of containing lithium and beryllium. The beryllium reacts with the fusion neutrons to give even more neutrons and hence increased tritium production. However, the supply of beryllium is limited, making the material very expensive. Water, the main coolant for fission reactors, is not favoured because of the high pressure needed: the water itself, and the pipework needed to contain the high pressures, would occupy a lot of room and make it difficult to fit in sufficient lithium for breeding; also low pressures are preferred until there is more information on materials that can withstand the fast neutron irradiation.

The more recent conceptual designs mostly use helium. As explained in Chapter 8 helium is one of the best gases from the point of view of heat-carrying capacity versus pumping power, and it is chemically inert. The high frictional pressure drop and pumping power associated with a gas are minor disadvantages compared to the disadvantages of the other coolants. A compound containing lithium is still required in the blanket to breed tritium, but this compound is not part of the coolant.

TRANSIENT HEATING PROBLEMS

The first wall of a laser fusion reactor will be subjected to very short bursts of energy immediately after each micro-explosion. The charged ions leaving the remains of the pellet will have a range of velocities and so arrive at the wall at different times. For typical postulated chamber dimensions the charged ion energy deposition would last a few μs. This energy will all appear in the first few μm of the wall.

We can estimate the temperature rise of the surface by considering two extreme cases. Firstly, for a long pulse, the energy will have time to diffuse beyond the initial few μm and the volume affected is determined by thermal diffusion. Secondly, for a short pulse, the volume affected is just the few μm thick surface layer.

It is a standard result of diffusion theory that when the thermal diffusivity is K ($= k/\rho c$) the heat will diffuse a distance Δz in a time t given by $\Delta z^2/t = K$ (these parameters appeared in the transient heating analysis of Chapter 7). So the heat penetrates to a depth Δz given by

$$\Delta z = (Kt)^{1/2}. \tag{10.10}$$

If the total energy in the pulse is E per unit area of the wall then the temperature rise is $\Delta T = (E/\rho c)\,(Kt)^{-1/2}$. Rigorous analysis of this problem, for energy deposited at a uniform rate at the surface, gives [8]

$$\Delta T = \frac{2E}{\rho c}(\pi K t)^{-1/2}. \tag{10.11}$$

Provided the thermal diffusion depth Δz given by equation (10.10) exceeds the depth of penetration of the charged ions d then equation (10.11) gives a reasonably close upper limit to the temperature rise.

For shorter times, when Δz is less than d, the temperature rise is just

$$\Delta T = \frac{E}{\rho c d}. \tag{10.12}$$

For a numerical example we will take the same thermal first wall loading that we suggested for the magnetically confined reactor, 1 MW m^{-2}, and assume 10 micro-explosions per second. If 10% of the energy arrives in the form of charged ions then $E = 10^4$ J m^{-2}. For a stainless steel wall $\rho = 8000$ kg m^{-3}, $c = 500$ J kg^{-1} K^{-1} and $K = 5 \times 10^{-6}$ m^2 s^{-1}. Also we assume $d = 5\ \mu$m.

If the pulse lasts 10 μs then equation (10.10) gives the diffusion depth as 7.1 μm, greater than d, so the temperature rise comes from equation (10.11) and is 399 K.

If the pulse lasts 1 μs (or any shorter time) the thermal diffusion depth is less than d, and equation (10.12) gives a temperature rise of 500 K.

The values chosen for the calculation were not particularly pessimistic, and it is unlikely that repeated temperature excursions of this order could be tolerated. One solution is to coat the first wall on the inside with a layer of liquid lithium that is continuously replenished. Some lithium would evaporate from the surface after each micro-explosion, but it seems that the vapour pressure of lithium is low enough for the vapour not to impede the subsequent passage of the laser beam.

References

1. STEINER, D. The technology required for power by fusion. *Nucl. Sci. Engng* **58,** 107–165 (1975).
2. PEASE, R. S. The potential of controlled nuclear fusion. *Cont. Phys.* **18,** 113–135 (1977).
3. RIBE, F. L. Recent developments in the design of conceptual fusion reactors. *Nucl. Technology* **34,** 179–208 (1977).

4. HOFFMANN, M. A., WERNER, R. W., CARLSON, G. A. and CORNISH, D. N. Review of heat transfer problems associated with magnetically confined fusion reactor concepts. A.I. Chem. E. Symposium, Series No. 168, 1977, pp. 9–44 (also other papers in this volume).
5. FRANK, T. G., BOHACHEVSKY, I. O., BOOTH, L. A. and PENDERGRASS, J. M. Heat transfer problems associated with laser fusion. *Ibid.*, 1977, pp. 77–85.
6. CARLSON, G. A. Magnetohydrodynamic pressure drop of lithium flowing in a conducting wall pipe in a transverse magnetic field, theory and experiment, UCRL–75307, Lawrence Livermore Lab., 1974.
7. HUNT, J. C. R. and HANCOX, R. The use of liquid lithium as coolant in a toroidal fusion reactor. Part I. Pumping power, CLM–R 115, UKAEA, Culham, 1971.
8. CARSLAW, H. S. and JAEGER, J. C. *Conduction of heat in solids*, 2nd edn., Oxford Univ. Press, 1959, p. 57.

Notation

A Flow cross-sectional area
A_1, A_2 Smaller, larger, flow area
a Radius: of fuel pellet; inner radius of tube; half-width of duct in direction of magnetic field (Ch. 10)
B Various constants defined in text; magnetic flux strength (Ch. 10)
B_m^2, B_g^2 Material, geometrical, buckling
B_1, B_2 Constants in equation (4.3)
b Outer radius of cladding; half-width of duct in direction perpendicular to magnetic field (Ch. 10)
C Various constants defined in text
C_c, C_f Thermal capacity per unit length of cladding, fuel
c Specific heat at constant pressure
c_p, c_v, c_m Specific heat at constant pressure, at constant volume, molar specific heat
D Diffusion coefficient (Ch. 1); fuel-rod diameter; constant (Ch. 8)
d Characteristic dimension of channel (Ch. 4); penetration depth of charged ions (Ch. 10)
d_e Equivalent diameter
E Various constants defined in text
F Various functions defined in text
F_s Defined by equation (5.24)
$F_q^N, F_z^N, F_r^N, F_q^E, F_q, F_{\Delta h}, F_{\Delta h}^E$ Hot-channel factors defined in Chapter 8
f Friction factor
f' Darcy–Weisbach friction factor
$f(\ )$ Various functions defined in text
G Mass velocity, m/A
g Acceleration due to gravity
$g(\ )$ A function
H Rate of energy production per unit volume of fuel; total enthalpy (Ch. 9)
h Heat-transfer coefficient; specific enthalpy (Chs. 5, 6, 9 and, with subscripts, Ch. 8)
h' Heat-transfer coefficient (Ch. 6)
Δh Specific enthalpy of subcooling
h_g Gap heat-transfer coefficient, gap conductance
h_0 Specific enthalpy in reservoir
h_{CF} Specific enthalpy of cross-flow
h_{mix} Specific enthalpy of turbulent mixing flow
i Electrical current

K Thermal diffusivity, $k/\rho c$; overall loss coefficient (Ch. 6)
k Thermal conductivity: of fuel (Chs. 3 and 7); of coolant (Ch. 4); of first wall (Ch. 10)
Pressure loss coefficient (Ch. 6); grid-loss coefficient (Ch. 8)
Multiplication constant (Ch. 7)
k_0 Thermal conductivity of 100% dense fuel
k_e Pressure-loss coefficient for expansion
k_c Pressure-loss coefficient for contraction (Ch. 6); thermal conductivity of cladding
k_∞ Multiplication constant for an infinite reactor
k_p Multiplication constant for the prompt neutrons
$k_{p'}$ Multiplication constant for the prompt neutrons, new value
L Length of channel; fundamental quantity of length (Ch. 4); length of fin (Ch. 4); diffusion length (Ch. 1)
L_s Slowing-down length
L' Extrapolated length of channel; extended length of fin (Ch. 4)
l Gap: between fuel and can (Ch. 3); between fins (Ch. 4)
Distance from start of nucleate boiling to critical heat-flux position (Ch. 5)
Length of current path (Ch. 10)
M Mass (fundamental quantity, Ch. 4); two-phase friction multiplier (Ch. 6); molecular weight (Ch. 8)
m Mass flow rate
$2h/k_c t$ (equations (4.35) to (4.44))
Exponent in equation (7.2)
δm Mass of particle of fluid
N Critical heat flux ratio; number of atoms per unit volume (Ch. 1)
N_i Number of delayed neutron emitters per unit volume
Nu Nusselt number, hd_e/k
n Number of neutrons per unit volume (Chs. 1 and 7); number of nuclei per unit volume (Ch. 10); various meanings in other chapters, defined in text
P Porosity (Ch. 3); pitch of fuel rods (Ch. 4); ideal pumping power
P' Actual pumping power
Pe Peclet number, $RePr$
Pr Prandtl number, $\mu c/k$
p Pressure
p_1, p_2 Inlet, outlet, pressure
p_b, p_0 Back pressure, reservoir pressure
Q Rate of heat supply
q Heat flux
q_0 Maximum value of heat flux
q_{crit} Critical heat flux
R Linear rating, i.e. rate of heat supply per unit length of fuel rod
Reaction rate (Ch. 1)
Gas constant per unit mass (Ch. 6)
r Radius
r_0 Outer radius of core
r_h Radius of hole in centre of fuel pellet

S Slip ratio, u_v/u_l
St Stanton number, $h/\rho uc$
s Perimeter of fuel rods in channel (Ch. 4); total perimeter of channel (Ch. 6)
Specific entropy
Source of neutrons (Ch. 1)
s_0 Specific entropy in reservoir
T Temperature
T_{of} Temperature on the outside of the fuel pellets
T_{ic} Temperature on the inside of the cladding
T_s Temperature of the cladding surface in contact with the coolant; temperature of other heated surfaces in contact with the coolant
T_1, T_2 Temperature of coolant at inlet, outlet, of the channel
T_b Bulk coolant temperature
T_f Film temperature
ΔT Can to coolant temperature difference; transient temperature rise (Ch. 10)
t Time; thickness of fin (Ch. 4)
t_w Thickness of duct wall
t_0 Time of reactor operation
u Flow velocity
u_{CF} Axial velocity of cross-flow
u_{mix} Axial velocity of turbulent mixing flow
u_1, u_2 Velocity at the edge of the laminar sublayer, velocity one turbulent eddy width into the flow
v Specific volume
Velocity of neutrons (Ch. 1)
Velocity of turbulent eddies (Ch. 4)
x Vapour quality; steam dryness
x_{do} Vapour quality at dryout position
y Various quantities defined in text
Y Defined by equation (5.15)
z Distance beyond mid-point of channel; distance along fin (Ch. 4)
Δz Incremental distance along channel; thermal diffusion depth (Ch. 10)
W Rate of work output
w_{CF} Cross-flow mass flow rate between subchannels
w_{mix} Turbulent mixing mass flow rate between subchannels
α through to ζ Powers in equaton (4.3)
α Void fraction; geometrical factor in equation (3.11)
α_n Roots of $J_0'(\alpha) = 0$
β Geometrical factor in equation (3.12); delayed neutron fraction (Ch. 7)
γ c_p/c_v
δ Thickness of laminar boundary layer (Ch. 4); gap between fuel rods (Ch. 8); pinch-point temperature difference (Ch. 9); linear dimension of turbulent eddy (Ch. 10)
ε_m Maximum value of eddy diffusivity of momentum
η Overall pump efficiency
θ $T - T_b$
λ Fuel diffusion length

λ_i Decay constants of the delayed neutron emitters
μ Viscosity
ν Kinematic viscosity
ρ Density
ρ_1 Density at the pump
σ Microscopic reaction cross-section (Ch. 1); surface tension (Ch. 5); electrical conductivity of the coolant (Ch. 10)
σ_w Electrical conductivity of the duct wall
Σ Macroscopic reaction cross-section
τ Wall shear stress; confinement time (Ch. 10)
ϕ Neutron flux
ϕ_0 Neutron flux in normal operation
ψ Ratio of eddy diffusivities of heat and momentum

Subscripts

c cool
f feed water
h hot
l property of the saturated liquid
lv change in property on going from liquid to vapour
p primary
s secondary (note T_s is surface temperature)
v property of saturated vapour

APPENDIX 1

Temperature Distribution Following Sudden Total Loss of Cooling

APPENDIX 1a. DIFFERENTIAL HEAT-CONDUCTION EQUATION

Equation (7.1) is for radial flow of heat in a cylinder, and can be obtained by considering a heat balance on an annular element, of thickness dr and unit length (see Fig. A.1).

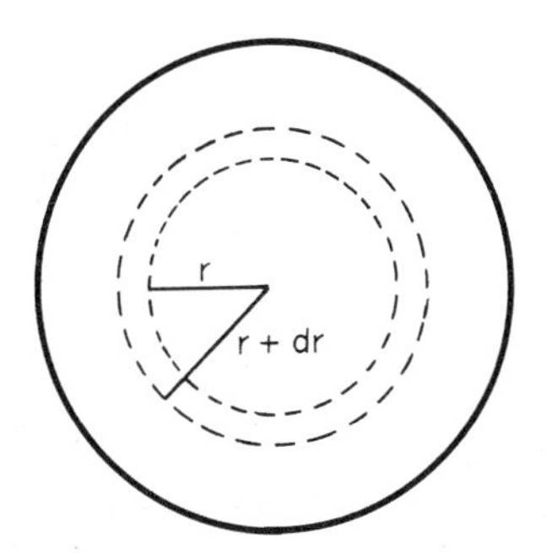

The rate of heat flow into the element at radius r is

$$-k\,2\pi r\frac{\delta T}{\delta r}$$

and the rate of heat flow out of the element at r + dr is

$$-k\,2\pi(r+\mathrm{d}r)\left\{\frac{\delta T}{\delta r}+\frac{\delta^2 T}{\delta r^2}\mathrm{d}r\right\}.$$

So the net rate at which heat is conducted into the element is, ignoring the $(\mathrm{d}r)^2$ term,

$$k\,2\pi r\frac{\delta^2 T}{\delta r^2}\mathrm{d}r+k\,2\pi\mathrm{d}r\frac{\delta T}{\delta r}.$$

Also, heat is generated within the element at a rate $2\pi r \mathrm{d}r H$. This supply of heat causes the element to warm up, at a rate $\delta T/\delta t$ given by

$$2\pi r \mathrm{d}r \rho c \frac{\delta T}{\delta t} = 2\pi r \mathrm{d}r k \left\{ \frac{\delta^2 T}{\delta r^2} + \frac{1}{r}\frac{\delta T}{\delta r} \right\} + 2\pi r \mathrm{d}r H$$

or

$$\rho c \frac{\delta T}{\delta t} = \frac{k}{r}\frac{\delta}{\delta r}\left\{ r \frac{\delta T}{\delta r} \right\} + H.$$

APPENDIX 1b. INTEGRATION OF BESSEL FUNCTIONS

We wish to perform the following integration (from equation (7.3))

$$\int_0^a r f(r) J_0 \left(\frac{\alpha_n r}{a} \right) \mathrm{d}r$$

where $f(r)$ is given by

$$f(r) = \frac{R}{4\pi k}\left\{ 1 - \frac{r^2}{a^2} \right\}.$$

Substituting, the integral becomes

$$\frac{R}{4\pi k a^2}\left[\int_0^a a^2 r J_0 \left(\frac{\alpha_n r}{a} \right) \mathrm{d}r - \int_0^a r^3 J_0 \left(\frac{\alpha_n r}{a} \right) \mathrm{d}r \right].$$

These are standard integrals (see, for example, reference [2] of Chapter 7), and the result is

$$\frac{R}{4\pi k a^2}\left[\frac{a^4}{\alpha_n} J_1(\alpha_n) - \frac{a^4}{\alpha_n} J_1(\alpha_n) + \frac{2a^4}{\alpha_n^2} J_2(\alpha_n) \right]$$

$$= \frac{R a^2}{2\pi k \alpha_n^2} J_2(\alpha_n). \quad \text{(A.1)}$$

Now J_2 is related to J_0. Generally

$$2nJ_n(z) = zJ_{n-1}(z) + zJ_{n+1}(z)$$

so with $n = 1$ and $z = \alpha_n$

$$2J_1(\alpha_n) = \alpha_n J_0(\alpha_n) + \alpha_n J_2(\alpha_n)$$

or

$$J_2(\alpha_n) = -J_0(\alpha_n) + \frac{2}{\alpha_n} J_1(\alpha_n)$$

and since the α_n are the roots of $J_1(\alpha) = 0$ we are left with

$$J_2(\alpha_n) = -J_0(\alpha_n). \tag{A.2}$$

Substituting (A.1) and (A.2) into equation (7.3) gives equation (7.4).

APPENDIX 1c. ESTIMATE OF TIME DELAY DUE TO FUEL CLAD GAP

Strictly speaking the transient response of the cladding is connected with that of the fuel, and the two should be considered together. However, it is possible to check whether or not the gap between the fuel and cladding will delay the cladding temperature rise so much that the 7 s estimated in Chapter 7 becomes much less than the time constant for the complete fuel rod. Suppose that the main barrier to heat transfer in the fuel rod is the gap between fuel and cladding, then the fuel temperature T_f will be approximately constant throughout the fuel volume at a given time, and similarly the cladding temperature can be represented by a single value T_c.

If the thermal capacities of fuel and can are C_f and C_c respectively per metre length, and h the gap heat-transfer coefficient, then the rate of loss of stored heat by the fuel must equal the rate at which heat is transferred across the gap, that is

$$C_f \frac{dT_f}{dt} = -2\pi ah(T_f - T_c) \tag{A.3}$$

and this same heat transferred across the gap increases the can temperature,

$$C_c \frac{dT_c}{dt} = 2\pi ah(T_f - T_c), \tag{A.4}$$

multiplying equation (A.4) by C_f/C_c and subtracting the result from equation (A.3) gives

$$C_f \frac{d}{dt}(T_f - T_c) = -2\pi ah(T_f - T_c)\left(1 + \frac{C_f}{C_c}\right)$$

which integrated between $t = 0$ and $t = t$ becomes

$$\frac{T_f - T_c}{T_{f_1} - T_{c_1}} = e^{-2\pi ah(1/C_f + 1/C_c)t} \tag{A.5}$$

where T_{f_1} and T_{c_1} are the initial temperatures.

So the initial fuel to cladding temperature difference decreases exponentially to zero with a $1/e$ time constant of $2\pi ah(1/C_f + 1/C_c)^{-1}$.

If the 10-mm diameter fuel rod in the example in Chapter 7 has a 0.8 mm thick Zircaloy cladding then the thermal capacities (volume $\times$ density $\times$ specific heat) calculated using the data in Table 3.1 are 260 J m^{-1} K^{-1} and 60 J m^{-1} K^{-1} for the fuel and can respectively. With $h = 5000$ W m^{-2} K^{-1} this gives a $1/e$ time constant of 0.3 s, and the time for the fuel to can temperature difference to decrease to 3% of its initial volume is 1.1 s. In other words, the initial assumption that the temperatures within the fuel would have time to even out before much heat was transferred to the can was not justified, and equation (A.5) cannot be used for detailed predictions. It is fairly clear that the barrier to heat transfer presented by the gap will not delay the attainment of equilibrium very much.

APPENDIX 2

Properties of Coolants

TABLE A.1. THERMODYNAMIC PROPERTIES OF SATURATED WATER AND STEAM
(reproduced with permission from [1])

Abs. press. (bar)	Temperature (°C)	Specific enthalpy (kJ/kg)			Specific entropy (kJ/kg K)			Specific volume (10^{-3} m^3/kg)	
p_{sat}	T_{sat}	h_l	h_{lv}	h_v	s_l	s_{lv}	s_v	v_l	v_v
0.040	28.98	121.4	2433.1	2554.5	0.4225	8.0530	8.4755	1.0040	34803.3
0.050	32.90	137.8	2423.8	2561.6	0.4763	7.9197	8.3960	1.0052	28194.5
0.060	36.18	151.5	2416.0	2567.5	0.5209	7.8103	8.3312	1.0064	23740.6
0.070	39.03	163.4	2409.2	2572.6	0.5591	7.7176	8.2767	1.0074	20530.4
0.080	41.54	173.9	2403.2	2577.1	0.5926	7.6370	8.2295	1.0084	18103.8
0.090	43.79	183.3	2397.9	2581.1	0.6224	7.5657	8.1881	1.0094	16203.4
0.100	45.83	191.8	2392.9	2584.8	0.6493	7.5018	8.1511	1.0102	14673.7
0.200	60.09	251.5	2358.4	2609.9	0.8321	7.0773	7.9094	1.0172	7649.2
0.300	69.13	289.3	2336.1	2625.4	0.9441	6.8254	7.7695	1.0223	5229.0
0.400	75.89	317.7	2319.2	2636.9	1.0261	6.6448	7.6709	1.0265	3993.2
0.500	81.35	340.6	2305.4	2646.0	1.0912	6.5035	7.5947	1.0301	3240.1
0.60	85.95	359.9	2293.6	2653.6	1.1455	6.3872	7.5327	1.0333	2731.7
0.70	89.96	376.8	2283.3	2660.1	1.1921	6.2883	7.4804	1.0361	2364.7
0.80	93.51	391.7	2274.0	2665.8	1.2330	6.2022	7.4352	1.0387	2086.9
0.90	96.71	405.2	2265.6	2670.9	1.2696	6.1258	7.3954	1.0412	1869.1
1.00	99.63	417.5	2257.9	2675.4	1.3027	6.0571	7.3598	1.0434	1693.7
1.20	104.81	439.4	2244.1	2683.4	1.3609	5.9375	7.2984	1.0476	1428.1
1.40	109.32	458.4	2231.9	2690.3	1.4109	5.8356	7.2465	1.0513	1236.3
1.60	113.32	475.4	2220.9	2696.2	1.4550	5.7467	7.2017	1.0547	1091.1
1.80	116.93	490.7	2210.8	2701.5	1.4944	5.6677	7.1622	1.0579	977.18
2.00	120.23	504.7	2201.6	2706.3	1.5301	5.5967	7.1268	1.0608	885.40
3.0	133.54	561.4	2163.2	2724.7	1.6717	5.3192	6.9909	1.0735	605.53
4.0	143.63	604.7	2132.9	2737.6	1.7764	5.1179	6.8943	1.0839	462.20
5.0	151.85	640.1	2107.4	2747.5	1.8604	4.9588	6.8192	1.0928	374.66
6.0	158.84	670.4	2085.0	2755.5	1.9308	4.8267	6.7575	1.1009	315.46
7.0	164.96	697.1	2064.9	2762.0	1.9918	4.7134	6.7052	1.1082	272.68
8.0	170.41	720.9	2046.5	2767.5	2.0457	4.6139	6.6596	1.1150	240.26
9.0	175.36	742.6	2029.5	2772.1	2.0941	4.5251	6.6192	1.1213	214.82
10.0	179.88	762.6	2013.6	2776.2	2.1382	4.4447	6.5828	1.1274	194.30
12.0	187.96	798.4	1984.3	2782.7	2.2160	4.3034	6.5194	1.1386	163.21
14.0	195.04	830.1	1957.7	2787.8	2.2836	4.1815	6.4651	1.1489	140.73
16.0	201.37	858.5	1933.2	2791.7	2.3436	4.0740	6.4176	1.1586	123.70
18.0	207.11	884.5	1910.3	2794.8	2.3976	3.9776	6.3751	1.1678	110.33
20.0	212.37	908.6	1888.7	2797.2	2.4468	3.8899	6.3367	1.1766	99.549
25.0	223.94	961.9	1839.0	2800.9	2.5542	3.6994	6.2537	1.1972	79.915
30.0	233.84	1008.3	1794.0	2802.3	2.6455	3.5383	6.1838	1.2163	66.632
35.0	242.54	1049.7	1752.2	2802.0	2.7252	3.3976	6.1229	1.2345	57.028

TABLE A.1. (cont.)

Abs. press. (bar)	Temperature (°C)		Specific enthalpy (kJ/kg)		Specific entropy (kJ/kg K)			Specific volume (10^{-3} m^3/kg)	
p_{sat}	T_{sat}	h_l	h_{lv}	h_v	s_l	s_{lv}	s_v	v_l	v_v
40.0	250.33	1087.4	1712.9	2800.3	2.7965	3.2720	6.0685	1.2521	49.749
45.0	257.41	1122.1	1675.6	2797.7	2.8612	3.1579	6.0191	1.2691	44.035
50.0	263.92	1154.5	1639.7	2794.2	2.9207	3.0528	5.9735	1.2858	39.425
55.0	269.94	1184.9	1605.0	2789.9	2.9758	2.9551	5.9309	1.3023	35.624
60	275.56	1213.7	1571.3	2785.0	3.0274	2.8633	5.8907	1.3187	32.433
65	280.83	1241.2	1538.3	2779.5	3.0760	2.7766	5.8526	1.3350	29.714
70	285.80	1267.5	1506.0	2773.4	3.1220	2.6941	5.8161	1.3514	27.368
75	290.51	1292.7	1474.1	2766.9	3.1658	2.6152	5.7810	1.3678	25.323
80	294.98	1317.2	1442.7	2759.9	3.2077	2.5393	5.7470	1.3843	23.521
85	299.24	1340.8	1411.6	2752.4	3.2480	2.4661	5.7141	1.4010	21.923
90	303.31	1363.8	1380.8	2744.6	3.2867	2.3952	5.6820	1.4179	20.493
95	307.22	1386.2	1350.2	2736.3	3.3242	2.3264	5.6506	1.4351	19.206
100	310.96	1408.1	1319.7	2727.7	3.3606	2.2592	5.6198	1.4526	18.041
110	318.04	1450.6	1258.8	2709.3	3.4304	2.1292	5.5596	1.4887	16.007
120	324.64	1491.7	1197.5	2689.2	3.4971	2.0032	5.5003	1.5267	14.285
130	330.81	1531.9	1135.1	2667.0	3.5614	1.8795	5.4409	1.5671	12.800
140	336.63	1571.5	1070.9	2642.4	3.6241	1.7564	5.3804	1.6105	11.498
144	338.86	1587.3	1044.6	2631.9	3.6488	1.7069	5.3557	1.6289	11.020
148	341.04	1603.0	1017.8	2620.8	3.6734	1.6573	5.3307	1.6480	10.564
152	343.18	1618.8	990.5	2609.3	3.6979	1.6073	5.3053	1.6678	10.128
156	345.27	1634.6	962.8	2597.3	3.7224	1.5570	5.2795	1.6885	9.7099
160	347.32	1650.4	934.5	2584.9	3.7470	1.5063	5.2533	1.7102	9.3099
170	352.26	1691.6	860.0	2551.6	3.8106	1.3749	5.1856	1.7695	8.3721

TABLE A.2. TRANSPORT PROPERTIES OF SATURATED WATER AND STEAM
(reproduced with permission from [1])

		Water				Steam			
T_{sat} (°C)	p_{sat} (bar)	c_p (kJ/kg K)	$\mu \times 10^6$ (N s/m²)	k (W/m K)	Pr	c_p (kJ/kg K)	$\mu \times 10^6$ (N s/m²)	$k \times 10^3$ (W/m K)	Pr
0.01	0.00611	4.218	1786	0.569	13.2	1.863	8.105	17.6	0.858
20	0.02337	4.182	1002	0.603	6.95	1.880	8.903	18.8	0.888
40	0.07375	4.179	653.9	0.631	4.33	1.900	9.701	20.2	0.912
60	0.19920	4.185	467.3	0.653	2.99	1.924	10.50	21.6	0.934
80	0.47360	4.198	355.4	0.670	2.23	1.970	11.29	23.2	0.959
100	1.01330	4.218	283.1	0.681	1.75	2.034	12.06	24.9	0.987
120	1.9854	4.244	231.0	0.687	1.43	2.125	12.83	26.7	1.02
140	3.6138	4.282	194.1	0.688	1.21	2.245	13.57	28.9	1.05
160	6.1806	4.334	167.7	0.684	1.06	2.406	14.30	31.3	1.10
180	10.027	4.403	148.5	0.677	0.967	2.615	15.02	34.1	1.15
200	15.549	4.494	133.9	0.664	0.906	2.883	15.72	37.4	1.21
220	23.198	4.613	122.4	0.648	0.871	3.223	16.42	41.5	1.28
240	33.478	4.769	112.9	0.628	0.850	3.656	17.14	46.5	1.35
260	46.943	4.985	104.8	0.603	0.866	4.221	17.90	52.8	1.43
270	55.058	5.134	101.1	0.589	0.882	4.575	18.31	56.6	1.48
280	64.202	5.307	97.5	0.574	0.902	4.996	18.74	60.9	1.54
290	74.461	5.520	94.1	0.558	0.932	5.509	19.21	66.0	1.61
300	85.927	5.794	90.7	0.541	0.970	6.148	19.73	71.9	1.69
310	98.700	6.143	87.2	0.523	1.024	6.968	20.30	79.1	1.79
320	112.89	6.604	83.5	0.503	1.11	8.060	20.95	87.8	1.92
330	128.63	7.241	79.5	0.482	1.20	9.580	21.70	99.0	2.10
340	146.05	8.225	75.4	0.460	1.35	11.87	22.70	114	2.36
350	165.35	10.07	69.4	0.434	1.61	15.8	24.15	134	2.84
360	186.75	15.0	62.1	0.397	2.34	27.0	26.45	162	4.40
370	210.54	55	51.8	0.340	8.37	107	30.6	199	16.4
374.15	221.2	∞	41.4	0.240		∞	41.4	240	

Carbon dioxide

Under reactor conditions ($T \geqslant 600$ K and $p \leqslant 40$ bar) the density of carbon dioxide gas is given within 1% by the universal gas equation, i.e. $1/\rho = v = R_0T/Mp$, where R_0 is the universal gas constant (8314.3 J (kg mol)$^{-1}$ K^{-1}) and M the molecular weight (44.01). T is in K and p in N m^{-2}. This accuracy is probably sufficient for any calculations involving the transport properties, since k, μ and Pr are only known to an accuracy of 2 to 3%.

TABLE A.3. PROPERTIES AT 40 BAR PRESSURE

Temperature (K)	Thermal conductivity [2] (10^{-3} W m^{-1} K^{-1})	Viscosity [3] (10^{-6} kg m^{-1} s^{-1})	Specific heat c_p [4] (J kg^{-1} K^{-1})	Prandtl no.
300	22.2	16.6	1407	1.05
400	26.5	20.6	1061	0.825
500	34.0	24.8	1071	0.781
600	41.8	28.7	1110	0.762
700	49.5	32.2	1148	0.747
800	56.7	35.5	1184	0.741
900	63.6	38.6	1215	0.737
1000	70.1	41.4	1243	0.734

TABLE A.4. PROPERTIES AT 1 BAR PRESSURE (THE INFLUENCE OF PRESSURE IS SMALL)

Temperature (K)	Thermal conductivity [2] (10^{-3} W m^{-1} K^{-1})	Viscosity [3] (10^{-6} kg m^{-1} s^{-1})	Specific heat c_p [4] (J kg^{-1} K^{-1})	Prandtl no.
300	16.6	15.1	853	0.776
400	24.4	19.8	942	0.764
500	32.5	24.2	1015	0.756
600	40.5	28.1	1076	0.747
700	48.1	31.7	1127	0.743
800	55.2	35.0	1169	0.741
900	62.0	38.1	1205	0.740
1000	68.5	41.0	1234	0.739

Helium

The density of helium under reactor conditions is also given to within 1% by the universal gas equation (molecular weight is 4). For helium the transport properties are nearly independent of pressure, so the values in Table A.5 can be used throughout the pressure range 0 to 80 bar. The variation with pressure in this range is less than 1%, whereas the estimated error in the quoted values is a couple of per cent.

TABLE A.5. PROPERTIES OF HELIUM AT 40 BAR PRESSURE
(reproduced with permission from [5])

Temperature (K)	Thermal conductivity ($W\ m^{-1}\ K^{-1}$)	Viscosity ($10^{-5}\ kg\ m^{-1}\ s^{-1}$)	Specific heat c_p ($J\ kg^{-1}\ K^{-1}$)	Prandtl no.
400	0.190	2.44	5192	0.666
500	0.222	2.84	5192	0.666
600	0.252	3.23	5191	0.666
700	0.280	3.60	5191	0.666
800	0.308	3.95	5191	0.666
900	0.335	4.29	5192	0.666
1000	0.360	4.62	5192	0.666
1100	0.386	4.94	5192	0.666
1200	0.410	5.26	5192	0.666
1300	0.434	5.56	5192	0.665

Liquid sodium

TABLE A.6. LIQUID SODIUM PROPERTIES [6]

Temperature (°C)	Density ($kg\ m^{-3}$)	Thermal conductivity ($W\ m^{-1}\ K^{-1}$)	Viscosity ($10^{-4}\ kg\ m^{-1}\ s^{-1}$)	Specific heat ($J\ kg^{-1}\ K^{-1}$)	Prandtl no.
100	927	86.9	6.80	1380	0.0108
200	904	82.0	4.52	1340	0.0074
300	880	77.1	3.45	1300	0.0058
400	856	72.2	2.85	1270	0.0050
500	832	67.3	2.46	1260	0.0046
600	808	62.4	2.07	1260	0.0042
700	784	57.6	1.81	1270	0.0040
800	760	52.6	1.62	1270	0.0039
900	736	47.7	1.47	1300	0.0040

References

1. *U.K. Steam Tables in S.I. Units*, 1970, Edward Arnold.
2. ALTUNIN, V. V. and SAKHABETDINOV, M. A. *Thermal Engineering* **20** (5), 121–126 (1973).
3. ALTUNIN, V. V. and SAKHABETDINOV, M. A. *Thermal Engineering* **19** (8), 124–129 (1973).
4. NATIONAL BUREAU OF STANDARDS CIRCULAR 564, Tables of thermal properties of gases, 1955.
5. MCCARTY, R. D. Thermophysical properties of Helium-4 from 2 to 1500 K with pressures to 1000 atmospheres, National Bureau of Standards Technical Note 631, 1972.
6. FOUST, O. J. (ed.) *Sodium–*NaK *engineering handbook*, Vol. 1, Gordon & Breach, 1972.

APPENDIX 3

Conversion Factors

Length: 1 m = 3.28 ft
Mass: 1 kg = 2.205 lb
Density: 1 kg m^{-3} = 0.062 43 lb-ft^{-3}
Pressure: 1 bar = 10^5 N m^{-2} = 14.50 lb-f/in^2 (psi)
Mass velocity: 1 kg m^{-2} s^{-1} = 737.3 lb-ft^{-2} h^{-1}
Temperature: 1 K = 1.8°F
Heat: 1 kJ = 0.9478 Btu
Heat flux: 1 W m^{-2} = 0.3170 Btu ft^{-2} h^{-1}
Thermal conductivity: 1 W m^{-1} K^{-1} = 0.5778 Btu ft^{-1} h^{-1} $°F^{-1}$
Heat transfer coefficient: 1 W m^{-2} K^{-1} = 0.1761 Btu ft^{-2} h^{-1} $°F^{-1}$
Specific heat: 1 kJ kg^{-1} K^{-1} = 0.2388 Btu lb^{-1} $°F^{-1}$
Specific enthalpy: 1 kJ kg^{-1} = 0.4299 Btu lb^{-1}

APPENDIX 4

Answers to Selected Problems

Chapter 3

Qn. 1. 379°C, 662°C, 2460°C
Qn. 2. (a) 0.15°C, (b) 1500°C
Qn. 7. 18.6 bar

Chapter 4

Qn. 3. 916°C
Qn. 4. 123 bar
Qn. 5. 632°C
Qn. 6. Two (new temperatures of first three clusters are 502, 601, 741°C)

Chapter 5

Qn. 1. (a) 0.79, (b) 0.56
Qn. 3. 798°C
Qn. 6. 2.06

Chapter 6

Qn. 1. 2.23×10^4 N m^{-2}
Qn. 2. (a) 2.2×10^4, (b) 5.19×10^4, (c) 0.19×10^4 N m^{-2}
Qn. 3. 0.60 tonne per day
Qn. 4. 3.36
Qn. 6. 38.6 bar
Qn. 8. 19,700 kg m^{-2} s^{-1}

Chapter 7

Qn. 2. (a) 110 MW, (b) 38 MW
Qn. 4. 1152°C

Chapter 8

Qn. 1. 327.2°C, 0.754 m
Qn. 4. (a) 0.45, (b) 0

Chapter 9

Qn. 2. (a) 0.06, (b) 0.31, (c) 0.42
Qn. 4. 0.23 (h.p.), 0.17 (l.p.)
Qn. 5. 300°C, 2540 kg s^{-1}, 39.6 MW, 0.417

APPENDIX 5

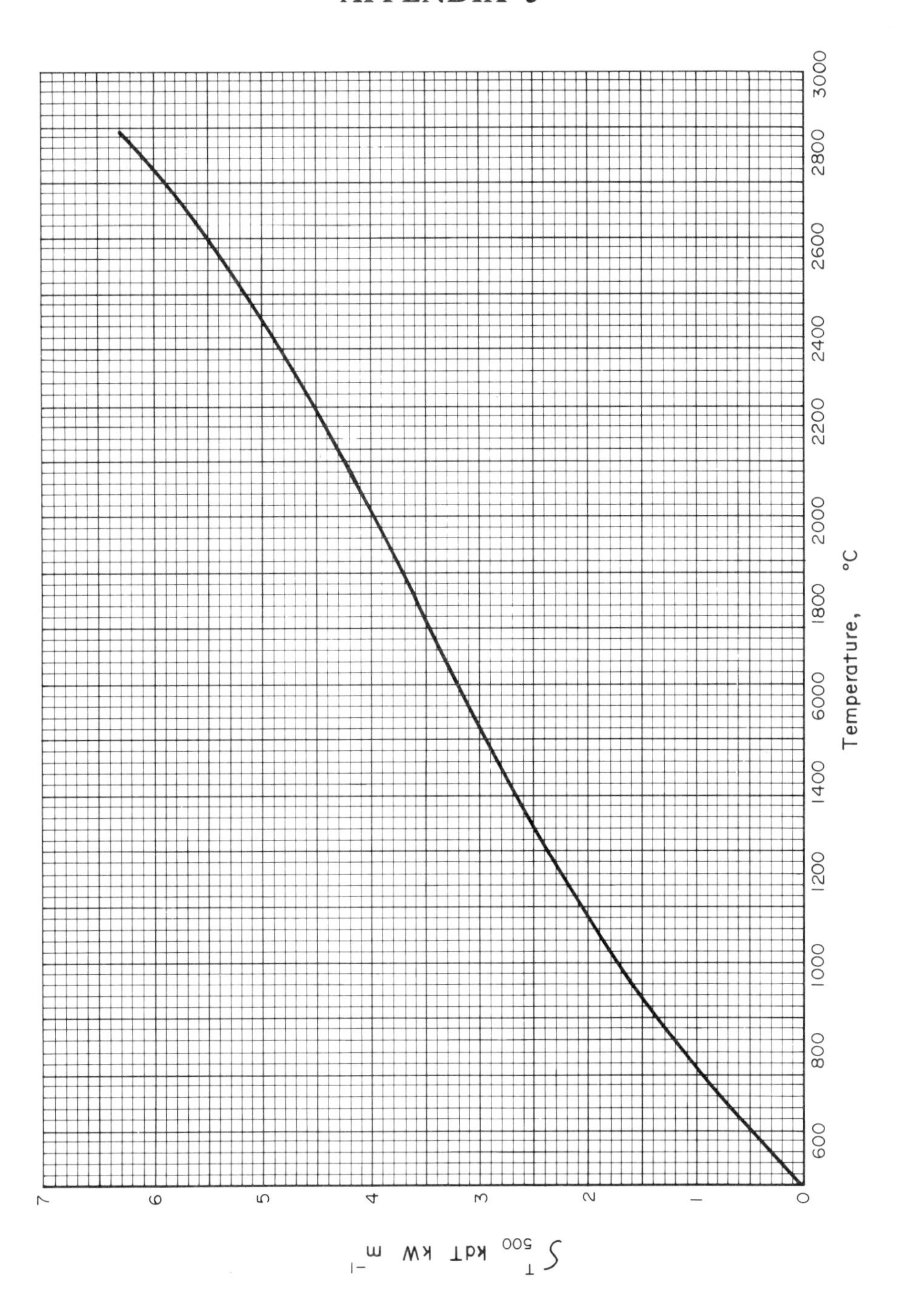
3000
2800
2600
2400
2200
2000
1800
6000
1400
1200
1000
800
600
Temperature, °C
7
6
5
4
3
2
1
0
$\int_{500}^{T} k\,dT$ kW m^{-1}

INDEX